ADVANCED PLANE GEOMETRY

ADVANCED
PLANE GEOMETRY

BY

C. ZWIKKER
TECHNICAL DIRECTOR LIGHT DIVISION PHILIPS EINDHOVEN

1950
NORTH-HOLLAND PUBLISHING COMPANY
AMSTERDAM

Sole distributors for U.S.A.:
Interscience Publishers Inc., New York

PRINTED IN THE NETHERLANDS

CONTENTS

PREFACE

Most textbooks on plane geometry show a certain onesidedness and concentrate the attention to an unduly great extent on conics, probably because these are so well suited to the illustration of general principles. Those properties, however, which require the introduction of differential quotients and integrals in the formulae are hardly mentioned at all in textbooks on analytical geometry and can be found in textbooks on the differential- and integral-calculus. Non-algebraic curves, finally, are mostly treated in textbooks on kinematics.

The present book is an attempt to combine the various parts of plane geometry. It gives a compilation of the most important properties of algebraic and transcendent curves together with their applications in physics and in technics; in the choice of the latter the author has been led by his own experience in physical engineering.

Another striking point is, in the author's opinion, the uneven way in which books on analytical geometry are distributed over the different levels of erudition required of the reader, there being found unduly great densities on the extreme ends of elementary treatise and of higher algebraic geometry, compared to which a certain scarcity exists in the middle regions. The present book belongs to these latter regions in so far as it presupposes a certain elementary knowledge of geometry but avoids on the other hand that field of abstract geometry which hardly requires the aid of any figures for its treatment.

To most readers the striking feature of this book will be the method used, as it is not the conventional Cartesian one, but is based on the possibility of representing a point with coordinates x and y by the complex quantity $z = x + jy$ $(j^2 = -1)$ as is already generally done in electrotechnics. To mathematicians, physicists and electricians the method will hardly appear revolutionary; chemically and mechanically trained readers will have to accustom themselves to the complex notation and calculus.

In the author's opinion the use of complex quantities in plane geometry has important pedagogic advantages. The student not only learns geometry but also gets trained in the handling of complex numbers. This method is, moreover, a most appropriate introduction to theoretical electrotechnics, modern acoustics, the theory of complex functions and to operational calculus.

But the treatment with complex numbers deserves attention also from the restricted standpoint of pure geometry. It turns out, namely, that formulae representing the curves give a much more direct description of their character than those occurring in Cartesian geometry. Many theorems can be deduced with surprising ease, as is shown throughout the book and in generality of scope the two methods are entirely equivalent.

So far as the author is aware, plane geometry is here for the first time treated consistently and completely as the geometrical interpretation of identities in complex numbers. Forerunners have been published as papers in periodicals and in an appendix the author presents a short historical review of the material available.

The figures have for the greater part been drawn by dr J. J. GELUK physicist and by mr W. MANINTVELD, chem. stud. The author is much indebted to them and to the publisher who so willingly complied with all his wishes relating to the make up of the book.

CHAPTER I

THE COMPLEX PLANE

1. *Introduction*

The representation of a complex number

$$z = x + jy \quad (j^2 = -1)$$

as a point with coordinates x and y in the mathematical plane dates from CASPAR WESSEL (1799) and from GAUSS (1831)[1]. z_i may stand for the point P_i (fig. 1) or for the vector from the

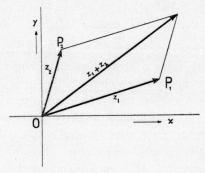

Fig. 1

origin to the point P_i. Addition and subtraction of two complex numbers may be accomplished geometrically by vectorial addition, respectively subtraction of the vectors denoted by z_1 and z_2. In Ch. II we shall extend this remark in such a way that we shall find for each analytical operation its geometrical equivalent.

This geometrical representation of the operations performed on complex numbers has been an important aid in the study of complex functions and in the treatment of complex impedances and admittances in electric engineering. The reverse procedure, using analytical calculations with complex numbers as a means of detecting or proving geometrical properties of plane figures has so far received but little attention.

---

[1] See also Appendix V for a historical review.

It will appear throughout this book that the application of complex numbers in analytical geometry often has marked advantages over the conventional Cartesian geometry, especially as regards physical and technical problems.

Now suppose x and y to be functions of a real parameter u and suppose we plot the corresponding z values in the plane for all values of u, we find a continuous locus of z values, a curve and a scale of u-values attached to it. The equation

$$z = f(u),$$

where $f(u)$ stands for a complex function of a real parameter u, is the equation of a curve and is equivalent to the Cartesian formula:

$$f(x, y) = 0$$

or rather we should say that it gives more than the Cartesian formula, as it also fixes a scale along the curve.

The method of representing a curve as the locus of the extremities of vectors, the components of which change in a continuous way with a parameter has been used in three-dimensional geometry [1] and it might look as if we were taking a two-dimensional cross-section of this more general treatment. This is not the case. The important property of the two-dimensional vector of being represented by a complex number has no simple analogon in three dimensions and the possibility of applying the often surprisingly simple calculation with complex numbers gives a special charm to two-dimensional vectorial geometry, or, expressed in a less exact way, to the geometry of the complex plane.

In the actually occurring cases various quantities may be introduced as the parameter. In kinematics, for example, it will usually be the time, while in purely geometrical problems the length of the curve, measured from a fixed point will be preferably used, especially in considerations of a more general nature. Further, the absciss x or the ordinate y and even the radius of curvature may occasionally be the most suitable one. Again, in electrotechnical problems the usual one is the angular frequency along the contours representing impedances as functions of the frequency

---

[1]   e.g. W. BLASCHKE, *Vorlesungen über Differentialgeometrie*, Berlin 1930.

and we shall, besides, meet many cases, in which still other quantities will play the part of parameter.

By changing from one parameter u to another v, being a real function of u, we do not change the character of the curve, the only thing that changes geometrically is the scale along the curve. It is therefore possible to represent one curve by different equations and we shall in each case choose the one that is most adapted to the problem in hand.

2. *First examples*

In order to familiarize the reader with the above notions we shall by way of introduction treat a number of curves and their analytical representation. It will strike us that simple functions always give rise to simple curves and vice versa.

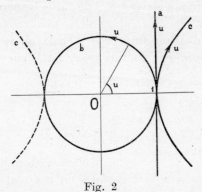

Fig. 2

a. $z = 1 + ju$ is in fig. 2 represented by curve a; it is a straight line with a uniform u-scale. Its direction is the same as that of the imaginary axis (y-axis).

b. $z = \exp(ju)$ (Fig. 2, curve b)

Separating real and imaginary parts with the aid of Euler's rule[1]),

$$\exp(ju) = \cos u + j \sin u,$$

we see that the curve is a circle with radius 1 round the origin as centre. The u-scale is uniform, but we may change to non-uniform scales by a transformation of the parameter. Each function

$$z = \exp(jf(u))$$

_____

[1]) Named after EULER (1707—1783) but already known to ROGER COTES (1682—1716).

represents the same circle. Anticipating later results, we may well state that the simple analytical representation of the circle is the reason why complex calculus is so well-adapted to the treatment of technical problems.

c. $$z = x + jy = \sqrt{1 + ju}.$$

In order to calculate real and imaginary parts we square the equation,

$$x^2 + 2jxy - y^2 = 1 + ju.$$

Separating now real and imaginary parts, we get

$$x^2 - y^2 = 1; \quad 2xy = u.$$

We recognize the first equation as that of the orthogonal hyperbola in Cartesian geometry. The curve is therefore a hyperbola (fig. 2, curve c).

The second equation fixes the u-scale along the curve, this scale being non-uniform in this case. Each curve

$$z = \sqrt{1 + jf(u)}$$

is identical with c.

d. $$z = \frac{1}{1 - ju} \quad \text{(Fig. 3)} \quad \ldots \ldots \ldots \quad (1)$$

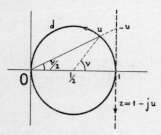

Fig. 3

is a circle with radius $\frac{1}{2}$ and with its centre on the real axis in the point $x = \frac{1}{2}$. To show the circle character we split z into real and imaginary parts:

$$z = \frac{1}{1 - ju} = \frac{1 + ju}{1 + u^2}$$

hence:

$$x = \frac{1}{1 + u^2}; \quad y = \frac{u}{1 + u^2}$$

and $(x - \frac{1}{2})^2 + y^2 = \frac{1}{4}$, which is the Cartesian equation of the circle.

In connection with example b we might have represented the same circle by the equation

$$z = \frac{1}{2}(1 + \exp(jv)) \quad \ldots \ldots \ldots \quad (2)$$

now using the letter v for the parameter to distinguish it from u.

The change from equation (1) to equation (2), however, is nothing but a transformation of the parameter. By putting

$$u = -\tan\frac{v}{2}$$

equation (1) is transformed into equation (2).

e. The evolvente of the circle $z = \exp{(ju)}$ is obtained by measuring on the tangent a distance u (BC in fig. 4). In complex notation the vector BC is

$u\,(\sin u - j\cos u)$.

Adding this to the vector OB we find for the point C of the evolvente:

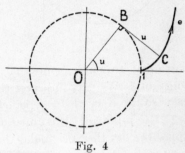

$z = (\cos u + j\sin u) + u\,(\sin u +$

$- j\cos u) = (1 - ju)\exp{(ju)}$.

So that the equation of the circle evolvente is:

Fig. 4

$$z = (1 - ju)\exp{(ju)}.$$

These five examples may suffice as a provisional introduction.

3. Intersection of two curves. Complex x- and y-values

The points of intersection of two curves

$$z_1 = f_1\,(u); \quad z_2 = f_2\,(v)$$

are found by solving the equation $z_1 = z_2$.

As this is a vector equation, it is equivalent to two normal equations, from which u and v may be calculated. Introduction of these values in z_1 or in z_2 respectively gives us the points of intersection.

Example: Let us take for the first curve the circle $z_1 = r\exp{(ju)}$ and for the second the straight line $z_2 = 1 + jv$. From $z_1 = z_2$ it follows by taking real and imaginary parts apart:

$$r\cos u = 1; \quad r\sin u = v$$

from which u is easily eliminated by squaring and adding, giving:

$$v = \pm\sqrt{r^2-1}$$

so that the two points of intersection are: $z = 1 \pm j \sqrt{r^2-1}$ which may be verified by applying elementary methods to fig. 5.

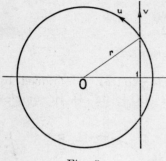

Fig. 5

If $r<1$ there are no points of intersection, v is imaginary.

In this connection, however, one should carefully avoid a treacherous pitfall, for substituting in that case $v = \pm j \sqrt{1-r^2}$ in z_2 would make $z = 1 \mp \sqrt{1-r^2}$ which are two points on the real axis and are certainly not the points of intersection.

This difficulty offers us an opportunity to enter somewhat deeper into the nature of the constant j. We may interpret the multiplication by j geometrically as a rotation in the x-y-plane counter-clockwise over an angle $\pi/2$. By repeating this operation the values obtained are the opposite of the original, thus $j^2 z = -z$. Therefore j can be treated in all calculations in the same way as $\sqrt{-1}$.

Now suppose we introduce imaginary values of x or even complex values $x = a + ib$, $i = \sqrt{-1}$. This may be interpreted in this way, that we consider the x-axis as the real section of a complex x-plane, in which multiplication by i means a rotation over an angle $\pi/2$. We now see that, although the square of both quantities j and i is equal to -1, they are not interchangeable and the product ij is certainly not -1. A third kindred quantity enters, when we admit complex values for y: $y = c + id$, $i = \sqrt{-1}$, where now i means geometrically a rotation over an angle $\pi/2$ in the complex y-plane. The complex x-plane and the complex y-plane are orthogonal planes in a four-dimensional space and by admitting complex values for x and for y we are doing four-dimensional geometry, a point being represented by the vector with four components:

$$z = a + ib + j \ (c + id).$$

Paying due attention to these considerations we see that in the case where $r < 1$ we might represent the points of intersection of circle and straight line by:

$$z = 1 \pm ji \sqrt{1-r^2}; \quad (i^2 = -1).$$

The introduction of complex values for x and y thus enables us to state that circle and straight line *always* have two points of intersection and this generalization appeals to our aesthetic sense. [1]

In general throughout this book we shall disregard complex values of x and y, as non-existent points are of no value in physical and technical applications of plane geometry. Nevertheless, these expatiations were necessary to correct the opinion that the vectorial treatment of plane geometry falls short of the Cartesian one. Both ways will always give identical results.

4. *The elements at infinity*

Another point that ought to be made clear in this introductory chapter regards the character of the infinitely remote parts of the plane. As in Cartesian geometry one usually speaks of the straight line at infinity and as we shall, as a rule, speak of the point at infinity in the present treatise, it is worth while to ascertain whether this is a contradiction or not.

One is led to the conception of the straight line at infinity by the properties of the perspective picture. All the infinitely remote parts of the original plane are found in the picture on a straight line. Now, as a straight line in the picture is always the image of a straight line in the original, it simplifies matters to consider the infinitely remote parts of the original as also constituting a straight line.

There are, however, other ways of portraying the plane. Take, for example, the transformation by which each point of the plane inverses its distance from the origin, thereby remaining on the same radius vector. Each point is transformed into another point with the exception of the infinitely remote parts of the plane

---

[1] E. LAGUERRE has given a general method for representing points with complex x — and (or) y — values by visible points of the plane. (Oeuvres, Paris 1905, vol. II, pp. 88 ff.) The points $z = 1 \mp \sqrt{1 - r^2}$ are the Laguerre-representation of the points of intersection we have been looking for and in general the Laguerre-representation is formed by just disregarding the difference between i and j.

which are all converted into the origin. Now, in order to make the one to one conjugation of the points a general rule, it is convenient to speak of *the* point at infinity of the plane.

From this we see that the conception of the character of the infinitely remote parts of the plane is dependent on the kind of transformation applied so that there is not the slightest contradiction in using at one time the expression "straight line at infinity" and at another time the expression "point at infinity". Because of its highly algebraic character Cartesian geometry mostly makes use of the straight line at infinity, whereas we shall often make use of the point at infinity. Let there be no mystery about the infinitely remote parts of the plane, it is just an infinite plane.

Historical note: GIRARD DESARGUES (1593—1662) introduced the general idea of elements at infinity. JEAN VICTOR PONCELET (1788—1868) contributed much to a better understanding. It was he who was the first to speak of the straight line at infinity.

x and y may become infinitely great for a certain value of u, so that the curve has a branch extending into infinity. As a rule, a second branch returns from the opposite side of the plane and although the two branches may be separate tracks, they behave in projection as if they were connected at infinity. By a perspective portrayal of the straight line l, its point at infinity is brought within finite distances (point I in fig. 6) and we see the two branches as one continuous line λ in the picture.

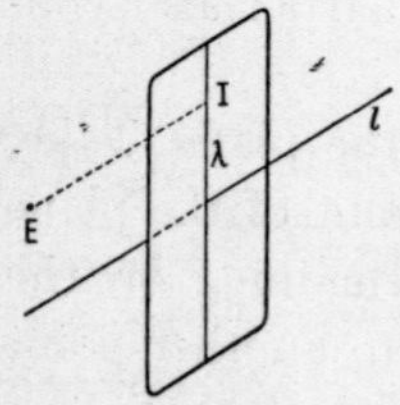

The hyperbola

Fig. 6

$$z = \sqrt{1 + ju}$$

extends into infinity for $u = \infty$ and for $u = -\infty$. As

$$\sqrt{j} = \pm \frac{1+j}{\sqrt{2}} \quad ; \quad \sqrt{-j} = \pm \frac{1-j}{\sqrt{2}},$$

$$x = \quad y = \infty \text{ or } x = \quad y = -\infty \text{ for } u = \quad \infty$$
$$x = -y = \infty \text{ or } x = -y = -\infty \text{ for } u = -\infty.$$

There are four points at infinity and they lie on the bisectors of the right angles between the coordinate axes. By any perspective projection the two points, denoted by $u = \infty$ will be made to coincide and likewise the two points denoted by $u = -\infty$. If we put it this way the hyperbola has not two separate tracks but consists of only one track, or with a technical term, is *unicursal*. In this projective language the hyperbola cuts the straight line at infinity in two points just as it cuts any normal straight line.

By applying the inversion we change the hyperbola into a lemniscate (fig. 7) and we bring the points at infinity together in the origin O. We see that the lemniscate reaches O from four different directions being opposite by pairs; inversely the hyperbola reaches the "point at infinity" from four different directions being opposite by pairs.

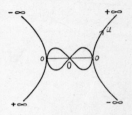

Fig. 7

The projective geometer assigns to the hyperbola two normal points at infinity, the inversion geometer one double point; both consider the hyperbola as consisting of one single track and both have a simpler idea of the hyperbola than the layman who assigns four infinitely remote points to it and who considers it as consisting of two separate branches. We may add that a comet flying past the sun behaves according to the layman's conception. It describes only one of the tracks, disappears into infinity, but does not come back from the opposite side.

5. *Complex values of u, deficient curves*

Suppose that both $x(u)$ and $y(u)$ assume real values for certain complex values of u. They then represent a real point in the plane not situated on the contour generated by the real u-values. From what has been said about the complex values of x and y it will be clear that by complex values of u we mean $a+ib$ and not $a + jb$. In these cases the curve may show more than one single track; it is no longer unicursal, but bicursal, tricursal and so on, in general multicursal.

In Ch. VI we shall treat at length the curve:

$$z = \mathsf{p}\,(u) + jd\mathsf{p}\,(u)/du,$$

where $\mathsf{p}\,(u)$ is Weierstrass' elliptic function. x and y are real for all real values of u but also for certain complex values, so that we find a curve consisting of two isolated tracks.

A simple example where x and y are real for complex values of u, although the curve remains unicursal, is furnished by the curve

$$z = \sin u + j \cos 2u \quad . \quad . \quad . \quad . \quad . \quad . \quad (1)$$

As $y = \cos 2u = 1 - 2 \sin^2 u = 1 - 2x^2$, curve (1) is identical with the parabola $y = 1 - 2x^2$. However, as long as u is real the curve

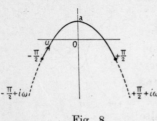

will consist only of a Lissajous-diagram, drawn as a thick line in fig. 8. The parts of the parabola beyond this stretch, correspond to complex values of u, namely for the right hand branch:

Fig. 8

$$u = \frac{\pi}{2} + i\omega.$$

For: $x = \sin u = \cosh \omega$

and $y = \cos 2u = - \cosh 2\omega$

are both real.

We have chosen this simple example in order to illustrate the possibility of the occurrence of complex u values. Of course, we may represent the complete parabola by a formula such as

$$z = u + j(1 - 2u^2),$$

where u takes only real values. However, this choice depends on the character of the physical problem and when we have to deal with a Lissajous problem form (1) is the more natural one.

Curves consisting of isolated tracks will be observed if x and y are at the same time real for certain values of u, real or complex, which in the complex u-plane describe two or more contours entirely separated from each other. Take for example:

$$z = u + j \sqrt{(1 - u^2)(1 - e^2 u^2)} \text{ with } e < 1.$$

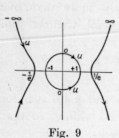

x is real for any real value of u; y only for those real values of u lying between -1 and $+1$ or lying beyond $\pm 1/e$. The curve consists of three tracks (fig. 9) of which the two outer ones may be considered as one in the sense of projective geometry. If e equals 1 the curve degenerates into a

Fig. 9

parabola like that of fig. 8, together with

its mirrored image:

$$y = \pm(1 - x^2).$$

In this limiting case the curve is unicursal in the projective sense and exhibits two double points. In general new branches occur at the cost of double points. Unicursal curves therefore are also called curves of *deficiency* zero, where the word deficiency refers to the number of double points.

CHAPTER II

THE GEOMETRICAL INTERPRETATION OF ANALYTIC OPERATIONS APPLIED TO COMPLEX NUMBERS

1. *Addition, subtraction, multitiplication*

As addition and subtraction of complex numbers consists in adding, respectively subtracting the real and the imaginary parts separately, this means geometrically that the components of the two vectors z_1 and z_2 have to be added or subtracted and the component sums, respectively differences, combined to a new vector. In other words, we have to apply the rules of vectorial addition and subtraction (fig. 1 p. 1).

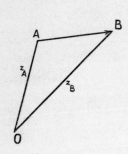

Fig. 10

The vector pointing from the point A to the point B may be expressed analytically by the difference $z_B - z_A$, the vector BA $=$ $= -$ AB by $z_A - z_B$. (fig. 10).

Adding a constant real value a to all z's is equivalent to a shift of the origin over a distance $-a$ along the real axis; addition of an imaginary constant equals a shift of the origin along the imaginary axis. In general we may shift the origin to any arbitrary point O' of the plane by adding a constant complex value $-z_0$ to all z-values, z_0 being the position of O' with respect to O as origin. (fig. 11).

Any formula of the character

$$z = z_0 + f(u)$$

where z_0 is a constant complex number may be simplified by leaving this constant out. This means geometrically that we either shift the curve parallel to itself over the vector $-z_0$ or that we shift the origin over the opposite value z_0.

In order to interpret the multiplication of two complex numbers

we remark that any complex number may be split up into two
factors:

$$z = |z| \exp\ (j\,\zeta)$$

where (fig. 12) $|z|$ is the *absolute value* or the *modulus* of the vector,
ζ is the angle which the vector makes with the x-axis and is called

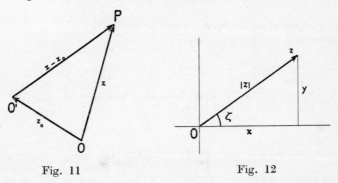

Fig. 11   Fig. 12

the *argument*; $\exp\ (j\,\zeta)$ will be called the *argument factor*. The
proof of the last equation follows from Euler's theorem:

$$\exp\ (j\,\zeta) = \cos \zeta + j\,\sin\ \zeta$$

and by remarking that $|z|\,\cos\ \zeta = x$; $|z|\,\sin\ \zeta = y$.

Multiplication of z by a real number means multiplying the
modulus by this factor without changing the argument; multiplication of z by a factor $\exp\ (j\,\varphi)$ means addition of φ to the
argument, that is a rotation of the vector over an angle φ counter-
clockwise without changing the modulus.

Any formula of the character

$$z = \exp\ (j\,\varphi)\,f\,(u)$$

where φ is a constant may be simplified by leaving the factor
$\exp\ (j\,\varphi)$ out. This means only that we have rotated the curve
over an angle $-\varphi$ round the origin without changing its form.
The curves

$$z = f\,(u)\ \text{and}\ z = \{f\,(u) - z_1\} \exp\ (j\,\varphi) + z_2$$

are congruent. Indeed, we can reduce the second equation to
the first by:

a.   shifting the origin over the distance z_2, by which z_2 drops
out of the formula;

b. rotating the curve round the new origin over an angle $-\varphi$ by which the factor exp $(j\,\varphi)$ disappears;

c. shifting the origin again, but now over the vector $-z_1$.

Exercise: Try to simplify the equation:

$$z = r\{1 - j\,(v + \tan\psi)\}\exp\{j\,(v - \psi)\}$$

where v is the parameter, r and ψ constants.

The curve is identical with

$$z = r\,(1 - ju)\exp\{j\,(u - \tan\psi - \psi)\}$$

as we have only introduced the parameter u for $v + \tan\psi$.

Now split off the factor $\exp\,(-j\,(\tan\psi + \psi))$, which means a rotation over the angle $(\tan\psi + \psi)$. What remains is:

$$z = r\,(1 - ju)\exp\,(ju)$$

and this we recognize as the evolvente of the circle of radius r.

The rotation over a right angle deserves special attention; it is accomplished by multiplication by the factor $\exp\,(\pm j\,\pi/2)$. But by Euler's rule:

$$\exp\,(\pm j\,\pi/2) = \cos\pi/2 \pm j\sin\pi/2 = \pm j$$

from which we see, that multiplication by $\pm j$ means a rotation counter-clockwise over an angle $\pm\pi/2$, a result anticipated in Ch. I when discussing the nature of j.

Multiplication of two complex numbers z_1 and z_2 gives:

$$|z_1| \cdot |z_2| \exp\{j\,(\zeta_1 + \zeta_2)\}.$$

The modulus of the product is the product of the two original moduli, the new argument is the sum of the two original arguments. Apart from the changes in the modulus, squaring a vector z doubles the argument, taking the square root halves the argument.

By way of example let us multiply $1 - ju$ by $\exp\,(ju)$. As ju is not constant, multiplication by $\exp\,(ju)$ does not mean an overall rotation over a constant angle. We have to multiply each vector $1 - ju$ by the corresponding factor $\exp\,(ju)$. Now $1 - ju$ is the tangent to the unit circle, running vertically (fig. 13) and by rotating it over the angle u it remains a tangent and point A moves to the position C. Now as BC equals u, the arc length of the circle, the locus of the points C, represented by the equation

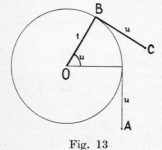

Fig. 13

$$z = (1 - ju) \exp{(ju)}$$

is evidently the circle evolvente. The same result was already found on page 5, but the present method is more illustrative of the possibilities of geometry in the complex plane.

We shall end this section with four remarks which are of a more purely analytical character, but which will be useful in several cases.

a. Raise both sides of the equation

$$j = \exp{(j\pi/2)}$$

to the j-th power. The result is

$$j^j = \exp{(-\pi/2)}$$

and, quite unexpectedly j^j is real. A Frenchman once called this formula ,,la plus belle formule de la mathématique''.

b. By taking logarithms on both sides, we find the Neperian logarithm of j:

$$lg\, j = j \cdot \pi/2.$$

c. By bisecting arcs, as is done in fig. 14, we find the often required values of $\sqrt{j}$ and $\sqrt{-j}$. They are:

$$\sqrt{j} = \pm \tfrac{1}{2}\sqrt{2}\,(1 + j)$$
$$\sqrt{-j} = \pm \tfrac{1}{2}\sqrt{2}\,(1 - j).$$

d. By dividing the circumference of the unit circle by a whole number n, we find the points which after being raised to the n-th power give 1, performing thereby one or more complete turns over the unit circle. The n values of $\sqrt[n]{1}$ form a regular n-angle (fig. 15) and are analytically expressed by:

$$z = \exp{\left(j \cdot \frac{2\pi k}{n}\right)} \qquad (k = 1,\ldots,n).$$

The unit circle may be represented by the formula:

$$z = \overset{v}{\sqrt{1}} = \exp\left(j\,\frac{2\pi}{v}\right)$$

which by the real transformation $v = \dfrac{2\pi}{u}$ is the transform of $z = \exp(ju)$ (fig. 16).

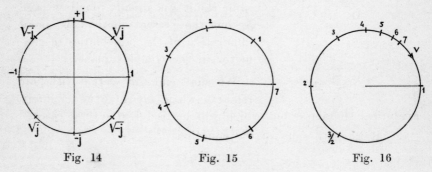

Fig. 14   Fig. 15   Fig. 16

2. *Decomposition of complex numbers*

In connection with the process of addition or for the sake of finding the Cartesian coordinates, and in many other cases, it is necessary to have a general method at our disposal for finding separately the real and imaginary parts of a complex number. The best way is to make use of the conjugate complex number obtained from z by converting j into $-j$ and which will be

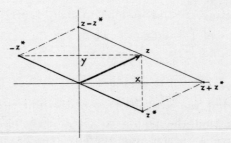

Fig. 17

designated by an asterisk: z^*. Changing the sign of j is geometrically equivalent to a reflection of z with respect to the real axis. The sum $z + z^*$ will be real and equal to twice the real value of z (fig. 17)

$$x = \mathrm{Re}(z) = \tfrac{1}{2}(z + z^*).$$

In a similar way we find for y:

$$jy = j\operatorname{Im}(z) = \tfrac{1}{2}(z - z^{*})$$

Example: take $z = (1 - ju)\exp(ju)$ (fig. 4)

$$x = \tfrac{1}{2}[(1 - ju)\exp(ju) + (1 + ju)\exp(-ju)] = \cos u + u \sin u.$$
$$jy = \tfrac{1}{2}[(1 - ju)\exp(ju) - (1 + ju)\exp(-ju)] = j\sin u - ju\cos u.$$
$$\text{(compare p. 5).}$$

The sum of any two conjugate numbers or functions will be real: as it does not change its value by interchanging j and $-j$, it is identical with its conjugate and this is only possible if it is real. For example $\tfrac{1}{2}[\exp(ju) + \exp(-ju)] = \cos u$ is real, and

$$z = \exp[jf(u) + jf^{*}(u)]$$

must be a point on the unit circle.

The difference of two conjugate numbers or functions will be purely imaginary. By interchanging j and $-j$ it changes its sign and conjugate numbers only differ in their sign if they are purely imaginary.

Example: $\tfrac{1}{2}[\exp(ju) - \exp(-ju)] = j\sin u$

and $$z = \exp[f(u) - f^{*}(u)]$$

must be a point on the unit circle.

Of equal importance is the availability of a general method for finding the modulus and the argument factor. This is also done by the intermediary of the conjugate value. We have:

$$z = |z|\exp(j\zeta) \;;\; z^{*} = |z|\exp(-j\zeta)$$

from which:

$$|z| = \sqrt{z \cdot z^{*}} \;;\; \exp(j\zeta) = \sqrt{\frac{z}{z^{*}}}.$$

The example of the circle evolvente (fig. 4; 13) goes as follows:

$$|z|^{2} = (1 - ju)\exp(ju) \cdot (1 + ju)\exp(-ju) = 1 + u^{2}$$

$$\exp(j\zeta) = \sqrt{\frac{1 - ju}{1 + ju}} \cdot \exp(ju).$$

Any function being the quotient of two conjugate functions will have unit modulus: $\left|\dfrac{z}{z^{*}}\right| = 1$, because $\dfrac{z}{z^{*}} \cdot \dfrac{z^{*}}{z} = 1$.

For example the function $\dfrac{1-ju}{1+ju}$, occurring in the last example, has unit modulus; it is a point on the unit circle and, indeed, by the transformation

$$u = \tan v$$

it assumes the form

$$\exp(-2jv)$$

from which $\zeta = u - v = u - \arctan u$ (fig. 13).

By combination with the method for finding real and imaginary parts we can split the argument function as follows:

$$\cos \zeta = \tfrac{1}{2}\left(\sqrt{\frac{z}{z^{*}}} + \sqrt{\frac{z^{*}}{z}}\right)$$

$$j\sin \zeta = \tfrac{1}{2}\left(\sqrt{\frac{z}{z^{*}}} - \sqrt{\frac{z^{*}}{z}}\right).$$

The argument itself is:

$$\zeta = \frac{1}{j}\lg\sqrt{\frac{z}{z^{*}}} = \frac{1}{2j}\lg\frac{z}{z^{*}}.$$

3.   Quotients

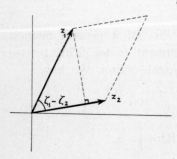

Fig. 18

Division of two vectors in the complex plane is graphically executed by the reversed process of multiplication, that is, by dividing the modulus of one vector by the modulus of the second one and by subtracting the arguments (fig. 18):

$$\frac{z_1}{z_2} = \frac{|z_1|}{|z_2|}\exp\{j(\zeta_1 - \zeta_2)\}.$$

If the two vectors are parallel, $\zeta_1 - \zeta_2 = 0$ and the quotient is purely real. As the imaginary part is in this case zero we have:

$$\frac{z_1}{z_2} - \frac{z_1^{*}}{z_2^{*}} = 0 \quad \text{or:} \quad z_1 z_2^{*} - z_1^{*} z_2 = 0.$$

This is the *criterion for parallel vectors*.

If, on the other hand, the vectors are orthogonal, we have

$\zeta_1 - \zeta_2 = \pm \pi/2$, $\exp j\,(\zeta_1 - \zeta_2) = \pm j$ and z_1/z_2 has no real part, in formula:

$$\frac{z_1}{z_2} + \frac{z_1^*}{z_2^*} = 0 \quad \text{or:} \quad z_1 z_2^* + z_1^* z_2 = 0$$

and this is the *criterion for orthogonal vectors*.

The two expressions occurring in these criteria are closely related with the vectorial and scalar products of two vectors as defined in normal vector calculus. The vector product is the area of the parallelogram, framed by the vectors z_1 and z_2:

$$A = |z_1| \cdot |z_2| \sin(\zeta_1 - \zeta_2).$$

But

$$z_1 z_2^* - z_1^* z_2 = |z_1| \cdot |z_2| \{\exp(j\,(\zeta_1 - \zeta_2)) - \exp_*(-j\,(\zeta_1 - \zeta_2))\}$$
$$= |z_1| \cdot |z_2| \cdot 2j \sin(\zeta_1 - \zeta_2),$$

so that the area of the parallelogram is:

$$A = \frac{1}{2j}\,(z_1 z_2^* - z_1^* z_2) = \operatorname{Im}(z_1 z_2^*).$$

In a similar way we find for the scalar product B:

$$B = |z_1| \cdot |z_2| \cdot \cos(\zeta_1 - \zeta_2) = \tfrac{1}{2}\,(z_1 z_2^* + z_1^* z_2) = \operatorname{Re}(z_1 z_2^*).$$

Scalar and vector products turn out to be the two components of the complex vector product $z_1 z_2^*$:

$$z_1 z_2^* = B + jA.$$

For the sake of completeness we may state that, expressed in the x's and the y's,

$$A = x_1 y_2 - x_2 y_1;$$
$$B = x_1 x_2 + y_1 y_2.$$

A proportionality of four vectors (fig. 19):

$$\frac{z_1}{z_2} = \frac{z_3}{z_4}$$

means that the moduli are proportional:

$$\frac{|z_1|}{|z_2|} = \frac{|z_3|}{|z_4|}$$

and that the enclosed angles are equal: $\zeta_1 - \zeta_2 = \zeta_3 - \zeta_4$.

The two triangles constructed on $z_1 z_2$ and $z_3 z_4$ are similar. The equality of the angles is already assured, if

$$\frac{z_1}{z_2} = \text{real factor times } \frac{z_3}{z_4}$$

or $z_1 z_4 = $ real factor times $z_2 z_3$;

and in the special case where z_2 and z_3 coincide, the two remaining vectors will make equal angles with this middle vector, if:

$$z_1 z_2 = \text{real factor times } z_2^2.$$

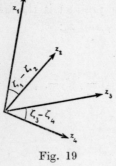

Fig. 19

These rules are always applied in order to prove equality of angles in geometrical figures. For example $z = \sqrt{f(u)}$ bisects the angle between $z = f(u)$ and the real axis $(z=1)$, whereas $z = \sqrt{jf(u)}$ bisects the angle between $z = f(u)$ and the imaginary axis $(z = j)$.

By the *anharmonic ratio, cross ratio* or *double quotient* D of four points we understand the expression:

$$D = \frac{z_1 - z_3}{z_1 - z_4} \div \frac{z_2 - z_3}{z_2 - z_4}.$$

D is in general complex and its argument is the difference of the arguments of $\frac{z_1 - z_3}{z_1 - z_4}$ and $\frac{z_2 - z_3}{z_2 - z_4}$. If this difference is zero, that is (fig. 20) if $\angle z_3 z_1 z_4 = \angle z_3 z_2 z_4$, D will be real. In this case the four points will be situated on a circle and the criterion for the concentric configuration of four points is the reality of the cross ratio.

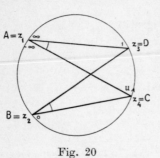

Fig. 20

Let three of the points be fixed on the circle and let z_4 move over it, then D will assume all the positive and negative real values. Now D can be considered as the parameter and the formula of the circle through z_1, z_2 and z_3 is evidently:

$$u = \frac{z_1 - z_3}{z_1 - z} \div \frac{z_2 - z_3}{z_2 - z}.$$

The value of the cross ratio depends on the order in which we take the four points. We shall denote the sequence by writing D (1 2 3 4) for the sequence chosen in the definition. One sees at once that interchanging 1 and 2 or 3 and 4 inverts the value. Interchanging 2 and 3 or 1 and 4 changes D into $1-D$ as may be seen by performing the calculation.

This leads to the *rules named after* Möbius:

I D (1 2 3 4)$=D$ (3 4 1 2)$=D$ (2 1 4 3) $=D$ (4 3 2 1)$=\delta$
II D (2 1 3 4)$=$ $=D$ (1 2 4 3) $=$ $=1/\delta$
III D (1 3 2 4)$=D$ (4 2 3 1)$=1-D$ (1 2 3 4)$=$ $=1-\delta$

and by further permutation of the indices the values $1-1/\delta$, $\dfrac{1}{1-\delta}$ and $\dfrac{\delta}{\delta-1}$ can be obtained.

In case D is real, it represents the double quotient of the lengths of the four vectors z_1-z_3, z_1-z_4, z_2-z_3 and z_2-z_4.

Möbius' third rule immediately gives us *Ptolemaios'* famous *theorem* (150 A.D), for (fig. 20)

$$D \ (1\ 2\ 3\ 4)=\frac{z_1-z_3}{z_1-z_4} \div \frac{z_2-z_3}{z_2-z_4}=\frac{AD.BC}{AC.BD}=\delta$$

$$D \ (1\ 3\ 2\ 4)=\frac{z_1-z_2}{z_1-z_4} \div \frac{z_3-z_2}{z_3-z_4}=\frac{AB.CD}{AC.BD}=1-\delta.$$

Since the sum is 1 we find:

$$AD.BC+AB.CD = AC.BD.$$

in words:

The product of the diagonals of a quadrilateral inscribed in a circle equals the sum of the products of the opposite sides.

4. *Conformal transforms, inversion.*

By a transformation $w=f(z)$, where w and z are complex values, one or more points of the complex w-plane correspond with one or more points of the z-plane. Let, furthermore, the function f be of such a nature, that the derivative dw/dz is a single-valued function of z, by which we mean that it is independent of the direction of dz. In this case dw makes a constant angle with dz, this angle being the argument of dw/dz. Two lines passing through

z and making a certain angle with each other will be transformed into two lines passing through w and making the same angle with each other as the original ones. Because of this property these transforms are called *conformal*. Conformity means in other words, that infinitely small polygons do not change their shape by this transformation.

In general, the function dw/dz, considered as a function of z, will, for a restricted number of z-values, be zero (so-called zero-points of dw/dz) and for a restricted number of values of z it will be infinite (so-called poles of dw/dz). Neither in the zero points, nor in the poles will it be clear what the meaning is of the argument of dw/dz and in these points we may find deviations from the conformity of the transforms. As these exceptional points are present only in a finite number, we shall nevertheless call these transformations conform.

For the transformation $w = \sqrt{z}$, $dw/dz = 1/2\sqrt{z}$, the point $z = 0$ is a pole, $z = \infty$ a zero point of dw/dz; the whole z-plane will be transformed conformally, but at $z = 0$ and $z = \infty$ we may expect deviations.

We shall consider here in some detail the transformation:

$$w = \frac{z - z_0}{z + z_0}$$

where z_0 is a complex constant. This transformation plays a role in the problem of the reflection of a plane wave, travelling in a medium of wave-resistance z_0 against a wall of impedance z. The number w is the complex reflection factor, the modulus being the ratio of the amplitudes of reflected and incident wave, the argument being the phase shift at reflection.

The argument $\triangle$ of w is constructed in fig. 21. It is constant along a circle going through the points $-z_0$ and $+z_0$ of the z-plane. The modulus of w is the ratio of the lengths of the vectors $z - z_0$ and $z + z_0$ and we know from elementary geometrics that this ratio is constant along a circle (circle of Apollonius) with its center on the straight line through $-z_0$ and $+z_0$.

Now, as in the w-plane the lines $|w| = $ constant (circles around the origin) and the lines $\triangle = $ constant (radii) are two orthogonal sets of curves, the two sets of circles in the z-plane for $|w| = $ constant and $\triangle =$ constant must by the property of conformal transforms also be orthogonal.

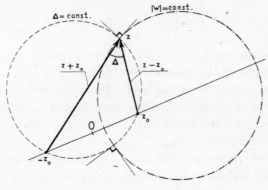

Fig. 21

We learn in passing from this example two geometrical conclusions:

a. The circle going through the points z_1 and z_2 lying in such a way that the chord $z_1 z_2$ subtends at any point of the circle the constant angle $\triangle$ is given by the equation:

$$u \exp (j\triangle) = \frac{z - z_1}{z - z_2}.$$

b. The circle of Apollonius, with the property that the ratio of the distances of any point of the circle to the two fixed points z_1 and z_2 is constant and equal to a, is given by the equation:

$$a \exp (ju) = \frac{z - z_1}{z - z_2}.$$

One of the most important transformations is the *inversion:*

$$w = \frac{1}{z^*}$$

by which the argument is not changed and only the modulus is inverted. We have seen already that the inversion of the vertical straight line $z = 1 + ju$ is a circle passing through the origin (we shall call it an O-circle). By an obvious generalization all straight lines will be converted into O-circles and conversely, the angle between two of these straight lines being equal to the angle at the intersection of the two corresponding O-circles.

Let us now see what the result is of a transformation by inversion of the cross ratio of four points. We find:

$$D\left(w\right)=\frac{w_1-w_3}{w_1-w_4}\div\frac{w_2-w_3}{w_2-w_4}=\frac{z_1^*-z_3^*}{z_1^*-z_4^*}\div\frac{z_2^*-z_3^*}{z_2^*-z_4^*}$$

and this is the conjugate value of the original $D(z)$. Although the cross ratio is in general changed by the inversion, it will remain the same, if it is real. In other words, if the four points are on a circle before the transformation, they will still be on a circle after the transformation, straight lines being included as circles of infinite radius.

We shall encounter pairs of curves which are mutual inversions: e.g. parabola and cardioid, orthogonal hyperbola and lemniscate. All the properties concerning angles between straight lines related to one member of the pair can immediately be converted into properties of angles between O-circles related to the second one. Concyclical location of four or more points will be invariant with respect to inversion.

5. *Non-conformal transforms, collineation*

There are, however, other transformations of the z-plane into the w-plane, where the angles do change. We shall call these transformations non-conformal and they are rather the general case.

A simple example is: $w=az+bz^*$

$$\frac{dw}{dz}=a+b\,\frac{dz^*}{dz}\,.$$

We now see that dw/dz is not merely a function of z but depends on the direction in which we choose dz, as dz^*/dz varies with this choice. As our argument in the last section was based on the fact that dw/dz was single-valued, the conclusion to the invariance of the angles can no longer be maintained.

The most important member of the family of non-conformal transformations is the *collineation*. Whereas the inversion converted circles into circles, the collineation has the even more important property of converting straight lines into straight lines, the straight line at infinity being included in the collection.

By way of introduction we wish to show that any straight line can be represented by a formula of the kind:

$$p^*z + pz^* - 2 = 0$$

where p is a constant complex number.

According to this equation the real part of p^*z is constant and equal to 1; p^*z therefore is a vertical straight line. Division by p^* shifts this line and turns it into a certain position in the plane dependent on the choice of p^*, but leaves it a straight line, q.e.d.

The collineation is defined as:

$$w = \frac{(p_2^*z + p_2 z^* - 2) + j\,(p_1^*z + p_1 z^* - 2)}{p_0^*z + p_0 z^* - 2}.$$

The real axis of the w-plane corresponds with the line

$$p_1^*z + p_1 z^* - 2 = 0$$

of the z-plane, the imaginary axis of the w-plane corresponds with:

$$p_2^*z + p_2 z^* - 2 = 0$$

and the infinitely remote line of the w-plane with the line

$$p_0^*z + p_0 z^* - 2 = 0$$

of the z-plane. The transforms of these three lines of the z-plane in the w-plane are represented schematically in fig. 22.

We may collect the terms with z in the numerator of the definition to one term $z_a z$, the terms with z^* to $z_b z^*$ and $-(2 + j2)$ to one complex number z_c and we see that the collineation may also be represented by the equation

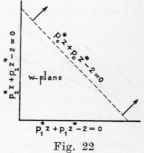

Fig. 22

$$w = \frac{z_a z + z_b z^* + z_c}{p_0^*z + p_0 z^* - 2}$$

where the numerator is now a trinomium, linear in z and z^*.

Let us now consider an arbitrary straight line in the w-plane, say:

$$w_0^* w + w_0 w^* - 2 = 0$$

where w_0 is a constant complex number.

Its transformation is

$$\frac{(w_0^{\cdot}z_a + w_0 z_b^{\cdot} - 2p_0^{\cdot})\,z + (w_0 z_a^{\cdot} + w_0^{\cdot} z_b - 2p_0)\,z^{\cdot} + (w_0^{\cdot} z_c + w_0 z_c^{\cdot} + 4)}{p_0^{\cdot} z + p_0 z^{\cdot} - 2} = 0$$

The left hand side has the form of a real factor times $(p^{\cdot}z + pz^{\cdot} - 2)$ and will, if equal to zero, represent a straight line in the z-plane.

The collineation is the analytical expression for the central projection of one plane (the original) on a second plane (the picture), placed, in general, inclined in space with respect to the original. It is therefore also called the *projective transformation*. It leaves the order of a curve — that is the number of points of intersection with any straight line — unaltered. The cross ratio, however, is in general changed by the collineation; it, therefore, does not always transform circles into circles. On the contrary it may be shown that any curve of the second order can be transformed into the unit circle with the aid of a collineation and this is equivalent to the fact that any second order curve can be considered as a section of a right-angled circular cone and therefore deserves the name of conic. (See later).

6. *The first derivative, tangents*

The vector z varies in a continuous way along a curve and

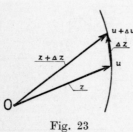

Fig. 23

we shall call the derivative dz/du the velocity of the point along the curve. The word velocity is borrowed from kinematics; dz/du is identical with the kinematic velocity, if u stands for the time. As dz is a vector and du a scalar, dz/du is also a vector. It has the direction of dz, that is of the tangent to the curve. Derivation with respect to the parameter will in future be denoted by a dot: $\dot{z} = dz/du$.

The argument of $\dot{z}$ has a definite geometrical meaning, it is the argument of the tangent and we shall denote it by the letter τ; therefore:

$$\exp{(j\tau)} = \sqrt{\frac{\dot{z}}{\dot{z}^{\cdot}}}.$$

The modulus of $\dot{z}$ has no definite geometrical meaning, it changes its value if we apply a real transformation to the parameter, by which, as we know, the curve does not change its nature. If u stands for the time $|\dot{z}|$ is the absolute value of the kinematic velocity. Special attention should be paid to the case where we choose the arc-length s along the curve as parameter; dz and ds are, apart from the argument factor, identical, $|\dot{z}| = |dz/ds| = 1$. For this choice of the parameter the curve is described with constant velocity 1, only the direction of the velocity being variable.

Plotting the velocity vector from the origin for all values of s brings the extremities of this vector on the unit circle, the s scale, marked on this circle is characteristic for the curve under consideration. The unit circle together with the s-scale is called the *velocity indicatrix* of the curve. Any curve is completely defined by its velocity indicatrix, apart from a parallel translation:

$$z = \int \dot{z} \ ds + z_0.$$

It is certainly tempting to use the arc length s as parameter because of the simplification of the formulae in which $\dot{z}$ occurs, but we are withheld by the fact that the formulae of many simple curves are not simple at all, if we try to express z in s. We shall make this choice in the case of general considerations where calculations in detail are not required (compare p. 136 and 144). But even if we start with the special parameter s, we are already compelled to follow the general procedure as soon as we consider the second derivative, this being the velocity of the velocity indicatrix, on which s is no longer identical with the arc-length.

Returning now to the general parameter u, not necessarily representing the arc-length, we find for the arc-length element:

$$ds = |dz| = \left| \frac{dz}{du} \right| du = |\dot{z}| \ du$$

and for the arc-length comprised between the points belonging to the values u_1 and u_2 of the parameter:

$$s = \int_{u_1}^{u_2} |\dot{z}| \ du$$

Examples:

a.   Circle: $z = \exp(ju)$; $\dot{z} = j\exp(ju)$; $|\dot{z}| = 1$.

Total perimeter: $s = \int\limits_{0}^{2\pi} du = 2\pi$

b.   Circle evolvente: $z = (1 - ju)\exp(ju)$; $\dot{z} = u\exp(ju)$; $|\dot{z}| = u$

Arc-length: $\int\limits_{0}^{u} u\,du = \tfrac{1}{2}u^2$

c.   Exponential curve: $y = \exp(x)$.

Take x as parameter: $z = x + j\exp(x)$; $\dot{z} = 1 + j\exp(x) = 1 + jy$.

In fig. 24 $\dot{z}$ is represented by the vector AB and we see at a glance that the subtangent AC is constant $= 1$. The arc-length

$$s = \int\sqrt{1 + \exp(2x)}\,dx$$

is not an elementary function of x and in the formula $z = f(s)$ the right-hand member would not be an elementary function, although the curve is a simple one.

d.   Logarithmic spiral, being the curve for which the radius vector grows exponentially with the argument, in complex notation:

$$\dot{z} = \exp(m + j)\,u$$
$$\ddot{z} = (m + j)\exp(m + j)\,u$$

and hence

$$\frac{\dot{z}}{z} = m + j = \text{constant}$$

which means that all tangents make the same angle with the radius vector, this angle being arc cotan m (fig. 25). The

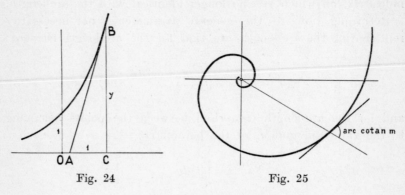

Fig. 24   Fig. 25

logarithmic spiral is the curve of „constant inclination". The arc-length is:

$$s=\int_{-\infty}^{u}\sqrt{1+m^2}\exp(mu)\,du=\sqrt{\frac{1+m^2}{m^2}}\exp(mu)$$

and therefore proportional to the radius vector.

How do we find the tangents to a given curve from a certain point P not lying on this curve? First suppose P to be the origin. The vector to the tangent point has the same or the opposite direction as the tangent $\dot{z}$, which can be formulated by:

$$\frac{z}{z^*}=\frac{\dot{z}}{\dot{z}^*}\quad\text{or}\quad z\dot{z}^*-z^*\dot{z}=0\quad\text{or}\quad \text{Im}\,(z\dot{z}^*)=0$$

and from this condition the parameter values of the tangent points can be calculated. If, more generally, P is not the origin, we substitute z by $z-z(P)$ and the condition is:

$$\text{Im}\,\{(z-z(P)).\dot{z}^*\}=0.$$

The order of this equation is the number of tangents which can be drawn to the curve from any point and is called the *class* of the curve.

Example: Take as the curve the unit circle and as the point P a point $z=a$ on the real axis. The condition for the tangents is:

$$\text{Im}\{(\exp(ju)-a)\cdot-j\exp(-ju)\}=$$
$$=\text{Im}\{-j+ja\exp(-ju)\}=$$
$$=-1+a\cos u=0$$

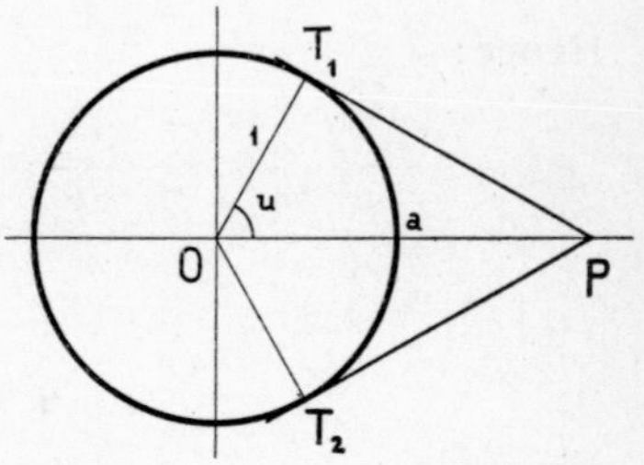

from which:

$$\cos u=\frac{1}{a}\ ;\quad \sin u=\pm\sqrt{1-\frac{1}{a^2}}$$

Fig. 26

and the tangent points are therefore: (fig. 26).

$$z_T=\exp(ju)=\cos u+j\sin u=\frac{1}{a}\pm j\sqrt{1-\frac{1}{a^2}}.$$

7. *The second derivative, curvature*

The second derivative, d^2z/du^2, or $\ddot{z}$ is called the *acceleration* of the point along the curve; it coincides with the kinematic acceleration, if u stands for the time. In general the acceleration has two components, one in the direction of the tangent being the derivative of the absolute value of the velocity, and one normal to the tangent and connected with the change in direction of the curve, that is with the curvature.

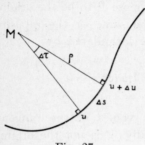

Fig. 27

The *curvature* is defined as the inverse value of the *radius of curvature* ϱ by the equation (fig. 27):

$$\frac{1}{\varrho}=\frac{d\tau}{ds}$$

where τ is the argument of the tangent. In order to express ϱ in z and its derivatives we calculate separately ds/du and $d\tau/du$. The first is simply $ds/du=$ $=|\dot{z}|=\sqrt{\dot{z}.\dot{z}^{*}}$. For the calculation of $d\tau/du$ we start from:

$$\tau=\frac{1}{2j}\lg\frac{\dot{z}}{\dot{z}^{*}}$$

from which:

$$\frac{d\tau}{du}=\frac{1}{2j}\frac{\dot{z}^{*}\,\ddot{z}-\dot{z}\ddot{z}^{*}}{\dot{z}\dot{z}^{*}}\;.$$

Hence:

$$\frac{1}{\varrho}=\frac{1}{2j}\frac{\dot{z}^{*}\ddot{z}-\dot{z}\,\ddot{z}^{*}}{(\dot{z}\dot{z}^{*})^{3/2}}$$

or:

$$\frac{1}{\varrho}=\frac{\operatorname{Im}(\dot{z}^{*}\ddot{z})}{|\dot{z}|^{3}}\;.$$

Examples:

a.   The unit circle: $z=\exp(ju)$; $\dot{z}=j\,\exp(ju)$; $|\dot{z}|=1$.

$$\dot{z}^{*}=-j\exp(-ju)\;\;;\;\;\ddot{z}=-\exp(ju).\;\;;\;\;\frac{1}{\varrho}=\operatorname{Im}(j)=1$$

as we might have expected.

b. Circle evolvente. $z = (1 - ju) \exp(ju)$; $\dot{z} = u \exp(ju)$; $|\dot{z}| = u$.

$$\dot{z}^{*} = u \exp(-ju) \;\; ; \;\; \ddot{z} = (1 + ju)(\exp ju)$$

$$\frac{1}{\varrho} = \frac{\mathrm{Im}\{u + ju^2\}}{u^3} = \frac{u^2}{u^3} = \frac{1}{u} \;\; ; \;\; \varrho = u.$$

Referring to fig. 13 we see that the centre of curvature lies on the circle which is developed and this could be expected if we consider this point to be the instantaneous centre of rotation during the evolvement of the circle.

The point M of fig. 27 is called the *centre of curvature* and the circle of radius ϱ with M as centre is called the *osculating circle*, it can be considered as having three points in common with the curve, the three points having coincided with each other.

A point of the curve for which the curvature is zero, is called an *inflection point*. This occurs, if $\ddot{z} = 0$.

A point for which the curvature is ∞, is called a *cusp*. This occurs if $\ddot{z} = \infty$. The curves treated up to now as examples show neither inflection points nor cusps, except the lemniscate, p. 9.

If we choose the arc-length s as parameter, $|\dot{z}|$ is always unity and the formula for the curvature takes the simple form:

$$\frac{1}{\varrho} = \mathrm{Im}\left(\frac{dz^{*}}{ds} \cdot \frac{d^2 z}{ds^2} \right).$$

The right-hand member is a certain function of s and this equation expresses the relation existing between the arc-length s and the radius of curvature ϱ. This relation is called the *natural equation* or the *intrinsic equation* of the curve. It defines the curve apart from its orientation and location in the plane and may be used as the starting-point for the deduction of all other properties of the curve. The natural equation of the unit circle is simply $\varrho = 1$; the natural equation of the circle evolvente follows from $\varrho = u, s = \frac{1}{2} u^2$, hence $s = \frac{1}{2} \varrho^2$. We may further refer to E. CESARO's book: Natürliche Geometrie.

We wish to state explicitly that the vector $\dfrac{d^2 z}{ds^2}$ is always normal to the curve z. This follows from the fact that the velocity dz/ds has always unit value, so that there exists no tangential component of the acceleration. But we can also give a purely analytical proof, as follows:

$$2 \operatorname{Re}\left(\frac{dz^*}{ds} \cdot \frac{d^2z}{ds^2}\right) = \frac{dz^*}{ds} \cdot \frac{d^2z}{ds^2} + \frac{dz}{ds} \cdot \frac{d^2z^*}{ds^2} = \frac{d}{ds}\left(\frac{dz}{ds} \cdot \frac{dz^*}{ds}\right).$$

Now $\dfrac{dz}{ds} \cdot \dfrac{dz^*}{ds} = \left|\dfrac{dz}{ds}\right|^2 = 1$ so that its derivative is zero. But if the real part of $\dfrac{dz^*}{ds} \cdot \dfrac{d^2z}{ds^2}$ is zero, the vectors $\dfrac{dz}{ds}$ and $\dfrac{d^2z}{ds^2}$ must be orthogonal, q.e.d.

As a consequence we can simplify the formula of the curvature still somewhat more. It becomes:

$$\frac{1}{\varrho} = \frac{1}{j}\frac{dz^*}{ds} \cdot \frac{d^2z}{ds^2}$$

and this is at the same time the natural equation of the curve.

We may consider the radius of curvature from the centre of curvature M to the curve as a vector. Its argument is $\tau - \pi/2$ and it is represented by:

$$z_r = \frac{\varrho}{j} \exp{(j\tau)}.$$

If we plot all vectors z_r from the origin we describe a curve which is called the *radial* of the original curve and which is represented also by the last equation. Expressing ϱ and τ in terms of z the formula for the radial can also be brought on the form:

$$z_r = \frac{2\dot{z}\dot{z}^*}{\dot{z}^*\ddot{z} - \dot{z}\ddot{z}^*}\dot{z}.$$

The radial of the circle $z = \exp(ju)$ is again this circle. The radial of the circle evolvente $z = (1 - ju)\exp{(ju)}$ turns out to be:

$$z_r = \frac{u}{j} \exp{(ju)}$$

and this is a spiral for which the modulus is proportional to the argument (spiral of Archimedes).

CHAPTER III

THE STRAIGHT LINE

1. *Collinearity of three points, concurrency of three straight lines*

We have already used the formula $z = 1 + ju$ for the straight line, passing through the point 1 in the direction of the vector j. If we wish to represent the line passing through the point z_1 in the direction of the vector z_2, we can generalize the above formula to $z = z_1 + z_2 u$.

The equation of the line passing through two given points z_1 and z_2, is however, more often required. Point P lying on this line in such a way that the distances from P to z_1 and z_2 are in the proportion u to 1 is given by: (fig. 28):

$$z = \frac{z_1 + u z_2}{1 + u}.$$

For $u = 0$, P coincides with z_1, for $u = \infty$, P coincides with z_2. Positive values of u occur between z_1 and z_2, negative values on

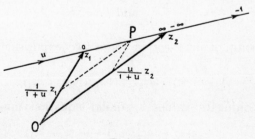

Fig. 28

both sides outside the stretch $z_1 z_2$; the point at infinity of the line is characterized by the parameter value $u = -1$.

Calculating u from the equation gives:

$$-u = \frac{z - z_1}{z - z_2}$$

and from this equation we see at once that the three points lie in one line as the reality of either side means that the vectors $z - z_1$ and $z - z_2$ have the same direction.

We can bring the criterion for collinearity of three points z_1, z_2 and z_3 in a more symmetrical form. The argument factor of

$$\frac{z_3 - z_1}{z_3 - z_2}$$

must equal ± 1, in formula:

$$\frac{z_3 - z_1}{z_3 - z_2} \cdot \frac{z_3^* - z_2^*}{z_3^* - z_1^*} = 1$$

and this can be written in the symmetrical form:

$$(z_1 z_2^* - z_1^* z_2) + (z_2 z_3^* - z_2^* z_3) + (z_3 z_1^* - z_3^* z_1) = 0$$

or, in the form of a determinant, the criterion of collinearity becomes:

$$\begin{vmatrix} 1 & 1 & 1 \\ z_1 & z_2 & z_3 \\ z_1^* & z_2^* & z_3^* \end{vmatrix} = 0.$$

We now proceed to calculate the point of intersection of the two lines passing through z_1 and z_2 and through z_3 and z_4 respectively. The two lines are:

$$z = \frac{z_1 + u z_2}{1 + u} \quad \text{and} \quad z = \frac{z_3 + v z_4}{1 + v}.$$

For the point of intersection these two expressions are equal, hence

$$(1 + v)\,(z_1 + u z_2) = (1 + u)\,(z_3 + v z_4)$$

For the conjugate values a similar equation must be valid:

$$(1 + v)\,(z_1^* + u z_2^*) = (1 + u)\,(z_3^* + v z_4^*)$$

and from these two equations u and v of the point of intersection can be calculated. Substituting these values into the line equations yields for the point of intersection:

$$z = \frac{(z_1 z_2^* - z_1^* z_2)\,(z_3 - z_4) - (z_3 z_4^* - z_3^* z_4)\,(z_1 - z_2)}{(z_1 - z_2)\,(z_3^* - z_4^*) - (z_1^* - z_2^*)\,(z_3 - z_4)}.$$

If the vectors $z_1 - z_2$ and $z_3 - z_4$ are parallel, the denominator equals zero by the criterion of parallellity and then $z=\infty$, as was to be expected.

If we cut the line $z_3 z_4$ by a third line $z_5 z_6$, we create a second point of intersection, the place of which is given by the last equation, if only we add 2 to each index. If the three lines have to pass through one point (in a technical term, if the lines are *concurrent*), the two expressions for the points of intersection have to be put equal to each other and the condition resulting from this equality can be brought into the symmetrical form of a determinant:

$$\begin{vmatrix} z_1 - z_2 & z_3 - z_4 & z_5 - z_6 \\ z_1^* - z_2^* & z_3^* - z_4^* & z_5^* - z_6^* \\ z_1 z_2^* - z_1^* z_2 & z_3 z_4^* - z_3^* z_4 & z_5 z_6^* - z_5^* z_6 \end{vmatrix} = 0.$$

We can check this formula by laying the origin in the common point of intersection. Each element of the third row is proportional to the area of the parallelograms on the vectors $z_1 z_2$, $z_3 z_4$ and $z_5 z_6$ respectively and all three must vanish if the origin is on the lines $z_1 z_2$, $z_3 z_4$ and $z_5 z_6$, but then the determinant is also zero.

2. *The theorems of Ceva, Menelaos and Desargues*

As applications of the general theory let us prove the theorems of MENELAOS and CEVA.

MENELAOS (58 A. D.): the three points P, Q, R, each lying on a side of the triangle ABC (fig. 29) in such a way that

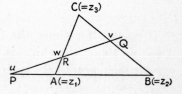

Fig. 29

$$\frac{AP \cdot BQ \cdot CR}{PB \cdot QC \cdot RA} = -1 \text{ are collinear.}$$

Let the three points be:

$$z_P = \frac{z_1 + u z_2}{1+u}; \quad z_Q = \frac{z_2 + v z_3}{1+v}; \quad z_R = \frac{z_3 + w z_1}{1+w}.$$

The condition is then equivalent to $u \cdot v \cdot w = -1$. The determinant occurring in the criterion for collinearity is

$$\begin{vmatrix} 1+u & 1+v & 1+w \\ z_1 + u z_2 & z_2 + v z_3 & z_3 + w z_1 \\ z_1^* + u z_2^* & z_2^* + v z_3^* & z_3^* + w z_1^* \end{vmatrix}.$$

Add the first row and $-u$ times the second to $-1/w=uv$ times the third row. The members of this row then become zero from which it follows that the determinant is zero and hence that the points PQR are collinear, q.e.d.

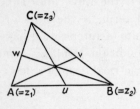

$\mathbf{C}(=z_3)$

w v

$\mathbf{A}(=z_1)$ u $\mathbf{B}(=z_2)$

Fig. 30

❦ CEVA (1700): the three lines joining the vertices of a triangle with the points PQR, each lying on one side so that

$$\frac{AP.BQ.CR}{PB.QC.RA}=1 \text{ are concurrent.}$$

Let the three points be:

$$z_P=\frac{z_1+uz_2}{1+u}; \quad z_Q=\frac{z_2+vz_3}{1+v}; \quad z_R=\frac{z_3+wz_2}{1+w},$$

then the condition leads to $u\cdot v\cdot w=1$. The determinant of the criterion of concurrency is:

$$\begin{vmatrix} (1+u)z_3-(z_1+uz_2) & (1+v)z_1-(z_2+vz_3) & (1+w)z_2-(z_3+wz_1) \\ (1+u)z_3^*-(z_1^*+uz_2^*) & (1+v)z_1^*-(z_2^*+vz_3^*) & (1+w)z_2^*-(z_2^*+wz_1^*) \\ (1+u)\{z_3(z_1^*+uz_2^*)-z_3^*(z_1+uz_2)\} & \text{cycl.} & \text{cycl.} \end{vmatrix}.$$

The sum of v times the first column, the second column and $1/w=uv$ times the third is zero; therefore the determinant is zero, which proves the concurrency of the three lines.

Each Ceva's point characterized by three definite values of u, v and w is correlated to one Meneloas' line, characterized by $-u$, $-v$, $-w$. They are taken together as *trilinear pole* and *trilinear polar*. The polar of the centre of gravity of the triangle $(u=v=w=1)$ is the straight line at infinity.

Another important theorem is Desargues' *theorem*, stating that corresponding sides of two perspective triangles intersect in three collinear points, ($\pm$1650), and we may see as follows, that it is a consequence of the theorems of MENELAOS and CEVA. Draw (fig. 31) the triangle ABC and mark the points u, v and w on its sides. By Ceva's theorem the triangles ABC and vwu are perspective if $u \cdot v \cdot w = 1$. Mark the points $-u$, $-v$ and $-w$ and draw the straight line m through these points, which is possible because of Menelaos' theorem. Now as $uvw = 1$, the points w, u, $-v$ must be collinear and also the points v, u, $-w$.... and also the points w, v, $-u$. We see thus that the corresponding sides

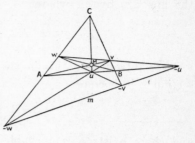

Fig. 31

of the triangles ABC and vwu intersect in three points of the live m, q.e.d.

3. *Line coordinates*

If in the criterion of collinearity of three points we substitute z for z_3, it becomes:

$$\begin{vmatrix} 1 & 1 & 1 \\ z_1 & z_2 & z \\ z_1^* & z_2^* & z^* \end{vmatrix} = 0$$

and this can be considered as the equation of the line passing through z_1 and z_2; written in one line the equation is:

$$(z_1^* - z_2^*) z + (z_2 - z_1) z^* + (z_1 z_2^* - z_2 z_1^*) = 0.$$

and this can be brought into the simple form:

$$p^* z + p z^* - 2 = 0 \qquad (\text{or } \operatorname{Re}(p^* z) = 1)$$

by introducing:

$$p = 2 \frac{z_2 - z_1}{z_1^* z_2 - z_1 z_2^*}; \quad p^* = 2 \frac{z_2^* - z_1^*}{z_1 z_2^* - z_1^* z_2}.$$

The straight line appears to be completely determined by the choice of p. p is called the vector of the line and its components are called the *line coordinates*. A point is determined by one vector or by two coordinates and we see that the same applies to a straight line.

The use of the line vector appears at once, if we introduce it into the formula for the point of intersection of two lines, deduced in a former section. Let the line $z_1 z_2$ be characterized by p_1 and the line $z_3 z_4$ by p_2, where

$$p_1 = 2\,\frac{z_2 - z_1}{z_1^* z_2 - z_1 z_2^*}\,; \quad p_2 = 2\,\frac{z_4 - z_3}{z_3^* z_4 - z_3 z_4^*}.$$

After introducing this in the formula for the point of intersection z it becomes:

$$z = 2\,\frac{p_2 - p_1}{p_1^* p_2 - p_1 p_2^*}$$

and there exists a remarkable reciprocity between the point of intersection z of the two lines determined by the vectors p_1 and p_2 and the line p connecting the two points determined by the vectors z_1 and z_2.

Let us also introduce the notion of the line vector into the condition for the concurrency of three lines. This takes then the form:

$$\begin{vmatrix} 1 & 1 & 1 \\ p_1 & p_2 & p_3 \\ p_1^* & p_2^* & p_3^* \end{vmatrix} = 0$$

which is formally identical with the condition for the collinearity of three points. Indeed we may say that three lines are concurrent, if their $p's$ are collinear.

We shall now investigate the geometrical nature of the vector p, defining the point P (fig. 32). As in the definition of p the denomi-

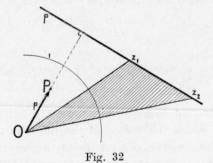

Fig. 32

nator is purely imaginary, we conclude that the vector from the origin to P is normal to the vector $z_2 - z_1$, that means normal to the line z_1z_2. As, furthermore, the absolute value of the denominator equals twice the area of the triangle Oz_1z_2, of which z_1z_2 is the base, we easily conclude that the modulus of p is the inverse of the length of the perpendicular let down from O on to the line. Point P is the inversion of the base of this perpendicular.

From now on we shall take point P and the corresponding line together as *pole* and *polar* with respect to the unit circle; both the pole and the line will be characterized by the letter p. As we have seen above, by the transformation of pole and polar a pencil of rays passing through one point is transformed into a point assemblage on a straight line. We can prove that this line is the polar of the point which carries the pencil of rays. Let this point be Q with coordinate q. The condition that Q shall lie on an arbitrary member p of the pencil is:

$$p^{\bullet}q + pq^{\bullet} - 2 = 0$$

but owing to the symmetry between p and q this is also the condition that P shall fall on the polar q of Q, q.e.d.

The polar of the point of intersection R of the lines p and q (fig. 33) must be the line PQ. PQR is a so-called *polar triangle*.

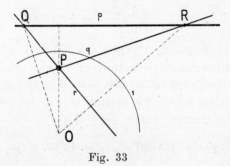

Fig. 33

By the transformation of pole and polar it is transformed into itself.

4. *Polar transformation, dual conceptions*

By the transformation of pole and polar a curve considered as a collection of points is transformed into a collection of straight lines. These lines will envelop a second curve which, therefore, may be considered as the transform of the original curve. A secant of the original curve, intersecting it in n (= the order) points will be transformed into a point carrying n lines from the collection that envelops the second curve. As these lines are tangents to this curve, the transform will be of the class n. Conversely the class of the original curve will equal the order of the transform. As conics are both of second order and second class, the transformation of pole and polar will transform conics into conics. We know that the inversion transforms circles into circles, but this is not the case with the transformation of pole and polar. By way of example we shall transform the circle, but first we have to indicate the general way of finding the formula of the polar transform.

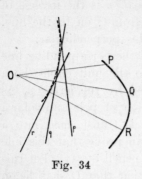

Fig. 34

The point of intersection of the lines p and q which are the transforms of the points P with coordinate p and Q with coordinate q is:

$$z = 2\,\frac{q-p}{p^{\bullet}q - pq^{\bullet}}\,.$$

Now let Q approach to P, then the line PQ will approach to a limiting position which is a tangent of the original curve. In the transform the point of intersection of p and q will approach a limiting position which by definition will be considered as a point of the transformed curve. Now if $q-p=dp$,

$$p^{\bullet}q - pq^{\bullet} = p^{\bullet}(p+dp) - p(p^{\bullet}+dp^{\bullet}) = p^{\bullet}dp - pdp^{\bullet}$$

and the point of the transformed curve is:

$$z = 2\,\frac{dp}{p^{\bullet}dp - pdp^{\bullet}}\,.$$

Performing the polar transformation for a second time that is, finding $2\,\dfrac{dz}{z^{\bullet}dz - zdz^{\bullet}}$ gives of course again the original curve p, as may be verified by actually performing the calculation.

We shall now apply this general result to the circle (fig. 35)

$$p = a + \exp(ju)$$
$$dp = j \exp(ju)\, du$$
$$dp^* = -j \exp(-ju)\, du$$

The transform is therefore:

$$z = \frac{\exp ju}{a \cos u + 1}$$

and this is not a circle, but a hyperbola (fig. 35).

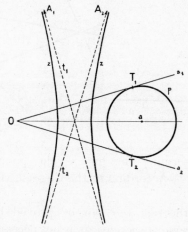

Fig. 35

Any property of the original figure will be found again in the transform, but in the so-called dual form (PONCELET). Dual expressions are point and line; collinearity of points and concurrency of lines; order and class; point on a curve and tangent. As examples of dual theorems we may nonsider the theorems of MENELAOS and CEVA. Another example is supplied by Pappos' theorems (300 A.D., fig. 36):

Take three points u_1, u_2, u_3 on one line and three points v_1, v_2, v_3 on a second line. The lines u_1v_2 and u_2v_1 intersect in C, the lines u_2v_3 and u_3v_2 in A, the lines u_3v_1 and u_1v_3 in B. The theorem says that A, B and C are collinear. It can be proved with the methods of the preceding sections.

The dual theorem is (fig. 37):

Take three lines u_1, u_2, u_3 through one point U and three lines v_1, v_2, v_3 through a second point V.

The points $u_1 v_2$ and $u_2 v_1$ determine the straight line c, the points

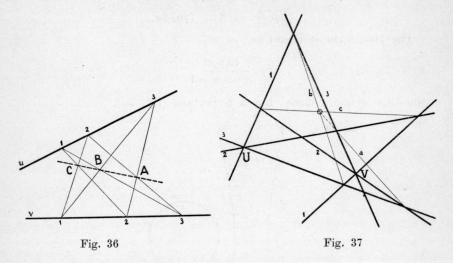

Fig. 36   Fig. 37

$u_2 v_3$ and $u_3 v_2$ determine the line a, the points $u_3 v_1$ and $u_1 v_3$ determine the line b. According to the theorem the lines a, b and c are concurrent.

Although this theorem too can be proved by means of the methods of the previous sections, it is not necessary to do so, once the dual theorem has been proved. More than that, the analytical proof of one of the theorems is identical with that of the second. We have merely to interpret the symbols in the dual way. Finally we may remind that Desargues' theorem is dual with itself.

5. *Projective point assemblages and ray pencils*

The point assemblage on the straight line:

$$z = \frac{z_1 + z_2 u}{1 + u} \quad . \quad . \quad . \quad . \quad . \quad . \quad . \quad (1)$$

may be compared with that on the arbitrary other straight line:

$$z' = \frac{z_3 + z_4 u}{m + n u} \quad (m \text{ and } n \text{ are real}). \quad . \quad . \quad . \quad (2)$$

The latter equation is of a more general character than the former. We remark here, that z_3 and z_4 are no longer points of the straight line; it passes through the points z_3/m $(u=0)$ and z_4/n $(n=\infty)$. We shall show that the transition from (1) to (2) can be accomplished by a combination of parallel translations, rotations and perspective projections.

By way of introduction we may remark that two lines:

$$z_A = \frac{z_1 + z_2 u}{m + nu} \quad \text{and} \quad z_B = \frac{z_1 + z_2 u}{p + qu}$$

are perspective with respect to the origin, by which we mean, that the points on the two lines with equal values of u lie on one straight line passing through O. Indeed, the quotient

$$\frac{z_A}{z_B} = \frac{p + qu}{m + nu}$$

is real and that means that z_A and z_B have the same direction.

The construction of the scale of (2)

$$z' = \frac{z_3 + z_4 u}{m + nu}$$

is shown in fig. 38. We first construct the line $z_3 + z_4 u$ which is

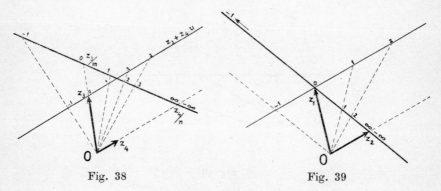

Fig. 38   Fig. 39

perspective with (2) and has a uniform scale (unit=modulus of z_4). Fig. 39 shows in the same way the construction of (1):

Now move one of the here mentioned uniform scales until both are parallel and at the same time perspective and the chain of operations leading from (1) to (2) is closed. In general two point assemblages of the type (2) will not be perspective, but we call them *projective*.

Perspective projection leaves certain properties intact; these are called *projective properties*, other properties may be lost in the projection; as opposed to the projective properties they are called *metric properties*.

Examples of projective properties are; incidence of point and line, collinearity of points, concurrency of lines, order and class of a curve, character of tangent, double point, inflection point, cusp. We shall now add one important example more to this collection: the cross ratio of four points *on a straight line* is invariant. To prove this, take four points $u_1u_2u_3u_4$ on the line (2) and calculate the cross ratio. We find:

$$D = \frac{z'(u_1) - z'(u_3)}{z'(u_1) - z'(u_4)} : \frac{z'(u_2) - z'(u_3)}{z'(u_2) - z'(u_4)} = \frac{u_1 - u_3}{u_1 - u_4} : \frac{u_2 - u_3}{u_2 - u_4}$$

and this is entirely independent of z_3, z_4, m and n.

The projective character of the cross ratio was already known to Pappos (300 A.D.).

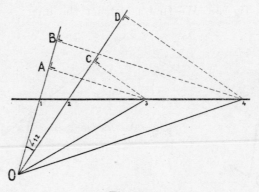

Fig 40

The cross ratio is, so to say, picked up by a projecting pencil of rays and transferred to a second line. We expect that it can be expressed in the angles of the pencil without the help of a secant. Indeed (fig. 40)

$$\frac{z_1 - z_3}{z_1 - z_4} = \frac{A\,3}{B\,4} = \frac{O\,3 \sin \angle 13}{O\,4 \sin \angle 14}$$

In the same way:

$$\frac{z_2 - z_3}{z_2 - z_4} = \frac{C\,3}{D\,4} = \frac{O\,3 \sin \angle 23}{O\,4 \sin \angle 24}$$

and the cross ratio:

$$D = \frac{\sin \angle 13}{\sin \angle 14} \div \frac{\sin \angle 23}{\sin \angle 24},$$

where $\angle 12$ is the angle between the two rays from O to the points z_1 and z_2 etc.; as the choice of O however is entirely arbitrary we have left O out of the expression for D.

A ray pencil projecting a linear point assemblage will be called projective with it. Two pencils projecting projective point assemblages will be called mutually projective; if, more in particular, corresponding rays of these two pencils intersect all on one straight line, we shall call them *perspective*. ,,Perspective pencils of lines" is the dual conception of ,,perspective point assemblages".

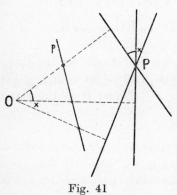

The poles of a ray pencil lie on the polar of the carrier point of the pencil and as the pole of each member is situated on the perpendicular let down from O on the line concerned, the arguments of the poles differ by the same amounts as the slopes of the lines of the original pencil (fig. 41). We come therefore, to the conclusion that the cross ratio is also invariant with respect to the transformation of pole and polar.

Fig. 41

6. *Projective geometry*

As a rule projective properties of figures are much more easily proved by direct projective methods than by analytical calculation.

We shall give a number of examples of theorems proved by the former methods.

a.   Harmonic point quadruples in the complete quadrangle.

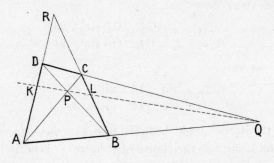

Fig. 42

The complete quadrangle ABCD has six sides and three diagonal points, P, Q and R (fig. 42). Connect P and Q by a line which intersects the two remaining sides in K and L, then the points P, Q, K and L are lying *harmonically* ($D=-1$). The proof is as follows:

$$D\,(\text{PQKL}) = (\text{projected from A on RB})) = D\,(\text{CBRL}).$$

$$= (\text{projected from D on KQ}) = (\text{QPKL}).$$

Now P and Q have changed places, but from the definition of the cross ratio it follows that it is inverted by changing two elements. So D must be either $+1$ or -1, and from the figure we see, that in this case it is -1.

b.   Desargues' theorem was proved analytically in a previous section. The projective proof is as follows: (fig. 31). The point quadruples $-wAwC$ and $-vBvC$ are both harmonic ($D=-1$) and as they have one point in common (C) they must be perspective, so that $w-v$ and $-w\,v$ must intersect on the side AB (in the point u); for the same reason $w\,v$ and $-w\,v$ must meet on AB.; q.e.d.

c. Pappos' theorem I follows from the fact, that in fig. 43, where the lines u_2C and u_3B are parallel and so on, defining three points v_1, v_2 and v_3 on the straight line at infinity, A, B and C are collinear for elementary reasons. By a collineation this figure is transformed into fig. 36 of page 42, but the three points A, B and C will remain collinear, and this is what the theorem states.

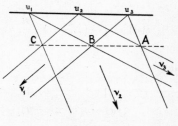

Fig. 43

7. *Involution*

We shall now return to the study of the point assemblage:

$$z=\frac{z_1+z_2u}{1+u}$$

lying on the straight line through the two points z_1 and z_2, and try to find the point which lies harmonically with the point u with respect to z_1 and z_2. This point u' has to be determined from

$$D\left(z_1z_2z\left(u\right)z\left(u'\right)\right)=-1.$$

or, as $u=0$ for z_1, $u=\infty$ for z_2, from:

$$\frac{u-0}{u'-0}\div\frac{u-\infty}{u'-\infty}=-1;\text{ hence }u'=-u.$$

The transformation transforming each point into the fourth harmonic with respect to two fixed points, is called the *involution*, its analytical expression is simply:

$$u'=-u.$$

Evidently the relation is reciprocal, the points u and $-u$ form a *pair of the involution*. There are two points which coincide with their partners, namely $u=0$ and $u=\infty$; these are precisely the points z_1 and z_2. Because of this property they are called the *double points* of the involution. The middle of the section z_1z_2 $(u=1)$ is the partner of the infinite point of the line $(u=-1)$.

The harmonic mean of the distances of two partners of the involution to one of the double points is constant;

$$z(u) - z_1 = (z_2 - z_1)\frac{u}{1+u}; \qquad z(-u) - z_1 = (z_1 - z_2)\frac{u}{1-u},$$

hence

$$\frac{1}{z(u) - z_1} + \frac{1}{z(-u) - z_1} = \frac{2}{z_2 - z_1} = \text{constant} = \frac{1}{f}$$

and as all vectors involved are in the same direction, the same relation holds for the absolute values. With respect to the second double point (z_2) we come to the same result with opposite sign:

$$\frac{1}{z(u) - z_2} + \frac{1}{(z-u) - z_2} = \frac{2}{z_1 - z_2} = \text{constant.}$$

Another theorem states that the product of the distances of the partners of a pair to the ,,*centre*" of the involution, that is the point $\frac{1}{2}(z_1 + z_2)$, is constant. Indeed:

$$\left(z(u) - \frac{z_1 + z_2}{2}\right)\left(z(-u) - \frac{z_1 + z_2}{2}\right) =$$

$$= \left(\frac{z_1 + z_2 u}{1+u} - \frac{z_1 + z_2}{2}\right)\left(\frac{z_1 - z_2 u}{1-u} - \frac{z_1 + z_2}{2}\right) = \left(\frac{z_1 - z_2}{2}\right)^2 = \text{constant}$$

and as all vectors involved are in the same direction the same holds for the absolute values.

This theorem provides us with a second definition of the involution: The involution transforms a point into its partner in such a way that the product of the distances of the two partners to a fixed centre is constant.

This definition is more general than the original one. If the two partners are situated on the same side of the centre, as was the case up to now, the product is positive, if, however, we choose the points on opposite sides of the center, the product is negative and there exist no real double points of the involution. We distinguish *hyperbolic* (product positive, real double points) from *elliptic* (product negative, imaginary double points) and *parabolic* (product zero, two coinciding double points) involutions. In the case of the parabolic involution one of the points of each pair coincides always with the double point.

Now the point $1/u$ lies symmetrical with the point u with respect to the centre $\frac{1}{2}(z_1 + z_2)$:

$$z(u) - \frac{z_1 + z_2}{2} = \frac{u-1}{u+1} \cdot \frac{z_2 - z_1}{2}; \quad z\left(\frac{1}{u}\right) - \frac{z_1 + z_2}{2} = \frac{1-u}{1+u} \cdot \frac{z_2 - z_1}{2};$$

and, as the pairs $(u, -u)$ form a hyperbolic involution, the pairs of points $(u, -1/u)$, form an elliptic involution. The basic points $z_1 (u = +0)$ and $z_2 (u = -\infty)$ are no longer double points, but form a pair. The double points are imaginary $(u = \pm i)$ and with respect to these imaginary double points the harmonic configuration of the pairs is maintained.

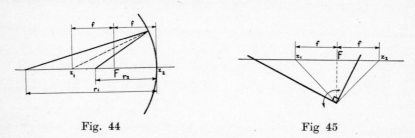

Fig. 44   Fig 45

An example of a hyperbolic involution is provided by the pairs of objects and images in the case of reflection of light by a spherical mirror, for which the equation $1/r_1 + 1/r_2 = 1/f$ holds. This case is depicted in fig. 44; the mirror is placed in the point z_2, the centre of the spherical surface is placed in z_1.

An example of an elliptic involution is provided by the pairs of points of insersection of the sides of a right angle with a straight line, if the right angle is rotated round its vertex, fig. 45.

A point involution can be picked up by a projecting ray pencil and projected on a second line. If in particular, as is the case in fig. 45, the rays of each pair of the ray involution are at right angles we speak of an *orthogonal involution*. In projecting an involution on an other line carrier, the double points are perspective, but the centre is not projected as the centre of the new involution; the centre is not a projective but a metric characteristic of the involution.

CHAPTER IV

THE TRIANGLE

1. *Centre of gravity, orthocentre, circumcentre*

The line connecting one of the vertices with the middle of the opposite side of the triangle is called a *median*. The three medians pass through one point called the *centre of gravity* (point G in fig. 46).

This theorem is a special case of Ceva's theorem ($u = v = w = 1$)

The middle of the side z_2z_3 is $\dfrac{z_2 + z_3}{2}$. Connect this point with z_1.

Take on this median the point G that divides the median in ratio 2 to 1. Its position is:

$$z_G = \tfrac{1}{3}\,(z_1 + z_2 + z_3).$$

As this result is symmetrical in the indices, we should have found the same point on the two other medians, so that all three medians pass through this point G.

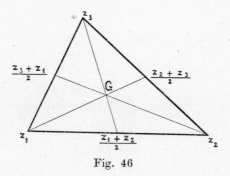

Fig. 46

Taking G as origin changes the last equation into:

$$0 = z_1 + z_2 + z_3$$

and as this is a vector equation, it means that separately:

$$\Sigma\, x_i = 0 \quad \text{and} \quad \Sigma\, y_i = 0$$

A rotation of the triangle round the centre of gravity does not change the relation:

$$0 = z_1 + z_2 + z_3$$

and by separating once more real and imaginary parts we conclude that the sum of the perpendiculars let down from the three vertices on any straight line through the centre of gravity is zero.

Divide the three sides by the points PQR in the same ratio (fig. 47):

$$z_P = \frac{z_1 + u z_2}{1 + u}; \quad z_Q = \frac{z_2 + u z_3}{1 + u}; \quad z_R = \frac{z_3 + u z_1}{1 + u}.$$

The center of gravity of the triangle PQR is

$$\tfrac{1}{3}(z_P + z_Q + z_R) = \tfrac{1}{3}(z_1 + z_2 + z_3)$$

and coincides with the centre of gravity of the whole triangle ABC (PAPPOS). The centre of gravity of the subtriangle CRQ is:

$$\tfrac{1}{3}(z_3 + z_R + z_Q) = \tfrac{1}{3}\frac{(z_1 + 2z_3) + (z_1 + 2z_3)u}{1 + u}$$

and when u varies, this point decribes a straight line through

$$\frac{z_1 + 2z_3}{3} \ (u = 0) \text{ and}$$

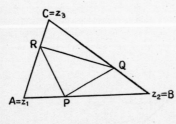

$$\frac{z_1 + 2z_3}{3} \ (u = \infty),$$

Fig. 47

these being the points lying on one third from C on the two sides BC and CA of the triangle. This theorem is also due to PAPPOS.

The *area* of the triangle is half the vector products of the vectors $z_2 - z_1$ and $z_3 - z_1$ (compare p. 19), that is:

$$A = \frac{1}{4j}\left\{ (z_3 - z_1)(z_2^* - z_1^*) - (z_3^* - z_1^*)(z_2 - z_1) \right\}$$

$$= \frac{j}{4}\begin{vmatrix} 1 & 1 & 1 \\ z_1 & z_2 & z_3 \\ z_1^* & z_2^* & z_3^* \end{vmatrix}$$

It is zero if the three points are collinear.

In order to find the common point of intersection of the three perpendiculars, we calculate the point of intersection of two of them. If the result is symmetrical in the indices we may infer that the three perpendiculars are concurrent (orthocentre O, z_0, fig. 48).

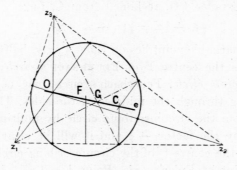

Fig. 48

The vector $z_0 - z_3$ should be perpendicular to $z_2 - z_1$ and $z_0 - z_1$ should be perpendicular to $z_3 - z_2$, in formula:

$$\frac{z_0 - z_3}{z_0^* - z_3^*} \cdot \frac{z_2^* - z_1^*}{z_2 - z_1} = \frac{z_0 - z_1}{z_0^* - z_1^*} \cdot \frac{z_3^* - z_2^*}{z_3 - z_2} = -1$$

which after figuring out gives the symmetrical result:

$$z_0 = \frac{z_1 \{ z_1 (z_2^* - z_3^*) + z_1^* (z_2 - z_3) \} + \text{cycl.}}{4jA}.$$

Let us next calculate the centre C of the circumscribing circle (fig. 48). It is at equal distances from the three vertices and therefore determined by the equations:

$$(z_C - z_1)(z_C^* - z_1^*) = (z_C - z_2)(z_C^* - z_2^*) = (z_C - z_3)(z_C^* - z_3^*) = R^2$$

where R is the radius of the circumscribing circle. Figuring out, we find for C the symmetrical expression:

$$z_C = \frac{z_1 z_1^* (z_3 - z_2) + \text{cycl.}}{4jA}$$

and for the radius R:

$$R = \frac{|z_2 - z_1| \cdot |z_3 - z_2| \cdot |z_1 - z_3|}{4A}.$$

2. *Euler's axis, nine points circle*

The line connecting the centre of the circumscribing circle C with the orthocenter O is called EULER's *axis* (line e in fig. 48). This axis contains also the centre of gravity and this lies at one third of the distance CO, reckoned from C, for:

$$\tfrac{2}{3} z_C + \tfrac{1}{3} z_0 = \tfrac{1}{3} (z_1 + z_2 + z_3).$$

A fourth remarkable point lies on Euler's axis, halfway between C and O. It is the centre F of FEUERBACH's *circle*, also known as the *nine points circle*. Feuerbach's circle can be defined as the circle going through the middles of the sides. This circle can be deduced from the circumscribing circle by multiplication with respect to G by the factor $-\tfrac{1}{2}$ and it will be clear that by this multiplication the centre C of the circumscribing circle is brought to another point of Euler's axis. Point $F = \tfrac{1}{2} z_C + \tfrac{1}{2} z_0$ is:

$$z_F = \frac{z_1^2 (z_2^{*} - z_3^{*}) + \text{cycl.}}{8jA}.$$

If we lay the origin in the circumcentre C we find the auxiliary points by the following formulae:

Circumcentre   : $z = 0$
Centre of gravity   : $z = \tfrac{1}{3} (z_1 + z_2 + z_3)$
Orthocentre   : $z = z_1 + z_2 + z_3$
FEUERBACH's point: $z = \tfrac{1}{2} (z_1 + z_2 + z_3)$

Because FC=FO, the bases of the perpendiculars let down from C and O on any of the three sides of the triangle, have the same distance to F. Therefore, Feuerbach's circle not only passes through the middles of the sides of the triangle, but also through the bases of the perpendiculars.

Furthermore, Feuerbach's circle may also be considered as the multiplication of the circumscribing circle with respect to the orthocentre by the factor $\tfrac{1}{2}$. Therefore the middles of the stretches of the perpendiculars comprised between the orthocentre and the vertices will also lie on FEUERBACH's circle. All this explains its second name: *nine points circle*.

If z_4 is any fourth point on the circumscribing circle, the point S halfway between the orthocentre and z_4 will be $\tfrac{1}{2} (z_1 + z_2 + z_3 + z_4)$. This point is situated on Feuerbach's circle.

3. *Base points of perpendiculars, Wallace's theorem*

We found in the last chapter (p. 39) that the base of the perpendicular let down from the origin on a line p is simply $1/p^*$, the inversion of the pole P.

Inserting the values for the triangle $z_1 z_2 z_3$ (fig. 49):

$$\frac{1}{p_2^*} = \tfrac12 \frac{z_1 z_3^* - z_1^* z_3}{z_3^* - z_1^*} \; ; \; \frac{1}{p_1^*} = \tfrac12 \frac{z_2^* z_3 - z_2 z_3^*}{z_2^* - z_3^*} \; ,$$

yielding for the vector w_3, connecting these two bases:

$$w_3 = \frac{1}{p_1^*} - \frac{1}{p_2^*} = \tfrac12 \left(\frac{z_3 - z_1}{z_3^* - z_1^*} - \frac{z_2 - z_3}{z_2^* - z_3^*} \right) z_3^* \; .$$

The form between brackets is independent of the location of O and only depends on the directions of the two lines. Indeed it equals, if τ_1 and τ_2 are the arguments of the two lines:

$$e^{2j\tau_2} - e^{2j\tau_1} = e^{j(\tau_1 + \tau_2)} \left\{ e^{j(\tau_2 - \tau_1)} - e^{-j(\tau_2 - \tau_1)} \right\}$$

$$= 2j\, e^{j(\tau_1 + \tau_2)} \sin(\tau_2 - \tau_1)$$

so that $|w_3| = |z_3|$. $\sin(\tau_2 - \tau_1)$.

Further, it appears that w_3 is proportional to z_3^*. If, therefore, O moves over a circle having z_3 as its centre, the absolute value of w_3 remains constant. Conversely: if a line of constant length moves with its extremities along the two legs of an angle, the locus of the points of intersection of the normals erected on the legs of the angle at the extremities of the moving line will be a

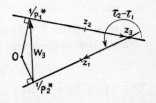

Fig. 49

circle of which the centre coincides with the vertex of the angle.

In the second place we find, that Oz_3 and w_3 rotate with the same angular velocity, only in opposite directions.

Now, draw the line $z_2 z_1$ and find the base point vector, if z_2 is the vertex of the angle $z_3 z_2 z_1$. This line is

$$w_2 = \tfrac12 \left(\frac{z_2 - z_3}{z_2^* - z_3^*} - \frac{z_1 - z_2}{z_1^* - z_2^*} \right) . z_2^* .$$

The ratio w_2/w_3 is:

$$\frac{w_2}{w_3} = -\frac{(z_2 - z_1)(z_2^* - z_3^*) - (z_2^* - z_1^*)(z_2 - z_3)}{(z_3 - z_2)(z_3^* - z_1^*) - (z_3^* - z_2^*)(z_3 - z_1)} \cdot \frac{(z_3^* - z_1^*) \cdot z_2^*}{(z_2^* - z_1^*) \cdot z_3^*}.$$

The first factor is the quotient of two imaginary values and thus real. The rest is real if z_1, z_2, z_3 and the origin lie on one circle; w_2 and w_3 have then the same direction and coincide.

By the above we have proved *Wallace's* theorem (1798):

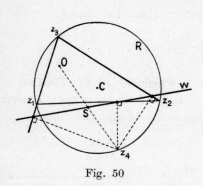

The bases of the perpendiculars let down from any point of the circumscribing circle on the three sides of a triangle are collinear. This common base points line will be called Wallace's line. (fig. 50).

If this point, from now on to be called z_4, moves over the circumscribing circle with angular velocity ω, all three vectors

Fig. 50

from z_4 to z_1, z_2 and z_3 rotate with half this velocity, Wallace's line rotates also with the velocity $\omega/2$ but in the opposite sense.

4. *Steiner's cycloid*

We now again lay the origin in the circumcentre. For this choice of the origin (fig. 50):

$$z_1 z_1^* = z_2 z_2^* = z_3 z_3^* = z_4 z_4^* = R^2 \quad \ldots \ldots \quad (1)$$

The place of the bases of the perpendiculars let down from z_4 on the sides of the triangle can be borrowed from the last section, provided we subtract z_4 from all vectors mentioned there: The base on the side $z_1 z_3$ will be:

$$\tfrac{1}{2}\frac{(z_1 - z_4)(z_3^* - z_4^*) - (z_1^* - z_4^*)(z_3 - z_4)}{(z_3^* - z_1^*)} + z_4$$

for which we can write with the help of (1):

$$\tfrac{1}{2}(z_1 + z_2 + z_3 + z_4) - \tfrac{1}{2}\frac{z_1 z_3 + z_2 z_4}{z_4}.$$

Now $\tfrac{1}{2}(z_1 + z_2 + z_3 + z_4)$ is the point S, situated on Feuerbach's circle midway between the orthocentre and point z_4 on the circumscribing circle. The vector from the base point to this point S is:

$$\frac{1}{2}\,\frac{z_1 z_3 + z_2 z_4}{z_4}$$

and its direction is determined by the argument factor

$$\frac{z_4^{\cdot}\,(z_1 z_3 + z_2 z_4)}{z_4\,(z_1^{\cdot} z_3^{\cdot} + z_2^{\cdot} z_4^{\cdot})}$$

which again with the aid of (1) appears to be:

$$\frac{1}{R}\,\sqrt{\frac{z_1 z_2 z_3}{z_4}}$$

and is therefore independent of the choice of the base, so that we have not only proved once again that the three bases lie in one line, but also that this line passes through the point S, and that, moreover, this line rotates with half of the velocity with which z_4 rotates and in opposite sense.

If z_4 moves on the circumscribing circle, point S moves with the same angular velocity over Feuerbach's circle. At the same time Wallace's line, always passing through S, rotates with half this angular velocity. As we shall see in Ch. XIX the envelope of lines which move in this way is a hypocycloid with three cusps. It is also the track of a point of a circle of radius $R/2$ rolling within a circle of radius $3R/2$. This cycloid is called *Steiner's cycloid* (fig. 51).

If z_4 coincides with a vertex of the triangle, Wallace's line coincides with the perpendicular drawn from this vertex on to the opposite side. If z_4 lies diametrically opposite z_2, $z_1 z_3$ is Wallace's line. In this way we easily find 6 Wallace lines, namely the three sides of the triangle and the three perpendiculars. But if we consider the three vertices and the orthocentre as a complete quadrangle, having six sides, each joining two of the points, we see that sides and perpendiculars of the triangle are equivalent with respect

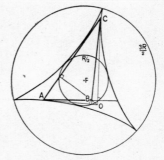

Fig. 51

to this quadrangle and may be interchanged. A complete

quadrangle of which two opposite sides are orthogonal, as is the case with the configuration of the sides and perpendiculars of a triangle is called an *orthogonal* complete quadrangle.

Feuerbach's circle and Steiner's cycloid are, strictly speaking, related to the orthogonal complete quadrangle, of which the triangle from which we started is only a part.

CHAPTER V

THE CIRCLE

1. *Properties of constant angle and of constant power*

In the preceding chapters the circle has been of frequent occurrence and so far, we have in our applications simply borrowed its proporties from elementary euclids. This refers in particular to the theorems of constant angle and of constant power. For consistency, however, we shall now prove these theorems along the lines of the present treatise. For the proof of Ptolemaios' theorem we refer to page 21.

Proof of the constant angle theorem: Let A, B and P be points on the circle $z = r \exp(ju)$; B is situated on the real axis $(u = 0)$, A is fixed $(u = \varphi)$ and P is arbitrary (fig. 52).

Vector AP is: $r \exp(ju) - r \exp(j\varphi)$.
Vector BP is: $r \exp(ju) - r$.

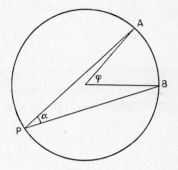

Fig. 52

The quotient of these two vectors contains the factor $\exp(ja)$ as argument function:

$$\text{Real function} \cdot \exp(ja) = \frac{r \exp(ju) - r \exp(j\varphi)}{r \exp(ju) - r}.$$

Divide this by the conjugate equation, we find:

$$\exp(2ja) = \frac{\exp(ju) - \exp(j\varphi)}{\exp(ju) - 1} \cdot \frac{\exp(-ju) - 1}{\exp(-ju) - \exp(-j\varphi)} = \exp(j\varphi)$$

from which: $a = \varphi/2$, q.e.d.

Proof of the constant power theorem: Choose point A on the negative real axis at a distance a from O (fig. 53). Draw a secant through A; its formula is:

$$z = -a + s \exp(j\varphi).$$

It cuts the circle

$$z = r \exp(ju),$$

where:

$$- a + s \exp{(j\varphi)} = r \exp{(ju)}.$$

Multiplying this equation by its conjugate, we shall find:

$$a^2 - 2\ as\ \cos\varphi + s^2 = r^2.$$

This equation has two roots, s_1 and s_2, the product of which equals $a^2 - r^2$, independent of the choice of φ, q.e.d.

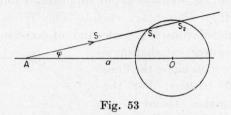

Fig. 53

2. General circle formula

We shall now prove that each of the curves represented by the equation:

$$z = \frac{z_1 + z_2 u}{z_3 + z_4 u} \quad \cdot \quad \cdot \quad \cdot \quad \cdot \quad \cdot \quad \cdot \quad \cdot \quad (1)$$

is a circle. The curve passes through point $A = z_1/z_3\ (u = 0)$ (fig. 54) and through point $B = z_2/z_4\ (u = \infty)$.

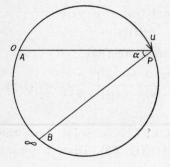

Fig. 54

Let P be a point on the curve, represented by (1). The vector PA is:

$$\frac{z_1 + z_2 u}{z_3 + z_4 u} - \frac{z_1}{z_3} = \frac{u}{z_3} \frac{z_2 z_3 - z_1 z_4}{z_3 + z_4 u}.$$

The vector PB is:

$$\frac{z_1 + z_2 u}{z_3 + z_4 u} - \frac{z_2}{z_4} = - \frac{1}{z_4} \frac{z_2 z_3 - z_1 z_4}{z_3 + z_4 u}$$

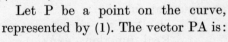

so that the quotient $\dfrac{PA}{PB} = - \dfrac{z_4}{z_3} u.$

Now, as z_3 and z_4 are constant and u is real, the argument of this quotient is constant. Therefore the angle α in fig. 2 is independent of u from which we may conclude that P describes a circle.

All formulae used up to now to represent circles can be brought to the general form (1) by a real transformation of the parameter. We saw already (p. 4) that

$$z = \tfrac{1}{2}\left(1 + \exp\left(jv\right)\right)$$

can be transformed into:

$$z = \frac{1}{1 - ju}$$

by the transformation:

$$u = -\tan\left(v/2\right)$$

By the same transformation

$$z = \exp\left(jv\right)$$

is transformed into:

$$z = \frac{1 + ju}{1 - ju}.$$

Appollonius' circle was found (p. 23) in the form:

$$a \exp\left(jv\right) = \frac{z - z_1}{z - z_2}$$

and by the same transformation it is changed into:

$$z = \frac{a\left(1 + ju\right)z_2 - \left(1 - ju\right)z_1}{a\left(1 + ju\right) - \left(1 - ju\right)}$$

of the character of (1), which proves that Appolonius' curve is indeed a circle.

On p. 20 we found the equation for the circle passing through the three points z_1, z_2, and z_3:

$$u = \frac{z_1 - z_3}{z_1 - z} \div \frac{z_2 - z_3}{z_2 - z}$$

and indeed, solving this equation for z, gives, again in accordance with (1):

$$z = \frac{\left(z_1 - z_3\right)z_2 - \left(z_2 - z_3\right)z_1 u}{z_1 - z_3 - \left(z_2 - z_3\right)u}.$$

What is the radius r and the centre z_c of the circle represented by (1)? Solve the equation for u:

$$-u = \frac{z_1 - zz_3}{z_2 - zz_4}.$$

As this is real, it must also equal the conjugate value of the right hand side, so that the circle is represented by the equation:

$$(z_1 - z z_3)(z_2^* - z^* z_4^*) = (z_1^* - z^* z_3^*)(z_2 - z z_4)$$

and if we arrange the symbols so that we find the form:

$$(z - z_c)(z^* - z_c^*) = r^2$$

equating corresponding terms will give us z_c and r. This leads to

$$z_c = \frac{z_1 z_4^* - z_2 z_3^*}{z_3 z_4^* - z_3^* z_4} \quad \text{and} \quad |z_c|^2 - r^2 = \frac{z_1 z_2^* - z_1^* z_2}{z_3 z_4^* - z_3^* z_4}.$$

The last expression gives us the power of the circle for the origin acting as the pole.

3. *Circuit impedance and admittance.*

Circle diagrams are constantly encountered in electrotechnical circuit theory. The impedance of a circuit, containing a resistance R, selfinduction L and capacity C in series, when applying an electromotive force of angular frequency ω; is:

$$z = j \omega L + R + \frac{1}{j \omega C},$$

or with the new parameter $u = \omega L - \dfrac{1}{\omega C}$:

$$z = R + ju$$

and this is a straight line in the complex z-plane. The admittance $\dfrac{1}{z} = \dfrac{1}{R + ju}$, however, is a circle.

Connecting a resistance R, a capacity C and a selfinduction L in parallel leads to an admittance:

$$\frac{1}{z} = \frac{1}{R} + \frac{1}{j \omega C} + j \omega L$$

which with the new parameter $u = \omega C - \dfrac{1}{\omega L}$ becomes:

$$\frac{1}{z} = \frac{1}{R} + ju$$

and represents a straight line in the complex-plane. Now, however, the impedance z will be a circle.

In more complicated cases both impedance and admittance will be circles. The admittance of the circuit of fig. 55 is:

$$\frac{1}{R_1} + \frac{1}{R_2 + j\omega L} = \frac{R_1 + R_2 + j\omega L}{R_1 R_2 + j\omega LR_1}$$

and this as well as its inversion represents a circle.

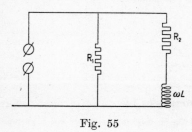

Fig. 55

It is not always the frequency which acts as the varying parameter. In BOUCHEROT's circuit (fig. 56) we find a variable resistance u. The impedance is:

$$z = \frac{a^2}{j(b-a) + u}$$

and this is again represented by a circle. As a matter of electro-technical interest we may observe that i_2 is independent of u. For:

$$e = ja(i_1 + i_2) + v_2; \quad v_2 = -jai_1 \therefore e = jai_2.$$

In other cases, again, it may be the power output which functions as parameter. The circle diagram named after HEYLAND

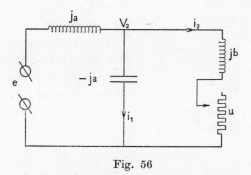

Fig. 56

is obtained by plotting the admittance of a motor as a function of the load.

If one tries to find out why circular diagrams occur so often in electrical engineering one sees that the reason is the linear character of the fundamental equations. And as mechanical vibrations obey similar equations as the electrical ones, the field of application includes mechanics and acoustics.

4. *The circle transformation*

The transformation

$$w = \frac{az+b}{cz+d} \quad (a,\ b,\ c \text{ and } d \text{ complex}) . \quad . \quad . \quad . \quad (1)$$

transforms the circle:

$$z = \frac{z_1 + z_2 u}{z_3 + z_4 u}$$

into another circle:

$$w = \frac{az_1 + bz_3 + (az_2 + bz_4)\,u}{cz_1 + dz_3 + (cz_2 + dz_4)\,u}$$

and for this reason the transformation (1) is called the *circle transformation*.[1]) Straight lines will have to be considered as special cases of circles, as the straight line

$$z = \frac{z_1 + z_2 u}{m + nu}$$

will also be transformed into a circle and it is not impossible that reversely it will turn out as the transform of a circle.

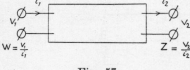

Fig. 57

The technical realization of the circle transformation is furnished by the linear four terminal network. Suppose that linear relations exist between the quantities of the primary and of the secondary sides of the network:

$$v_1 = a\,v_2 + b i_2 \quad . \quad . \quad . \quad . \quad . \quad . \quad (2a)$$

$$i_1 = c v_2 + d i_2 \quad . \quad . \quad . \quad . \quad . \quad . \quad (2b)$$

---

[1]) See e.g. J. L. Coolidge, Treatise on the circle and the sphere. Oxford 1916. A. Feldkeller, Vierpoltheorie.

then we find by dividing:

$$w = \frac{az+b}{cz+d} \quad ; \quad w = \frac{v_1}{i_1} \quad ; \quad z = \frac{v_2}{i_2},$$

so that the impedance is transformed according to the scheme (1) and if z is a circle impedance, w will again have circular character.

Four terminal networks can be of electrical, mechanical, acoustical or even optical character, they may be electromechanical couplings and so on. [1]

Of special interest are symmetrical networks in which case the values v_2 and v_1 for resp. v_1 and v_2, and $- i_2$ and $- i_1$ for resp. i_1 and i_2 must not infringe equ. (2).

In addition to (2), therefore, the equations:

$$v_2 = av_1 - bi_1 \quad \cdots \quad \cdots \quad \text{(3a)}$$
$$- i_2 = cv_1 - di_1 \quad \cdots \quad \cdots \quad \text{(3b)}$$

must hold. Eliminate v_1 from (2a) and (3a):

$$i_1 = \frac{a^2 - 1}{b} v_2 + ai_2$$

and identify this with (2b). Comparison of the corresponding coefficients shows that in the case of a symmetrical network the coefficients must fulfil the conditions:

$$a = d \quad \text{and} \quad a^2 - bc = 1$$

The following considerations will all relate to symmetrical networks so that we shall put $d = a$, the second relation is of no consequence for what follows, but from a purely physical point of view it is even more important than the first one. [2]

For a symmetrical four terminal network the transformation is:

$$w = \frac{az+b}{cz+a} \cdot \quad \cdots \quad \cdots \quad \text{(4)}$$

Characteristic values of z are $z = \infty$ (secondary terminals open) and $z = 0$ (secondary terminals shortcircuited). The corresponding

---

[1] A remarkable relation exists between the circle transformation and the rotation of a solid body in space. See e.g. E. T. WHITTAKER. Analytische Dynamik, p. 13.

[2] E. M. Mc. MILLAN. Jl. Acoust Soc. Am. **18, 344** (1946).

values of w, denoted by w_∞ and w_0 are:

$$w_\infty = a/c \ ; \ w_0 = b/a.$$

Furthermore, the case where $w = z$ is of importance. This value of z is called the wave impedance. An arbitrary number of networks, put in cascade, would not change the impedance. From (4) it follows that this value is $\sqrt{b/c}$, we shall denote it by w_z. We may note that $w_z^2 = w_0 w_\infty$, which means geometrically that the triangles $w_\infty O w_z$ and $w_z O w_0$ are similar (fig. 58).

The transformation (4) can be written as:

$$\left(w - \frac{a}{c}\right)\left(z + \frac{a}{c}\right) = \frac{b}{c} - \frac{a^2}{c^2}$$

or, keeping in mind the meaning of a/c and b/c:

$$(w - w_\infty)(z + w_\infty) = w_z^2 - w_\infty^2 = (w_z - w_\infty)(w_z + w_\infty).$$

Still more explicitly:

$$\frac{w - w_\infty}{w_z - w_\infty} = \frac{w_z + w_\infty}{z + w_\infty}.$$

which means that the triangles $w, -w_\infty, w_z$ and w, w_∞, z are similar (fig. 59).

Now, as w_∞, $-w_\infty$, w_z are fixed points in the plane, this offers

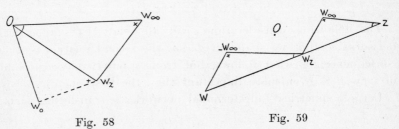

Fig. 58   Fig. 59

us a method to construct point w for any given place of z, thereby performing the transformation point for point.

Besides, it is very instructive to follow how the z-plane is transformed as a whole. (Fig. 60, 61). All radii, emanating from O in the z-plane (fig. 61) will be transformed into w-circles through the fixed points w_0 and w_∞ (fig. 50). The straight line $w_0 w_\infty$ is one of these circles, it contains the point $w = \infty$, corresponding to $z = -a/c$

$(=-w_\infty)$. This point is indicated in the z-plane and the radius
vector through this point makes angles α and β with the coordinate
axis. The transformation is conform and plotting these same angles
α and β in the point w_0 leads us to the w-circles which are the trans-

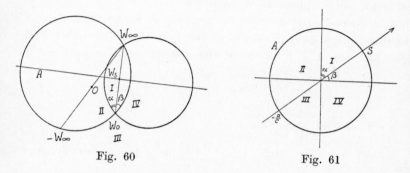

Fig. 60   Fig. 61

forms of the coordinate axes of the z-plane. The circles of the
z-plane having O as center will be transformed into w-circles,
cutting the first set of circles orthogonally. One of these w-circles
is the straight line A. This line contains the point $w=\infty$ and
the corresponding z-circle will contain the point $z=-a/c$. Roman

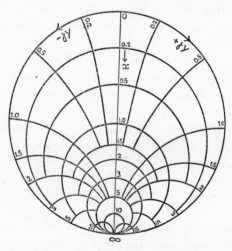

Fig. 62

ciphers indicate where the four quadrants of the z-plane within
the circle A will be represented in the transform.

The entire right half of the z-plane is represented within the right hand circle, drawn in the w-plane. As in many problems only the positive values of the real part of the electric impedance are of importance this circular image of the complete infinitely extended semi-z-plane is of great use.

As a special case of the circle transforms we mention RIECKE's diagram, often used in papers of the Bell Telephone Laboratories (See fig. 62). Use is made of the special circle transformation:

$$w = j \frac{1-z}{1+z}.$$

5. *Projective properties*

Considering the circle $z = \dfrac{z_1 + z_2 u}{z_3 + z_4 u}$ as a point assemblage we may inquire what the cross ratio is of four points characterized by the values u_1, u_2, u_3 and u_4 of the parameter.

By figuring out it appears that:

$$D = \frac{z(u_1) - z(u_3)}{z(u_2) - z(u_3)} \div \frac{z(u_1) - z(u_4)}{z(u_2) - z(u_4)} = \frac{u_1 - u_3}{u_2 - u_3} \div \frac{u_1 - u_4}{u_2 - u_4}.$$

The anharmonic ratio is thus independent of the choice of the four vectors z_1, z_2, z_3 and z_4 and, moreover, is real as we had already expected from what was said on p. 20.

As the circle transformations only change the values of the vectors z_i but leave u unchanged in its character of parameter we infer that the cross ratio is invariant with respect to circle transformations.

It is possible to correlate a circular point assemblage to a linear one. Indeed, by a suitable circle transformation the circle can always be transformed to:

$$z = \frac{m + nu}{z_1 + z_2 u}.$$

This is a circle through the origin, as for $u = -m/n$, $z = 0$.

The circle character may also be concluded from the fact that this z is the inversion of the straight line

$$z = \frac{z_1^* + z_2^* u}{m + nu}.$$

Circle and straight line are perspective in the sense that points of the same u-value are [seen from O in the same direction. Indeed the quotient of the two z-values is real:

$$\frac{m+nu}{z_1+z_2u} : \frac{z_1^\bullet+z_2^\bullet u}{m+nu} = \frac{(m+nu)^2}{|z_1+z_2u|^2}$$

and this proves the property mentioned (fig. 63).

As the linear point assembly

$$\frac{z_1^\bullet+z_2^\bullet u}{m+nu}$$

and also the pencil of rays projecting it from O is projective with any linear point assemblage of the form

$$z = \frac{z_a+z_bu}{k+lu}$$

we see that any circular point assemblage

$$z = \frac{z_1+z_2u}{z_3+z_4u}.$$

is projective with any of these linear point assemblages, provided we project the circular point assemblage from a point situated on the circle itself.

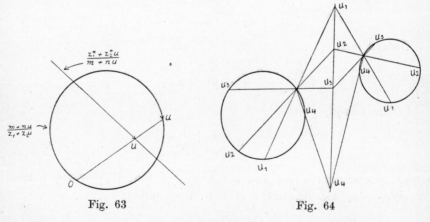

Fig. 63   Fig. 64

Fig. 64 shows how by the intermediary of a straight line we can construct two point quadruples on two circles of the same cross ratio.

The circular point assemblage

$$z = \frac{m + nu}{z_1 + z_2 u}$$

is not only perspective with its inversion but also with any linear assemblage

$$z = \frac{z_1^* + z_2^* u}{k + lu}$$

and particularly also with $z = z_1^* + z_2^* u$. This furnishes an easy way to construct the assemblage

$$z = \frac{m + nu}{z_1 + z_2 u}$$

(fig. 65). First construct the uniform assemblage $z_1^* + z_2^* u$. Then find the points m/z_1 on the radius vector of z_1^* and n/z_2 on the radius vector of z_2^*. Draw the circle through the points O, m/z_1 and n/z_2 and finally project the linear point assemblage on the circle.

By taking together as pairs the rays with opposite parameter values we obtain an involution. The double rays are the rays through z_1^* and z_2^* ($u = \pm 0$; $u = \pm \infty$). Join the points $+u$ and $-u$ on the circle. This line has a line vector $p(u)$, determined by

$$p(u) = 2 \frac{z(+u) - z(-u)}{z^*(+u) z(-u) - z(+u) \cdot z^*(-u)}$$

figured out:

$$p(u) = 2 \frac{z_1^{*2} - z_2^{*2} u^2}{m^2 - n^2 u^2} \cdot \frac{mz_2 - nz_1}{z_1^* z_2 - z_1 z_2^*}.$$

The factor

$$2 \frac{mz_2 - nz_1}{z_1^* z_2 - z_1 z_2^*}$$

is independent of u and hence we see that by varying u the poles $p(u)$ will describe a straight line, similar to:

$$\frac{z_1^{*2} - z_2^{*2} v}{m^2 - n^2 v} \; ; \; v = u^2,$$

but if the poles of all the lines joining $+u$ and $-u$ are on a straight

line, the lines themselves pass through a single point Q (fig. 66).
By the above we have correlated by projective means the ray

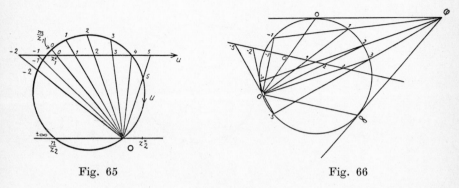

Fig. 65   Fig. 66

pencil O with the ray pencil Q in such a way however, that one
ray of Q corresponds to two rays of O. It is therefore, preferable
to say that we have correlated the involution in O with the ray
pencil in Q.

The involution in O may be transformed by projective means
into point or ray involutions of the general formula:

$$z = \frac{z_1 + z_2 u}{m + nu}, \text{ resp. } p = \frac{p_1 + p_2 u}{m + nu} \qquad (m \text{ and } n \text{ are real})$$

and the ray pencil in Q into point assemblages or ray-pencils of
the formula:

$$z = \frac{z_3 + z_4 u^2}{r + su^2}, \text{ resp. } p = \frac{p_3 + p_4 u^2}{r + su^2} \qquad (r \text{ and } s \text{ are real}).$$

and we shall call all these involutions, point assemblages and ray
pencils mutually projective.

We now have the following construction for the pairs of an
involution *fig.* 67. Cut a ray pencil Q by a circle. Project the points
of intersection from a point O of the circle by a ray involution. The
double rays of the involution point to the tangent points of the
tangents from Q to the circle.

The rays u and $-u$ lie harmonically with respect to the double
rays.

We may add here that the role of the circle in the correlation

of involution and pencil may be taken over by any curve of the
second order (conic). This follows from the fact that the correlation

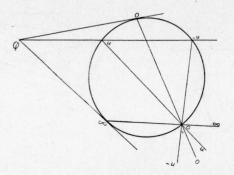

Fig. 67

belongs to the projective properties and as the conics are projections
of the circle the argument holds for conics in general as well.

CHAPTER VI

ALGEBRAIC CURVES

1. *Unicursal curves of the n-th order*

In general the curve of the formula

$$z = \frac{z_0 + z_1 u + z_2 u^2 \ldots + z_n u^n}{m_0 + m_1 u + m_2 u^2 \ldots + m_n u^n} \quad \cdot \quad \cdot \quad \cdot \quad \cdot \quad (1)$$

is of the *n-th* order, by which we mean that it cuts a straight line in n points apart from the point at infinity. The *m's* are all real. Curves of this kind are encountered in alternating current theory as soon as we consider impedances and admittances (as functions of frequency) for circuits consisting of two and more parallel loops. [1])

However (1) is not the most general curve of the *n-th* order as defined in Cartesian geometry:

$$a_0 x^n + a_1 x^{n-1} + a_2 x^{n-1} y + \ldots + a_k y^n = 0$$

possessing

$1 + 2 + 3 + \ldots + (n+1) = \frac{1}{2} (n+1)(n+2) = k+1$ coefficients.

As only the ratio of the coefficients is of importance there are ∞^k curves of the *n-th* order. Formula (1) contains $3(n+1)$ coefficients, and consequently, we find here $\infty^{3(n+1)-1}$ different forms.

Now by the linear transformation

$$u = \frac{p + qv}{r + sv}$$

numbering ∞^3, we can transform the formula into another one

---

[1]) Litterature: O. BLOCH: Die Ortskurven der Wechselstromtechnik. A. BLONDEL: Revue Gén. de l'Electr. 1938, p. 739, 773, 803. F. M. COLEBROOK: Alternating Currents and Transients. M. J. DE LANGE: Beginselen der vectormeetkunde.

of the family (1), but the curve remains the same, so that the number of curves denoted by (1) is actually only ∞^{3n-1}.

For $n = 2$: $k = 5$ and $3n - 1 = 5$ too so that formula (1) represents indeed all curves of the second order, but for $n = 3$: we have $k = 9$, whereas $3n - 1 = 8$, so that (1) represents only part of the third order curves.

For $n = 4$; we have $k = 14$, and $3n - 1 = 11$, and formula (1) represents only a small part of all fourth order curves.

The curves denoted by (1) are called n-th order *unicursal* curves or curves of deficiency[1]) zero. The word deficiency refers to the number of double points (including cusps), the unicursal curves being characterized by a maximum number of double—or higher multiple points. By a continuous change in the coefficients in the equation of the curve, the curve may change from a to b (fig. 68)

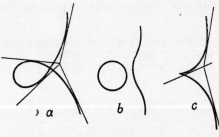

Fig. 68

and then consists of two branches and this goes at the cost of a double point; cf. fig. 8 and 9, p. 10.

Although the deficient curves are the more general type they are of less importance than the unicursal type for all technical and physical applications. In many cases the separate loops may be considered as separate curves being more or less incidentally represented by the same Cartesian formula. We shall treat in section **5** a third order curve of the multicursal type (conchoide).

The class v of a curve of the n-th order is our next point of discussion.

---

[1]) In German texts: Geschlecht.

Let the formula of the curve be:

$$z = \frac{f(u)}{g(u)}$$

where f and g are of the n-th order in u, $g(u)$ having real doefficients.

The formula for the tangent is

$$\dot{z} = \frac{g\dot{f} - f\dot{g}}{g^2}$$

and we find the tangents from the origin by establishing the condition that $\dot{z}$ and z shall have the same direction, in formula:

$$z\dot{z}^* - z^*\dot{z} = 0$$

or

$$f(g\dot{f}^* - f^*\dot{g}) - f^*(g\dot{f} - f\dot{g}) = 0$$

from which as the second and fourth terms cancel out;

$$f\dot{f}^* - f^*\dot{f} = 0 \quad . \quad . \quad . \quad . \quad . \quad . \quad . \quad . \quad (2)$$

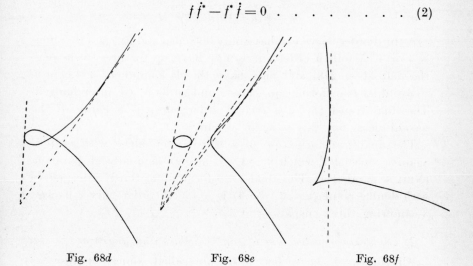

Fig. 68d   Fig. 68e   Fig. 68f

and this is an equation in u of the order $n + n - 1 = 2n - 1$, but the coefficient of the term of the highest order in u cancels out automatically, so that the order is $2n - 2$. In this way we find the general rule:

The class of a unicursal curve of the n-th order is $\nu = 2n - 2$.

The second order curves are of the second class, the third order curves of class 4, fourth order curves of class 6.

This number $2n - 2$ for the class of the curve has to be considered as a maximum, as equation (2) may be reduced to a lower order for special values of the coefficients of f and because it may have complex u-roots. If the double point degenerates into a cusp one tangent vanishes and the class changes into the next lower one (fig. 68c, f). Multicursal curves in general have higher classes, v jumping up by 2 for each new loop that appears (fig. 68c).

Double points are found by solving the equations

$$z(u_1) = z(u_2) \quad ; \quad z^*(u_1) = z^*(u_2)$$

for u_1 and u_2. By a similar method as used for finding the class we find that the maximum number of double points is:

$$d = \tfrac{1}{2}(n-1)(n-2).$$

From this we infer, that the deficiency may be defined as

$$m = \tfrac{1}{2}(n-1)(n-2) - d.$$

A third order curve can have only one cusp and its class therefore is 3 or 4. A fourth order curve may have up to three cusps (e.g. the deltoid, p. 248) and may have the class numbers, 3, 4, 5 or 6.

By dual transformation, class v and order n are interchanged. The dual transform of a second order curve is a curve of the second class, but this is again a conic.

The dual transformation of a third order curve with cusp is again a curve for which $n = 3$, $v = 3$, e.g. semi-cubical parabola (NEIL's parabola). The dual transform of a third order curve with double point ($n = 3$, $v = 4$) is a fourth order curve of class 3 (showing three cusps).

2. *Synthetic construction of conics, cubics and quartics*

All curves of the second order are called conics, because, as will be proved later, they can all be generated by cutting a right circular cone by a plane. If the points of intersection with the line at infinity are real, we call the curve a *hyperbola*, if they are non-existent, the curve is an *ellipse* and if they coincide, the curve is a *parabola*. All three types are to be considered as unicursal and they are all projective transforms of each other.

A synthetic way of generating conics is provided by the mutual intersecting of two projective ray-pencils, that is: the locus of the points of intersection of corresponding rays is a conic. For, let the two pencils be:

$$p = \frac{p_1 + p_2 u}{m_1 + m_2 u} \; ; \qquad q = \frac{q_1 + q_2 u}{n_1 + n_2 u} \cdot$$

Corresponding rays intersect in the point:

$$z = 2 \frac{q - p}{p^* q - p q^*} \cdot$$

This is the quotient of two quadratic functions in u, of which the denominator is purely imaginary, so that z is a curve of the second order, q.e.d.

The carrier points P and Q are situated on the conic. As the ray p approaches point Q, the corresponding ray q becomes the tangent in Q ($u = 40$ in fig. 69). Conversely as the ray q reaches P, the corresponding line p becomes tangent in P ($u = -2.8$ in fig. 69).

In the same way as the curve of the second order was built up synthetically by the cutting of two projective ray pencils we

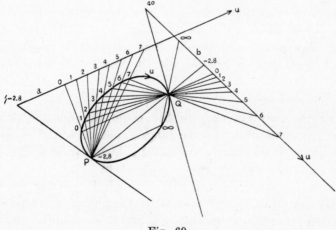

Fig. 69

may build up a curve of the third order (cubic) by cutting a ray involution with a projective ray-pencil.

The corresponding rays are:

$$p = \frac{p_1 + p_2 u}{m_1 + m_2 u}; \qquad q = \frac{q_1 + q_2 u^2}{n_1 + n_2 u^2}.$$

Corresponding rays cut each other in the point:

$$z = 2 \frac{q - p}{p^* q - p q^*}$$

and this is the quotient of two cubic functions in u, of which the denominator is purely imaginary, q.e.d. Again the points P and Q, carrying the involution and the pencil will be points of the curve.

It may, further be proved in exactly the same way that the two projective ray involutions:

$$p = \frac{p_1 + p_2 u^2}{m_1 + m_2 u^2} \text{ and } p = \frac{q_1 + q_2 u^2}{n_1 + n_2 u^2}$$

cut each other along a curve of the fourth order (quartic).

Dualistically, the connecting lines of the corresponding points of two projective linear point series will envelop a curve of the second class, which, however, is also a conic.

In fig. 69 we projected a linear point series on the conic. We want to emphasize that in doing so the cross ratios are changed. In the linear series all cross ratios are real. If they are still to be real after projection on the conic, this conic should be a circle. As this is not the general case, the cross ratio will be changed.

3. *Pole and polar*

Apply the two tangents to the conic through the point P outside the conic. Connect the tangent points A and B by the line p. Point P and line p are called pole and polar with respect to the conic (fig. 70).

Draw an arbitrary secant PRS through P, cutting the polar in Q. We can prove that P and Q lie harmonically with respect to the cone, that is with respect to R and S. For: project the point quadruple PQRS from B on the conic, giving BRAS, then project these points from A again on PS, giving QRPS. Now the cross ratios of PRQS and QRPS are the same, but as two letters are exchanged it must also be reversed. So the cross ratio is either 1 or − 1; the figure says that it is − 1. q.e.d.

Therefore:

The polar is the locus of the points separated harmonically from the pole by the conic.

This provides us at the same time with a definition of the polar

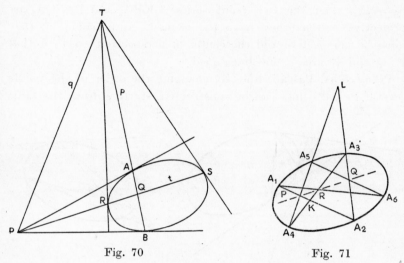

Fig. 70   Fig. 71

for a point like Q, situated within the conic. This polar, q, will have to go through the point T on p, harmonically separated from Q by A and B. The triangle PQT is a polar triangle, by which we mean that each vertex is the pole of the opposite side.

If P moves along the line RS, the polar will also move and so does the point Q. P and Q describe an involution.

This conception of pole and polar is a generalization of the same phenomenon for the circle which we used to define the line coordinates and line vector and on which we based the duality of the geometric theorems, using the unit circle round the origin as reference conic.

4. *Pascal's and Brianchon's theorems*

Important projective properties of the conics are the theorems named after PASCAL (1640) and BRIANCHON (1806).

PASCAL: Take 6 points on a conic (fig. 71), $A_1 \ldots A_6$, connect

them in this order so that a hexagon is created. Opposite
sides A_1A_2 and A_4A_5 meet in P; A_2A_3 and A_5A_6 in Q, A_3A_4
and A_6A_1 in R. Now the theorem states that P, Q and R are
collinear.

We shall give a projective proof of the theorem. Project the
points from A_1 and A_5, cut the first pencil by A_4A_3, the second
by A_2A_3, then the two point series A_4KRA_3 and $LA_2\,QA_3$ are
projective, but as they have the element A_3 in common, they
must be perspective and the center of perspectivity is P, so that
P, Q and R are in one line, q.e.d.

PQ is called Pascal's line. By changing the order of the points
several Pascal's lines can be constructed, starting from the same

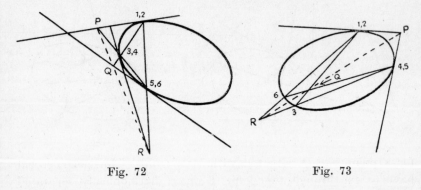

Fig. 72   Fig. 73

6 points. The configuration of these lines have many remarkable
properties, so that the hexagon, inscribed in a conic is known
by the name of *hexagramma mysticum*, but we shall not enter
further into this matter.

Special cases of Pascal's theorem are those where one or more
pairs of points coincide so that the corresponding chord becomes
a tangent. Fig. 72 shows the case where A_1A_2, A_3A_4 and A_5A_6
have become tangents: The tangent triangle is perspective with
the corresponding chord triangle.

In fig. 73 only two sides: A_1A_2 and A_4A_5 have become tangents.
We see here that the tangents in two consecutive points of
a quadrangle inscribed in a conic, intersect on the line joining
two diagonal points (Q and R). If we apply this result to any
other pair of consecutive points of the quadrilateral we get the

property shown in fig. 74 and known as *Simson's theorem* (1735); in words: The diagonals and the lines joining opposite tangent points of a quadrilateral circumscribed to a conic are concurrent.

Brianchon's *theorem* is the dual theorem of Pascal's and may be considered as proved once Pascal's theorem is proved. We borrow from section 1 the result that the dual curve of a conic is again a conic. Now take 6 tangents, producing a circumscribing

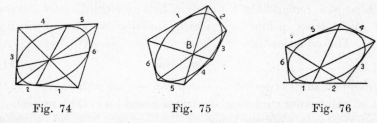

Fig. 74   Fig. 75   Fig. 76

hexagon. Brianchon's theorem states that the three lines connecting opposite vertices of the tangent hexagon are concurrent. (fig. 75).

Special cases arise if two of the tangents coincide, in which case the point of intersection becomes a tangent point and at the same time the hexagon degenerates to a multilateral with less sides.

Fig. 76 shows the case where a pentagon is circumscribed; fig. 77 for a quadrilateral. On the same diagonal we may find another

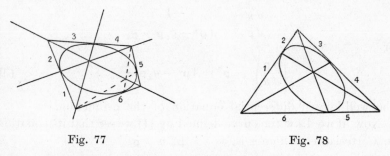

Fig. 77   Fig. 78

point of Brianchon, again as the intersection of two lines joining each a vertex with a tangent point.

Simson's theorem may be derived from Brianchon's by assigning numbers to the tangents as indicated in fig. 74.

Finally, fig. 78 shows the case of three pairs of coinciding tangents. This figure depicts MacLaurin's *theorem*, stating that in a circumscribed triangle the three lines joining the vertices with the opposite tangent points are concurrent, or that the tangent triangle is perspective with the tangentpoint-triangle, the dual case of fig. 72 (compare Desargues' theorem, p. 36).

5. *Cubics, Newton's classification*

There is a remarkable connection between third order curves and Weierstrass' p-function, which function we shall presently define. The equation

$$z = \mathsf{p} + j\,\dot{\mathsf{p}} \,. \quad . \quad . \quad . \quad . \quad . \quad . \quad (1)$$

represents a third order curve and it can be shown (Newton, 1711) that *all* third order curves can be transformed into (1) by projective transformations (collineations).

The definition of Weierstrass' function $\mathsf{p}(u)$ is formulated by:

$$u = \int\limits_{\mathsf{p}}^{\infty} \frac{d\,x}{\sqrt{4\,x^3 - g_2 x - g_3}} \quad . \quad . \quad . \quad . \quad . \quad (2)$$

where g_2 and g_3 are real constants. u considered as a function of p is called the elliptic integral, inversely, p considered as a function of u is called Weierstrass'-p-function.

From (2) it follows that:

$$\frac{d\,u}{d\,\mathsf{p}} = \frac{-1}{\sqrt{4\,\mathsf{p}^3 - g_2\mathsf{p} - g_3}}$$

or

$$\left(\frac{d\,\mathsf{p}}{d\,u}\right)^2 = \dot{\mathsf{p}}^2 = 4\,\mathsf{p}^3 - g_2\mathsf{p} - g_3 \quad . \quad . \quad . \quad . \quad (3)$$

the well-known differential equation of the p-function.

Now, if we draw the curve defined by (1) we see that its equation in Cartesian coordinates is, as $x = \mathsf{p}$, $y = \dot{\mathsf{p}}$:

$$y^2 = 4\,x^3 - g_2 x - g_3 \quad . \quad . \quad . \quad . \quad . \quad (4)$$

and this obviously is a curve of the third order.

Newton's theorem stating that (4) is the transform of *any* third order curve is proved as follows: Project the curve in such a way that a point of inflection coincides with the point ∞ of the y-axis and that the line at infinity is tangent. Of the third order terms only x^3 remains and the curve is then represented by:

$$a x^3 + b x^2 + c x y + d y^2 + e x + f y + g = 0.$$

Take as new variables:

$$x' = x + b/3a; \, y' = y + \frac{c}{2\,d}\,x + \frac{f}{2\,d}$$

the equation is then transformed into:

$$a x'^3 + d y'^2 + e x' + g = 0.$$

By an appropriate choice of the unit on the x-axis a/d can always be made equal to 4, so that equation (4) is obtained, q.e.d.

The curve (1) will assume different characters, according as the constants g_2 and g_3 have different values. $\dot{\mathsf{p}}$ is zero if the right-hand member of (4) is zero. Let the three roots be p_1, p_2 and p_3, p_1 being algebraically the largest (corresponding to the point of intersection of the curve with the x-axis most to the right). Then

$$4 x^3 - g_2 x - g_3 \equiv 4 (x - \mathsf{p}_1)\ (x - \mathsf{p}_2)\ (x - \mathsf{p}_3) \quad . \quad . \quad (5)$$

and by equating the coefficients of equal powers of x on both sides:

$$\mathsf{p}_1 + \mathsf{p}_2 + \mathsf{p}_3 = 0$$

$$\mathsf{p}_1 \mathsf{p}_2 + \mathsf{p}_2 \mathsf{p}_3 + \mathsf{p}_3 \mathsf{p}_1 = -\tfrac{1}{4} g_2$$

$$\mathsf{p}_1 \mathsf{p}_2 \mathsf{p}_3 = \tfrac{1}{4} g_3$$

NEWTON now distinguishes five classes:

I. *Parabolic class.* Let two of the p's be conjugate complex, one real. As representative of this class we take the equi-anharmonic case, that is the case where p_1, p_2 and p_3 are the three third power roots of unity. They are 1, $\exp(j\,\tfrac{2}{3}\,\pi)$ and $\exp(j\,\tfrac{4}{3}\,\pi)$ cf. p. 15. The name equi-anharmonic is suggested by the fact that if four points have a cross ratio equal to $\exp(j\,\tfrac{2}{3}\,\pi)$ or $\exp(j\,\tfrac{4}{3}\,\pi)$ the 6 cross ratio's obtained by combining the four points in all possible ways are the same in both cases, as the reader may check for himself by applying Möbius' rules (p. 21).

The values of $\mathbf{p}$ and $\dot{\mathbf{p}}$ as functions of u are tabulated (e.g. JAHNKE-EMDE. Funktionentafeln p. 72) and the curve may be constructed with the help of these tables (fig. 79). The curve consists of a single track. In the equi-anharmonic case: $g_2 = 0$, $g_3 = 4$ and in Cartesian coordinates the curve is:

$$y^2 = 4\,(x^3 - 1).$$

The cubical parabola $y = x^3$ belongs to this class; the point of inflexion which lies at infinity if we use form. (1) is now projected in the origin.

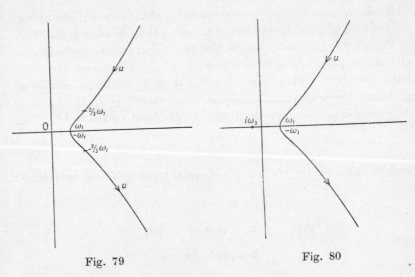

Fig. 79   Fig. 80

II.   *Acnodal class*: $\mathbf{p}_2$ and $\mathbf{p}_3$ are real and equal. As representative we shall take $\mathbf{p}_1 = 1$; $\mathbf{p}_2 = \mathbf{p}_3 = -\frac{1}{2}$ (fig. 80); The curve has an isolated double point or *acnode*, $g_2 = 3$, $g_3 = 1$.

The equation in Cartesian coordinates is:

$$y^2 = 4\,x^3 - 3\,x - 1.$$

III.   The three $\mathbf{p}$'s are real and all different. We shall call this the *conchoidal class*. As representative of this class we take (fig. 81):

$$\mathsf{p}_1 = 1 \quad ; \quad \mathsf{p}_2 = 0 \quad , \quad \mathsf{p}_3 = -1.$$
$$g_2 = 4 \quad , \quad g_3 = 0$$
$$y^2 = 4\,x\,(x^2 - 1)$$

These curves consist of two branches.

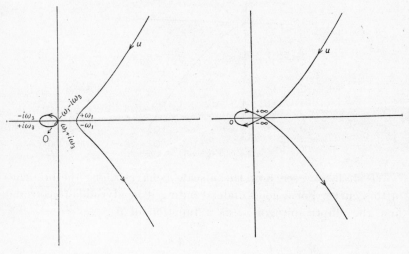

Fig. 81   Fig. 82

IV. p_1 and p_2 are equal, the *strophoidal or crunodal class*. The curve has a double point or *crunode*. As representative we take (fig. 82):

$$\mathsf{p}_1 = \mathsf{p}_2 = \tfrac{1}{2} \quad , \quad \mathsf{p}_3 = -1$$
$$g_2 = 3 \quad , \quad g_3 = -1$$
$$y^2 = 4\,x^3 - 3\,x + 1.$$

The strophoid belongs to this class.

V. All three p's are equal $= 0$;

$$g_2 = 0 \quad , \quad g_3 = 0.$$
$$y^2 = 4\,x^3$$

(NEIL's parabola fig. 83). The curve has a cusp and this case
is called the *cissoid or cuspidal* class. The cissoid belongs to
this class.

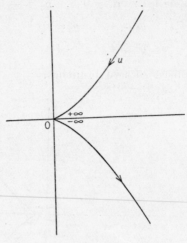

Fig. 83

We shall now see how the u-scale behaves along the branches
of this curve. For a good understanding it is advisable to consider
first the elliptic integral u as a function of $\mathbf{p}$.

$$u = -\int\limits_{\infty}^{\mathbf{p}} \frac{dx}{\sqrt{4\,(x-\mathbf{p}_1)\,(x-\mathbf{p}_2)\,(x-\mathbf{p}_3)}}.$$

Starting from $x = \infty$ and letting it decrease we see that the
denominator is real for all values of x from ∞ to $\mathbf{p}_1$ and u will
also be real (fig. 84). At $x = \mathbf{p}_1$ the denominator becomes imaginary
and the increase of u will be in the imaginary direction. This
goes on until $x = \mathbf{p}_2$, where the denominator becomes real again,
du will be real up to $x = \mathbf{p}_3$ where it again becomes imaginary
and remains so up to $x = -\infty$. As the root has double sign,
the minus sign in the definition of u has no sense. At each
corner we may even change the sign of the integrand and in this
way create adjacent rectangles in fig. 84, u is a multivalued
function of $\mathbf{p}$.

We now see that $\dfrac{du}{d\mathbf{p}}$ is real between $\mathbf{p} = \infty$ and $\mathbf{p} = \mathbf{p}_1$, and again

between $p = p_2$ and $p = p_3$. In these same intervals $y = \dot{p}$ will
be real. And as p is real all along the contour of the rectangle

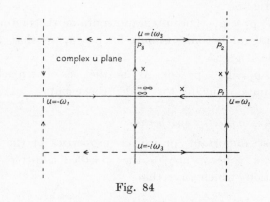

Fig. 84

there exist two intervals where we have at the same time real
values for p and $\dot{p}$ and for which the curve (1)

$$z = p + j\,\dot{p}$$

can be drawn. This corresponds to the two branches of the conchoidal class of the third-order curves.

Along the oval branch of class III the u-values are complex
but with a constant imaginary part $\pm i\,\omega_3$, which is the value
of u for $p = p_3$.

As u is a multi-valued function of p we may add to any
u-value an arbitrary multiple of $2\,\omega_1$, ω_1 being the value of u
for $p = p_1$ and $2i\,\omega_3$, but we shall choose the u-values as indicated in fig. 81. Conversely, we may say that p is a periodical
function of u with periods $2\,\omega_1$, and $2i\,\omega_3$.

Let us now see how the situation is changed when we consider
not the general case of class III, but the more or less special cases.

Class I, p_2 and p_3 are conjugate complex (fig. 79).

By giving to x all values between $+\infty$ and $-\infty$, the expression
under the root sign changes its sign only for $x = p_1$ and remains
negative for ever after. u follows the real axis down to $x = p_1$
and then moves in the imaginary direction without bending
again. There is no second branch.

Class II $p_2 = p_3$. The upper side of the rectangle in the u-plane is described with infinite velocity, that is to say within an infinitely small p-interval. The oval contracts to a single point (acnode) (fig. 80).

Class IV $p_1 = p_2$. The integrand contains the factor $1/(x - p_1)$ and the integral becomes infinite for $p = p_1$, so that $u = \infty$ lies in the node (fig. 82).

Class V: $p_1 = p_2 = p_3 = 0$. As is the case with class IV, u obtains infinite value in the node (the cusp).

6. Cubics, projective porperties

The most important projective properties of the third-order curves are a consequence of the so-called addition theorem of the p-function, which says that:

$$\begin{vmatrix} 1 & 1 & 1 \\ p\,(u_1) & p\,(u_2) & p\,(u_3) \\ \dot{p}\,(u_1) & \dot{p}\,(u_2) & \dot{p}\,(u_3) \end{vmatrix} = 0 \text{ if } u_1 + u_2 + u_3 = 0 \text{ (mod. per).} [1]$$

the analytical proof of which may be found in any textbook on elliptical functions. By elementary properties of determinants it follows that in this case also:

$$\begin{vmatrix} 1 & 1 & 1 \\ p\,(u_1) + j\,\dot{p}\,(u_1) & p\,(u_2) + j\,\dot{p}\,(u_2) & p\,(u_3) + j\,\dot{p}\,(u_3) \\ p\,(u_1) - j\,p\,(u_1) & p\,(u_2) - j\,\dot{p}\,(u_3) & p\,(u_3) - j\,\dot{p}\,(u_3) \end{vmatrix} = 0$$

that is:

$$\begin{vmatrix} 1 & 1 & 1 \\ z_1 & z_2 & z_3 \\ \dot{z}_1 & \dot{z}_2 & \dot{z}_3 \end{vmatrix} = 0 \text{ if } u_1 + u_2 + u_3 = 0 \text{ (mod per.)}$$

The geometrical interpretation of this is, that the three points of the third order curve represented by these three values of u lie on a straight line (are collinear).

This property leads to several interesting geometrical consequences.

_____

[1] By (mod. per) is expressed that an arbitrary entire number of each of the periods may be added.

Cut the curve by two straight lines u and v (fig. 85), let the points of intersection be characterized by u_1, u_2, u_3 and v_1, v_2, v_3. Then:

$$u_1 + u_2 + u_3 = 0 \quad . \quad . \quad , \quad . \quad . \quad . \quad . \quad (6)$$
$$v_1 + v_1 + v_3 = 0.$$

The line u_1v_1 cuts the curve in a third point w_1 and

$$u_1 + v_1 + w_1 = 0.$$

In the same way the lines u_2v_2 and u_3v_3 determine points w_2 and w_3, in such a way that

$$u_2 + v_2 + w_2 = 0$$
$$u_3 + v_3 + w_3 = 0.$$

Adding the three last equations gives in connection with (6):

$$w_1 + w_2 + w_3 = 0.$$

and the points w lie also on a straight line (fig. 86).

Dualistically (fig. 86): Apply to a curve of the third class the tangents u_1, u_2, u_3 running through point U and the three tangents v_1, v_2, v_3 running through point V. The third tangents through the points u_1v_1, u_2v_2 and u_3v_3 will again be concurrent (point W).

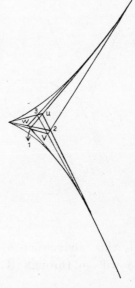

Draw the tangents in three points $P_1P_2P_3$

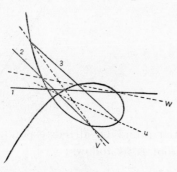

Fig. 85   Fig. 86

lying on a straight line, parameter values u_1, u_2, u_3. Each tangent cuts the curve in a third point Q (called the tangential copoint

of P). As the tangent is the limiting position of a transect
it cuts the curve with the parameter values $u(P)$, $u(P)$ and
$u(Q)$. Now, as the sum must be zero:

$$u (Q) = - 2 u (P)$$

So that the sum of the parameters of the three tangential copoints is

$$- 2 (u_1 + u_2 + u_3) = 0$$

and the three tangential copoints lie on a straight line (fig. 87).

Another property: Bring (fig. 88) through point Q of the curve
a line a; it cuts the curve in A_1
and A_2. Draw SA_1 and SA_2, where
S is another point of the curve.
SA_1 cuts the curve also in B_1,
SA_2 in B_2.
The line B_1B_2 (b) cuts the
curve in R. Now the property

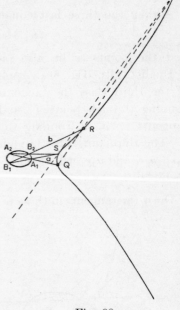

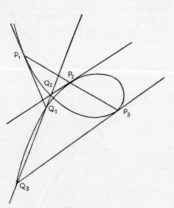

Fig. 87   Fig. 88

is this, that when a is rotated round Q, all corresponding lines
b will go through R. The proof is as follows:

$$u (Q) + u (A_1) + u (A_2) = 0$$
$$u (S) + u (A_1) + u (B_1) = 0$$
$$u (S) + u (A_2) + u (B_2) = 0$$
$$u (B_1) + u (B_2) + u (R) = 0$$

from which:

$$u(Q) - 2u(S) + u(R) = 0$$

and as Q and S are fixed, R is also fixed.

The u-value of S is midway between the u-values of Q and R. Another formulation of the theorem is therefore: Draw two secants through an arbitrary point S of the curve. They cut the curve in four further points. Draw the diagonals of this quadrangle. These diagonals cut the cubic further in two points Q and R on equal u-distances from S.

The tangent in S cuts the cubic in point T, such that $u(T) = -2 u(S)$, so that T is collinear with Q and R.

S is the carrier of a ray involution projective with either the ray pencil a in Q or the ray pencil b in R (comp. p. 77).

If a becomes a tangent, b becomes also a tangent. Curves of the conchoidal class have four tangents a and four tangents b and as the pencils are projective the cross ratio of the four tangents drawn from any point of the curve is constant. We can even calculate this constant. Take Q in the point $u = 0$, that is at infinity in the y-direction. The four tangent points are the points where the curve cuts the x-axis: p_1, p_2, p_3 and the point $x = \infty$. The cross ratio is

$$\frac{p_1 - p_2}{p_1 - p_3} \div \frac{\infty - p_2}{\infty - p_3} = \frac{p_1 - p_2}{p_1 - p_3},$$

which ratio is known as *Salmon's invariant*.

The inflection-points have to satisfy the equation

$$3u = 0 \ (\text{mod. per.})$$

One of them is $u = 0$, another one (fig. 79):

$$3u = \pm 2\omega_1, \ u = \pm \tfrac{2}{3} \omega_1$$

This fixes the location of the tangent points and we find that the three tangent points $u = 0$ and $u = \pm \tfrac{2}{3} \omega_1$ lie on a straight line as the sum is zero. As this is a projective property it holds for any third-order curve. Other inflection points are:

$$u = \pm \tfrac{2}{3} i \omega_3 \ ; \ u = \pm \tfrac{2}{3} \omega_1 \pm \tfrac{2}{3} i \omega_3$$

and in total there are 9 inflection points, of which three always lie on a straight line and each of them lies on four of such inter-connection lines.

For the point $u = \frac{2}{3} i \omega_3$ for example we have the four col-linearities:

$$\frac{2}{3} i \omega_3 \qquad\quad -\tfrac{2}{3} i \omega_3 \qquad +0 \qquad\qquad\qquad\qquad = 0$$

$$\tfrac{2}{3} i \omega_3 + (\tfrac{2}{3}\omega_1 - \tfrac{2}{3} i \omega_3) \qquad -\tfrac{2}{3}\omega_1 \qquad\qquad\qquad = 0$$

$$\tfrac{2}{3} i \omega_3 + (-\tfrac{2}{3}\omega_1 - \tfrac{2}{3} i \omega_3) \; +\tfrac{2}{3}\omega_1 \qquad\qquad\qquad = 0$$

$$\tfrac{2}{3} i \omega_3 + (\tfrac{2}{3}\omega_1 + \tfrac{2}{3} i \omega_3) + (-\tfrac{2}{3}\omega_1 + \tfrac{2}{3} i \omega_3) = 2\, i\, \omega_3 = 0 \;\; \text{(mod. per).}$$

We must, however, remark that only three of these inflection points are real points, namely $u = 0$ and $u = \pm \frac{2}{3}\, \omega_1$ and if $\omega_1 = \infty$ two of the real inflection points disappear into the node or into the cusp.

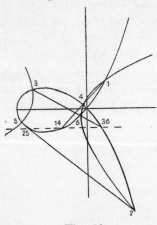

Fig. 89

Cut the third-order curve by a se-cond-order curve, there are 6 points of intersection and again as in the case of cutting a straight line $\Sigma u = 0$. We shall not prove this property. Its basis is a generalization of the addition theorem of the p-function mentioned above , for the proof of which we also referred to analytical text books. See e.g. B. L. van der Waerden: Al- gebraische Geometrie.

Let the 6 points of intersection with a conic be $u_1 \ldots u_6$.

Draw $u_1 u_4$; $u_2 u_5$; $u_3 u_6$, they cut the curve for the third time in u_{14}, u_{25} and u_{36}. Then:

$$u_1 + u_4 + u_{14} = 0$$
$$u_2 + u_5 + u_{25} = 0$$
$$u_3 + u_6 + u_{36} = 0$$

and because

$$\Sigma_1^6\, u_i = 0$$

$$u_{14} + u_{25} + u_{26} = 0$$

so that these three points are collinear (fig. 89).

CHAPTER VII

THE ELLIPSE

1. *Introduction*

For the sake of a simple definition we shall introduce the ellipse as the curve in Cartesian geometry represented by the formula:

$$\frac{x^2}{a^2} + \frac{y^2}{b^2} = 1.$$

Introducing the parameter u by the definition

$$x = a \cos u$$

we find from the above formula:

$$y = b \sin u$$

and in complex notation the formula of the ellipse is:

$$z = a \cos u + jb \sin u \quad . \quad . \quad . \quad . \quad . \quad . \quad (1)$$

from which follows at once the construction indicated in fig. 90.

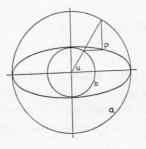

The x- and y-axes are called the *principal axes;* the longer one is the *major axis*, the shorter one the *minor axis*. The origin is called the *centre* of the ellipse, u the *eccentric angle*. The two circles of radii a and b are called the auxiliary circles, again distinguished as major and minor. The name ellipse (= falling short) is due to APOLLONIUS of PERGA (262—200 B.C.), who wrote a treatise in eight volumes on conics and to whom most

Fig. 90

of the names of characteristic points, lines and measures date back. EUCLID, who is older than APOLLONIUS (EUCLID approx. 360—300 B.C.) called the ellipse by the name of „thyreos" (= shield).

Equation (1) is the basis of the use of the *ellipsograph*, consisting (fig. 91) of a rod of length a carried by two rotary sledges which slide along two guiding bars placed perpendicular to each other. The sledges are placed at one end of the moving rod and

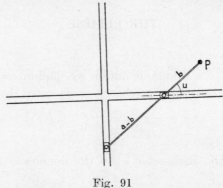

Fig. 91

at a distance a-b from this end. The other end of the rod carries the recording pen. Introducing the angle u between the direction of the moving rod and the x-axis as parameter we see from fig. 91 at once that $x = a \cos u$; $y = b \sin u$.

Many problems give immediately rise to a curve of the form of equation (1) so that the ellipse is one of the most important curves. We shall, for the time being, give only four examples:

a. *Projection of a circle.* Equ. (1) is created by shortening all ordinates of the circle

$$z = a \exp (ju) = a \cos u + ja \sin u$$

by the factor b/a. This may possibly be due to the projection of a circle placed in an inclined position with respect to the z-plane. From this way of generating the ellipse we may deduce, that its area is b/a times that of the circle, that is $A = \pi a b$.

b. *Lissajous-movement.* Suppose a point to perform simultaneously two harmonic movements in two mutually perpendicular directions with the same angular velocities ω and with a phase difference of $\pi/2$ radians.

Then:

$$x = a \cos \omega t; \; y = b \sin \omega t$$

and the resulting track is the ellipse (1) with $u = \omega t$.

c. *Central force.* The Lissajous movement may be originated by a force acting on a material point always in the direction of the origin and proportional to the radius vector r. These conditions apply to a pendulum of small amplitude. The mechanical equation, neglecting centrifugal forces, is:

$$m \frac{d^2 r}{dt^2} = - Dr$$

with $m =$ mass of the particle, $D =$ directive constant. As this is a vectorequation we may split it into its components:

$$m \frac{d^2 x}{dt^2} = - Dx \quad ; \quad m \frac{d^2 y}{dt^2} = - Dy$$

with particular solutions:

$$x = a \cos \sqrt{\frac{D}{m}} . t \quad ; \quad y = b \sin \sqrt{\frac{D}{m}} . t$$

giving rise to a motion along the curve (1), now with $u = \sqrt{\frac{D}{m}} t$.

d. *Tensional ellipse.* Let σ_1 and σ_2 be the principal tensions in a rigid body. The equilibrium of a small solid triangle with its sides perpendicular to the principle directions and the direction defined by u (fig. 90) requires that the components of the tension in the hypothenusal plane be:

$$\sigma_1 \cos u \quad \text{and} \quad \sigma_2 \sin u$$

and the total tension in the plane fixed by the angle u is given by the vector:

$$\sigma_u = \sigma_1 \cos u + j \sigma_2 \sin u,$$

the extremity of which lies on the ellipse (1). The same applies to the case of anisotropal dilatation (dilatation ellipse) and to other cases of tensorial quantities of the second order.

These four examples may suffice to show the direct lucidity of equation (1). By passing to exponentials we can bring it into the form:

$$z = \frac{a + b}{2} \exp (ju) + \frac{a - b}{2} \exp (- ju). \quad . \quad . \quad . \quad (2)$$

and this formula suggests the ellipse construction, indicated in

fig. 92, the so called flail construction. Combination of fig. 90
and fig. 92 gives the relations shown in fig. 93.

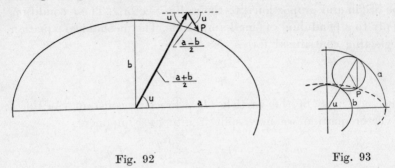

Fig. 92   Fig. 93

2. *Conjugate diameters*

Starting from equ. 2 we shall consider the location of two points
of the ellipse with parameters $u \pm q$ (fig. 94). They are:

$$z\,(u \pm q) = \frac{a+b}{2} \exp\{j\,(u \pm q)\} + \frac{a-b}{2} \exp\{-j\,(u \pm q)\}.$$

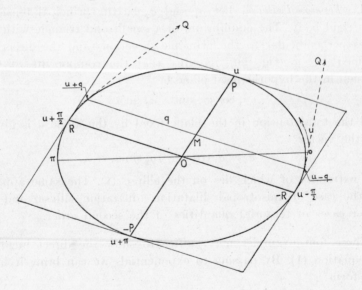

Fig. 94

The chord connecting these two points is indicated by the

letter q in fig. 94. Its middle is half the sum of the two values mentioned above:

$$z\ (\mathrm{M}) = \left\{ \frac{a+b}{2} \exp\ (ju) + \frac{a-b}{2} \exp\ (-ju) \right\}. \cos q$$

and we observe that this is $z\ (\mathrm{P})$, multiplied by the real factor cos q. This means, that M lies on the radius of P and as this conclusion holds for all values of q, all these middles lie on this radius.

Moreover, all these chords are parallel to each other. This results from the calculation of the difference of $z\ (u+q)$ and $z\ (u-q)$:

$$\tfrac{1}{2} \{ z\ (u+q) - z\ (u-q) \} =$$
$$= \left\{ \frac{a+b}{2} \exp\ (ju) - \frac{a-b}{2} \exp\ (-ju) \right\}. j \sin q \qquad (3)$$

which is a vector, the magnitude of which varies with q, but of which the direction is independent of q. The line OP, therefore, is the locus of the middles of a set of parallel chords and such a line is called a *diameter* or *median*. All straight lines through the centre of the ellipse are diameters.

If we allow q to decrease indefinitely, the vector (3) will approach to the tangent in the point P and we expect this tangent to be parallel to the set of chords (3). Indeed, by differentiating (2) we have:

$$\dot{z} = j \left\{ \frac{a+b}{2} \exp\ (ju) - \frac{a-b}{2} \exp\ (-ju) \right\},$$

which differs from (3) only by the real factor sin q so that the parallelism is proved.

Again, draw the tangents to the ellipse in the points $u \pm q$. Choosing uniform parameterscales v_1 and v_2 on these tangents, their equations are:

$$\begin{matrix} z_1 \\ z_2 \end{matrix} = \frac{a+b}{2} \exp\ \{ j\ (u \pm q) \} + \frac{a-b}{2} \exp\ \{ -j\ (u \pm q) \} +$$

$$+ \begin{matrix} v_1 \\ v_2 \end{matrix} j \left\{ \frac{a+b}{2} \exp\ \{ j\ (u \pm q) \} - \frac{a-b}{2} \exp\ \{ -j\ (u \pm q) \} \right\}.$$

Zwikker

7

By equating z_1 and z_2 we find the point of intersection Q of these two lines. The calculation gives:

$$- v_1 = v_2 = \tan q$$

$$z\,(Q) = (a \cos u + jb \sin u)\,\frac{1}{\cos q}$$

which just as M, is a point on the radius OP. Point Q is called the *pole* of the line q, q the *polar line* of Q. The line OP not only contains the middles of all chords q but also the poles of all chords q.

We observe, that $z\,(Q)\,.\,z\,(M) = z^2\,(P)$ which means that the points Q and M lie harmonically with respect to the extremities P and $-$ P of the diameter. By varying q, the points M and Q describe an involution.

One more observation: By elementary reasoning we conclude from fig. 94 that the tangent in P is cut by the tangents through Q in such a way that the intercepts between P and the tangents are equal.

Returning now to the set of chords (3), we observe that for

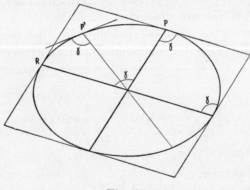

Fig. 95

$q = \pi/2$, M falls in the origin and the corresponding chord is a diameter with extremities R and $-$ R:

$$u\,(\pm R) = u\,(P) \pm \pi/2. \quad . \quad , \quad . \quad . \quad . \quad . \quad (5)$$

This diameter R, $-$ R is called the *conjugate diameter* to the diameter P, $-$ P. Now what will be the conjugate diameter to

R, $-$ R? From (5) it follows that the extremities of this diameter will have the parameter values u and $u + \pi$, but this leads to the points P and $-$ P. The conjugation of the diameters is therefore reciprocal.

If a circumscribing parallelogram touches the ellipse in the extremities of two conjugate diameters, these diameters are parallel to the sides of the parallelogram (fig. 95).

Apart from the sign, the angle γ between a diameter and the tangents in its extremities is the same for two conjugate diameters, namely equal to the angle between the diameters themselves. The minimum of γ is equal to $\pi/2$, if we choose the principal axes as conjugate diameters, it is a maximum for the diameters characterized by the parameter values $\pi/4$ and $3\pi/4$, as for reasons of symmetry (fig. 95) γ changes in the same direction on both sides of these points.

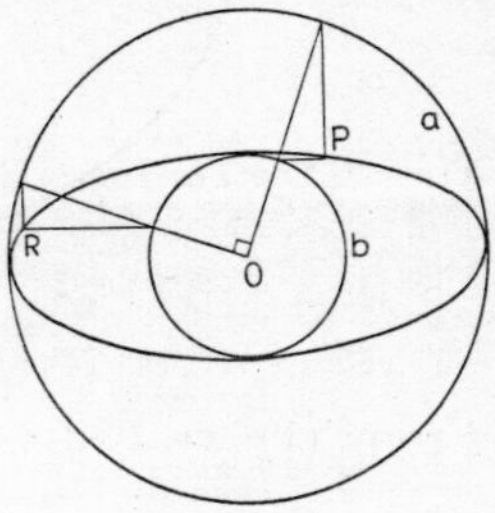

Fig. 96 shows a simple way of construction of two conjugate diameters, making use of the fact, that the eccentric angles differ by $\pi/2$.

Fig. 96

Passing to exponentials we find

$$z\,(\mathrm{P}) = \frac{a + b}{2} \exp\,(ju) + \frac{a - b}{2} \exp\,(-ju)$$

$$z\,(\mathrm{R}) = j \left\{ \frac{a + b}{2} \exp\,(ju) - \frac{a - b}{2} \exp\,(-ju) \right\}$$

and this suggests another costruction, shown in fig. 97. We first construct the point P as was already done in fig. 92 and the auxiliary point H:

$$z\,(\mathrm{H}) = \frac{a + b}{2} \exp\,(ju) - \frac{a - b}{2} \exp\,(-ju).$$

Turn the vector OH over $\pi/2$ (multiplying by j) in order to find the point R.

We must not leave the subject of the conjugate diameters without mentioning two metric theorems due to APOLLONIUS.

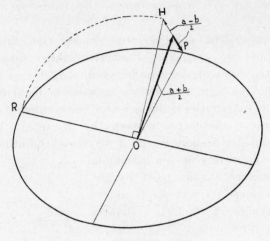

Fig. 97

From (1) we deduce for the square of the radius of P:

$$|z\,(\mathrm{P})|^2 = a^2\cos{}^2u + b^2\sin^2 u$$

and with the help of (5) for the radius of R:

$$|z\,(\mathrm{R})|^2 = a^2\sin^2 u + b^2\cos^2 u$$

adding:

$$|z\,(\mathrm{P})|^2 + |z\,(\mathrm{R})|^2 = a^2 + b^2;$$

in words: The sum of the squares of two conjugate half diameters is constant and equal to $a^2 + b^2$ (First theorem of APOLLONIUS). For $u = \pi/4$ the two conjugate diameters are equal, the semi-diameter being $\sqrt{\dfrac{a^2 + b^2}{2}}$. The sum of the diameters is not constant and it may be shown that this sum is a maximum in the case of the two equal conjugates.

The area of the parallelogram on two conjugate diameters is:

$$A = 4\,\mathrm{Im}\,\{z\,(\mathrm{P})\,.\,z^*\,(\mathrm{R})\}$$

with:

$$z\,(\mathrm{P}) = a\cos u + jb\sin u \quad ; \quad z\,(\mathrm{R}) = -\,a\sin u + jb\cos u$$

this gives $A = 4\,ab$ in words:

The area of a parallelogram on conjugate diameters is constant $= 4ab$ (Second theorem of APOLLONIUS).

3. The foci

The two foci of the ellipse are the points situated on the major axis at a distance $c = \sqrt{a^2 - b^2}$ from the centre. The ratio $e = c/a$ is called the *eccentricity* of the ellipse; it is zero if the ellipse degenerates into a circle $(a = b)$. Although the foci play a very important role, they seem to have been unknown to the Greeks; they are a contribution of the mathematicians of the 16-th century, who studied the optical and mechanical properties of the ellipse.

In order to write down the equation of the ellipse relatively

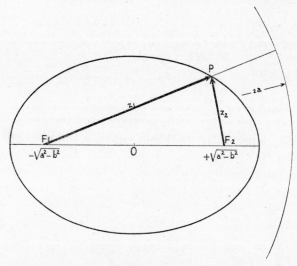

Fig. 98

to one of the foci as origin, we have to add or to substract the real amount $c = \sqrt{a^2 - b^2}$ to or from the values of z given by (1) or (2):

$$\begin{matrix} z_1 \\ z_2 \end{matrix} = a\cos u + jb \sin u \pm c . \quad . \quad . \quad . \quad . \quad (6)$$

resp.

$$\begin{matrix} z_1 \\ z_2 \end{matrix} = \frac{a+b}{2} \exp (ju) + \frac{a-b}{2} \exp (-ju) \pm \sqrt{a^2 - b^2}.$$

The right hand side is a full square:

$$\begin{matrix} z_1 \\ z_2 \end{matrix} = \tfrac{1}{2} \left\{ \sqrt{a+b}\, \exp\left(j\,\frac{u}{2} \right) \pm \sqrt{a-b}\, \exp\left(-j\,\frac{u}{2} \right) \right\}^2 \quad . \quad (7)$$

which is an equation of remarkable symmetry.

The absolute value of z_1 is:

$$|z_1| = \tfrac{1}{2} \left\{ \sqrt{a+b}\, \exp\left(j\,\frac{u}{2} \right) + \sqrt{a-b}\, \exp\left(-j\,\frac{u}{2} \right) \right\} \times$$

$$\times \left\{ \sqrt{a+b}\, \exp\left(-j\,\frac{u}{2} \right) + \sqrt{a-b}\, \exp\left(j\,\frac{u}{2} \right) \right\}$$

$$= a + c \cos u.$$

and in the same way we find for the absolute value of z_2:

$$|z_2| = a - c \cos u.$$

whence, by adding:

$$|z_1| + |z_2| = 2a;$$

in words: The sum of the radii vectores from the two foci to any point of the ellipse is constant and equal to $2a$. We shall refer to this theorem as to the *vectorsum law*. It is the basic property of the ellipse and, indeed, the most popular way of defining the ellipse is as the locus of the points for which the sum of the

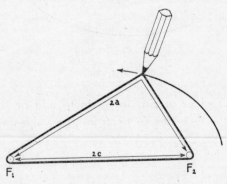

Fig. 99

distances to two fixed points is constant. This property is used in the so called cord- or gardeners construction (fig. 99). Attach the ends of a cord of constant length $2a$ to two fixed points, and keep it stretched by the lead pencil.

For the tops of the minor axis $|z_1|=|z_2|=a$. Fig. 100 illustrates

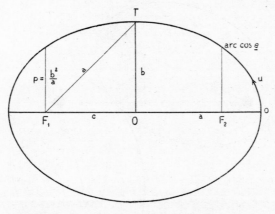

Fig. 100

the relation $a^2=b^2+c^2$. For a point just above one of the foci, the real part of z is zero; from (6) we deduce that in that case $\cos u=\pm c/a=\pm e$ consequently: $\sin u=\sqrt{1-e^2}=b/a$ and the value of y is $b \sin u = b^2/a$, a value, which is usually called the *parameter p* of the ellipse. Eccentricity e and parameter p are sufficient to fix shape and size of the ellipse, just as are a and b. Another name for $2p$ is *latus rectum*.

We shall now proceed to mention a number of applications of the vector sum law, without however, exhausting this prodigious theme.

a. *Directive circles:* The circles of radius $2a$ described round the foci as centres are called the *directive circles* (fig. 98). Each point of the ellipse lies at the same distance from the circle drawn round the first and from the second focus. The ellipse therefore, is the locus of points having the same distance to a fixed circle and a fixed point within this circle.

b. *Syntrepency:* Two curves are called *syntrepent*, if, when both rotate with constant or variable angular velocity round a fixed point, they roll over each other, always tangent to each other without sliding. If the two curves have the same size and shape, we say that this curve is *isotrepent*. Due to the vector sum law the ellipse is isotrepent (fig. 101). F_1 and F_1' are the centres

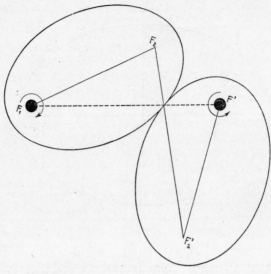

Fig. 101

of rotation, their distance apart is $2a$. If one of the ellipses rotates with constant angular velocity, the second one will show variations in velocity. A transmission like this may serve either to create a periodically varying angular velocity or to compensate for existing variations.

  c. *Elliptic bar system*: During the motion, illustrated in fig. 101 point F_2 describes a circle of radius $2c$ round the fixed point F_1 and F_2' describes likewise a circle of the same size round F_1'. Moreover, the distance $F_2 F_2'$ remains constant $= 2a$. One may just as well leave the contours of the ellipses out and apply a bar system consisting of only three bars of lengths $2c$, $2a$ and $2c$ with the extremities of the two outer bars fixed in the points F_1 and F_1', a distance $2a$ apart. This bar system serves the same purpose as the transmission by syntrepent ellipses (fig. 102).

  d. *Hyperbolic bar system*: In our case $2c < 2a$. One may also choose $2c > 2a$ in which case one speaks of a hyperbolic bar system (fig. 103). The point M, where the two bars of length $2c$ cross, has, for reasons of symmetry, distances from the fixed points F_1 and $F_1{}'$ so that their sum is always $2c$. M therefore, describes an ellipse and this suggests another ellipsograph. It

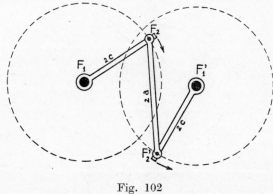

Fig. 102

may be added, that the point of intersection of F_1F_2 and $F_1{}'F_2{}'$ in the case of an elliptic bar system (fig. 102) describes a hyperbola.

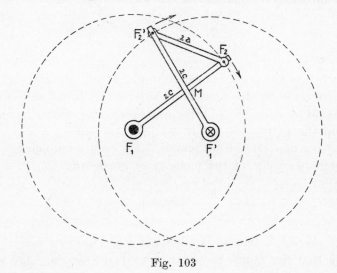

Fig. 103

4. *Kepler orbits*

What is the orbit of a particle moving in a central field of force in which the centripetal force varies inversely as the square of the distance? It will turn out that these orbits are either ellipses, parabolae or hyperbolae. The problem was solved in the reverse order by NEWTON (1687). He showed that in order to account for the elliptic orbits of the planets as found by KEPLER (Kepler's

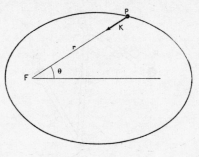

Fig. 104

first law) it is necessary to assume a central force inversely proportional to the square of the distance.

The mechanical equation for the radial component is:

$$-\frac{a}{r^2} = \frac{d^2r}{dt^2} - r\left(\frac{d\theta}{dt}\right)^2 \quad \ldots \ldots \quad (8)$$

in which a is the gravitational constant, θ the azimuth (fig. 104). The first term on the right hand side is the radial acceleration, the second term accounts for the centripetal acceleration necessary to keep the particle on a circular orbit of radius r.

The equation for the tangential component is supplied by the law of permanency of the moment of momentum:

$$r^2 \frac{d\theta}{dt} = \text{constant} = \beta. \quad \ldots \ldots \quad (9)$$

This second equation is identical with Kepler's second law, stating that the radius vector covers equal areas in equal times.

From (9):

$$\frac{d}{dt} = \frac{\beta}{r^2} \cdot \frac{d}{d\theta}$$

and hence:

$$\frac{dr}{dt} = -\beta \frac{d^1/r}{d\theta} \quad ; \quad \frac{d^2r}{dt^2} = -\frac{\beta^2}{r^2} \frac{d^2 1/r}{d\theta^2}$$

which, introduced into (8) gives as the differential equation of the orbit:

$$\frac{a}{\beta^2} = \frac{d^2 1/r}{d\theta^2} + \frac{1}{r}$$

integrated:

$$\frac{1}{r} = \frac{a}{\beta^2}(1 - e\cos\theta) \quad . \quad . \quad . \quad . \quad . \quad . \quad (10)$$

and we have still to prove that this can be an ellipse.

This is easily done with the aid of (6). This gives for the radius vector, as already carried out on page 102:

$$r = a + c \cos u.$$

For the focal azimuth we find:

$$\cos\theta = \frac{x}{r} = \frac{a\cos u + c}{a + c\cos u}.$$

Eliminating the parameter u from these two equations, we find the polar equation of the ellipse:

$$1/r = 1/p \,(1 - e\cos\theta)$$

identical with (10), if only we choose $p = b^2/a = \beta^2/a$.

Now in (10) e was an integration constant and may assume any value, whereas for the ellipse e is always less than 1. Equation (10) therefore only represents an ellipse if $e < 1$; if $e = 1$ the curve is a parabola (Ch. IX) and if $e > 1$, the curve is a hyperbola (Ch. VIII).

Having been forced to deduce the polar equation of the ellipse, we may as well use this opportunity to show another remarkable property of the ellipse. Extend the radius vector beyond the focus and let the chord be divided by the focus in the intercepts r_1 and r_2. From (10):

$$1/r_1 = 1/p\,(1 - e\cos\theta) \quad ; \quad 1/r_2 = 1/p\,(1 + e\cos\theta)$$

and

$$1/r_1 + 1/r_2 = 2/p,$$

so that we see, that each chord passing through the focus is divided by the focus into two parts in such a way, that their harmonic mean is constant and equal to the parameter of the ellipse.

5. *Conic sections*

The fact, that ellipse, parabola and hyperbola are to be considered as the sections of a plane with a right cone, was already

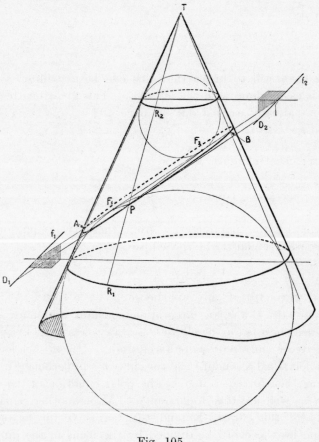

Fig. 105

discovered by MENAECHMUS in ± 350 B.C., but DANDELIN gave a most elegant proof in 1825.

Suppose a right circular cone cut by a plane (Fig. 105) and let P be any point of the section. Conceive two spheres placed so that they are inscribed in the cone and tangent to the plane, the two spheres touching the plane on opposite sides in the points F_1 and F_2. The spheres touch the cone along two parallel circles. Draw in P the generator of the cone, it intersects the parallel circles in R_1 and R_2. Now PF_1 and PR_1 are both tangents to the same sphere and will therefore be equal. Also and for the same reason $PF_2 = PR_2$. Now because $PR_1 + PR_2$ is the constant distance between the two parallel circles, $PF_1 + PF_2$ is also constant. The section, therefore, is an ellipse and F_1 and F_2 are its foci.

The sectional plane cuts the planes of the two parallel circles along straight lines f_1 and f_2. Let down the common normal from P on the lines f_1 and f_2, and let the base points of these normals be D_1 and D_2. Now:

$$PF_1 : PD_1 = PR_1 : PD_1 = R_1R_2 : D_1D_2 = \text{constant}.$$

In words: The ellipse is the locus of points for which the ratio of the distances to a fixed point F and to a fixed straight line f is constant and less than 1. The lines f_1 and f_2 therefore, have also a planimetric meaning; they are called the *directrices* of the ellipse. Applying the law of constant ratio to the tops of the major axis, we find that this ratio, which we shall call e, satisfies the equations:

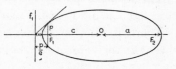

Fig. 106

$$e = \frac{a-c}{x} = \frac{a+c}{2a+x} \quad . \quad . \quad . \quad . \quad . \quad (11)$$

from which by elimination of x we calculate $e = c/a$, which result we had already anticipated when we denoted the ratio by the letter e, up to now reserved for the eccentricity.

By tilting the section plane of fig. 105 we may place it parallel to a generating line of the cone; in this case the conic is a parabola. We may tilt it still further so that it cuts the extension of the cone beyond the top; in this case the conic is a hyperbola. The parabola has only one focus and one directrix, the hyperbola two of each. The constant ratio e becomes 1 for the parabola,

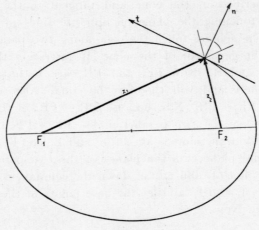

Fig. 107

> 1 for the hyperbola. We therefore repeat the last theorem in the following way:

The locus of points having a constant ratio e for its distances to a fixed point F and a fixed line f is a conic with eccentricity e.

There is another consequence which we can make from (11), viz. that the tops of the major axis lie harmonically with F and f;

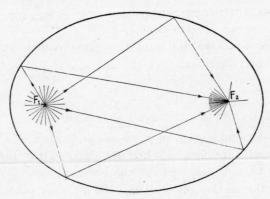

Fig. 108

f therefore is the polar of the corresponding focus F. Again from (11) we calculate for the distance between F and f the value $b^2/c = p/e$ (fig. 106).

6. *The reflection law*

The second basic property of the ellipse is also related to the foci, viz.: the two radii from the foci to any point of the ellipse make equal angles with the tangent in that point. (Fig. 107).

The proof follows from (7) by remarking that:

$$\dot{z} = j/2 \{\sqrt{a+b} \exp{(ju/2)} + \sqrt{a-b} \exp{(-ju/2)}\} \times$$
$$\times \{\sqrt{a+b} \exp{((ju/2)} - \sqrt{a-b} \exp{(-ju/2)}\}$$

so that

$$z_1/\dot{z} = - \dot{z}/z_2$$

which means that the angle between z_1 and the tangent equals the angle between the negative tangent and z_2.

All light rays emerging from F_1 will after reflection at the ellipse converge towards F_2 and it is this property which accounts for the name of focus for the points F_1 and F_2 (fig. 108).

In connection with the reflection law we shall mention a number of secondary properties, derived from it (fig. 109).

a. Let K be the image of F_2 mirrored in the tangent in the point P of the ellipse. By the reflection law F_1PK must be a straight line and its length must be the sum of F_1P and PF_2 that is $2a$, so that K lies on the directive circle of F_1

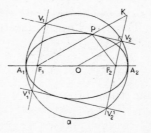

Fig. 109

b. The line F_2K is cut orthogonally by the tangent in its middle V_2. Since O too cuts the stretch F_1F_2 in two halves, OV_2 is half F_1K, that means that V_2 must be situated on the major auxiliary circle.

Generalizing: The bases of the normals let down from the foci on the tangents of the ellipse are located on the major auxiliary circle. In other words: the major auxiliary circle is a pedal.

c. F_1V_1 equals F_2V_2'. Now as V_2V_2' and the major axis are both chords of the major auxiliary circle intersecting in F_2,

$$V_2'F_2 \cdot F_2V_2 = A_1F_2 \cdot F_2A_2 = (a+c)(a-c) = a^2 - c^2 = b^2$$

and the product $F_1V_1 \cdot F_2V_2$ has this same value, in words: The product of the two normals let down from the foci on any tangent is constant and is equal to b^2.

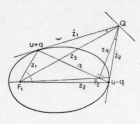

Fig. 110

The reflection law may be considered as a special case of a more general property of the ellipse, viz. the two tangents passing through a point Q located outside the ellipse make equal angles with the two lines connecting Q with the two foci (fig. 110).

From section 2 we take the two tangents:

$$\begin{matrix}\dot{z}_1\\\dot{z}_2\end{matrix} = j\left[\frac{a+b}{2}\exp\{j\,(u\pm q)\} - \frac{a-b}{2}\exp\{-j\,(u\pm q)\}\right].$$

Their product is:

$$-\dot{z}_1\dot{z}_2 = \left(\frac{a+b}{2}\right)^2 e^{2ju} + \left(\frac{a-b}{2}\right)^2 e^{-2ju} - \frac{c^2}{2}\cos 2\,q.$$

The two lines connecting Q with the foci are:

$$\begin{matrix}z_3\\z_4\end{matrix} = \frac{1}{\cos q}\left\{\frac{a+b}{2}\exp\,(ju) + \frac{a-b}{2}\exp\,(-ju)\right\}\pm c$$

and their product is:

$$z_3 z_4 = \frac{1}{\cos^2 q}\left[\left(\frac{a+b}{2}\right)^2 e^{2ju} + \left(\frac{a-b}{2}\right)^2 e^{-2ju} + \frac{c^2}{2}\right] - c^2$$

which, as $\cos 2q = 2\cos^2 q - 1$, differs from $\dot{z}_1\dot{z}_2$ only by the real factor $\cos^2 q$ and this is the proof of the stated theorem. When Q approaches the ellipse this theorem degenerates into the simple reflection law.

Again, draw the lines connecting F_1 with the two tangent points. These vectors are:

$$\begin{matrix}z_1\\z_2\end{matrix} = \frac{a+b}{2}\exp\{j\,(u\pm q)\} + \frac{a-b}{2}\exp\{-j\,(u\pm q)\} + c$$

and their product equals $\cos^2 q.z_3{}^2$, as may be verified by elementary calculation. The line F_1Q therefore makes equal angles with z_1

and z_2 (fig. 110). Of course the same applies to F_2. If in particular, as is nearly the case in fig. 110, F_2 lies on the polar q of Q, the two angles at F_2 are right. In that case Q must lie on the polar of F_2; that is on the directrix f_2.

We find in this way the theorem, that any line passing through a focus is normal to the polar q of the point Q where it intersects the corresponding directrix.

The two properties of constant vectorsum and equal angles are not independent of each other. Suppose (fig. 111) the point P to move over the ellipse over a distance ds. Let $|z_1|$ decrease by the amount $ds \cos \gamma_1$ and let $|z_2|$ increase by the amount $ds \cos \gamma_2$. If the vectorsum law holds, γ_1 and γ_2 must be equal. Conversely the vector sum law must hold if the reflection law be given.

We will now mention a generalization of the cord construction. Suppose we sling a cord round a polygon and keep it straight with the help of a recording pencil. The pencil will describe parts of ellipses, two corners of the polygon acting as temporary foci. In any point of the track of the pencil the two parts of the cord will make equal angles with the track described. Now suppose

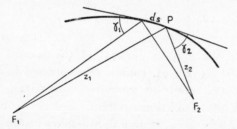

Fig. 111   Fig. 112

the number of sides to increase until a (continuously smooth curbed) curve is generated, then the track will, so to speak, consist of an infinite number of parts of ellipses and the reflection law will still hold. Each cord construction where the cord is slung round any closed contour will obey the reflection law.

Now suppose a cord slung round the ellipse of fig. 110 and kept stretched in Q. Execute the cord construction. Q will describe a track in a direction which makes equal angles with the two tangents of the ellipse. The angles between the direction in which

Q moves and the lines towards F_1 and F_2 will also be equal. The orbit of Q is therefore an ellipse having F_1 and F_2 as foci; with a technical term, it is *confocal* with the first ellipse. In order to generate an ellipse by the cord construction one may sling the cord round any smaller confocal ellipse (GRAVES 1850) and the straight line F_1F_2, described in both directions, may be considered as one of these confocal ellipses.

7. *The perimeter of the ellipse, radius of curvature*

Although the area of the ellipse could be given by a very simple formula there exists no elementary expression for its perimeter.

Starting from the ellipse equation:

$$z = a \cos u + jb \sin u$$

we have:

$$\dot{z} = - a \sin u + jb \cos u$$

and

$$|\dot{z}| = \sqrt{a^2 \sin^2 u + b^2 \cos^2 u} = a \sqrt{1 - e^2 \cos^2 u}$$

hence the arc length, starting from the bottom of the ellipse is:

$$s = a \int_{-\pi/2}^{u} du \sqrt{1 - e^2 \cos^2 u} = a \int_0^{\varphi} d\varphi \sqrt{1 - e^2 \sin^2 \varphi} \quad (\varphi = u + \pi/2)$$

and this integral, known as the elliptic integral of the second kind and as a rule designated by $E(e,\varphi)$, cannot be expressed in elementary functions. It is evaluated by numerical calculation and tabulated (e.g. JAHNKE-EMDE. Funktionentafeln).

The integral from $u = -\pi/2$ to $u = 0$ (φ from 0 to $\pi/2$) gives us the length of one quarter of the perimeter and is designated by a square letter: $E(e)$. The total perimeter, therefore, is:

$$s = 4a \, \mathrm{E} \, (e)$$

We find in mathematical tables:

$$e^2 = 0 \quad \text{(circle)}, \quad \mathrm{E} = 1{,}5708 \;\; (= \pi/2)$$
$$e^2 = {}^1/_4 \;\; (c = a/2) \qquad\qquad 1{,}4675$$
$$e^2 = {}^1/_2 \;\; (b = c) \qquad\qquad\quad 1{,}3506$$
$$e^2 = {}^3/_4 \;\; (b = a/2) \qquad\qquad 1{,}2111$$
$$e^2 = 1 \quad \text{(straight line)} \quad 1$$

An expansion of the function E(e), suitable for numerical evaluation is:

$$\frac{2}{\pi} E\,(e) = 1 - (\tfrac{1}{2})^2\, e^2 - \left(\frac{1.3}{2.4}\right)^2 \frac{e^4}{3} - \left(\frac{1.3.5}{2.4.6}\right)^2 \frac{e^6}{5} - \cdots$$

For the radius of curvature in point P (u) of the ellipse one calculates:

$$\varrho = \frac{\{2\,(a^2 + b^2) - 2\,c^2 \cos 2\,u\}^{3/2}}{8\,ab}$$

giving in the extremities of the major axis (cos 2u = 1):

$$\varrho = b^2/a = p$$

and in the extremities of the minor axis (cos 2u = − 1):

$$\varrho = a^2/b.$$

CHAPTER VIII

HYPERBOLA

1. *Introduction*

For an introductory treatment of the hyperbola we shall start from the CARTESIAN formula

$$\frac{x^2}{a^2} - \frac{y^2}{b^2} = 1.$$

We introduce a parameter u by putting

$$x = a \cosh u \quad \text{and hence} \quad y = b \sinh u$$

by which the formula in complex notation will be:

$$z = a \cosh u + jb \sinh u. \quad \ldots \ldots \quad (1)$$

Passing on to exponentials, this can also be written as:

$$z = \frac{a+jb}{2} \exp(u) + \frac{a-jb}{2} \exp(-u). \quad \ldots \quad (2)$$

The vectors $a + jb$ and $a - jb$ are indicated in fig. 113 and a point

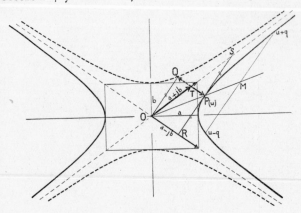

Fig. 113

of the hyperbola is found by a superposition of $\frac{1}{2} \exp(u)$ times the first (OT) and $\frac{1}{2} \exp(-u)$ times the latter vector (TP).

It may be observed that the product of OT and TP is constant

$$= \frac{a^2 + b^2}{4}.$$

By the *conjugate hyperbola* is meant the curve:

$$\frac{x^2}{a^2} - \frac{y^2}{b^2} = -1$$

or after introducing the same parameter u:

$$z = \frac{a + jb}{2} \exp(u) - \frac{a - jb}{2} \exp(-u) \quad \ldots \quad (3)$$

and this curve can be constructed in a way closely analogous to the first hyperbola, the vector $\frac{1}{2}(a - jb) \exp(-u)$ only being drawn in the opposite direction (TQ).

If u increases indefinitely the second term decreases more and more and both vectors z approach to the line $\frac{a + jb}{2} \exp(u)$.

This line and its counterpart $\frac{a - jb}{2} \exp(-u)$, to which both hyperbolae approach if u approaches to $-\infty$, are called the *asymptotes* of the two conjugate hyperbolae.

2. *Medians, conjugate directions*

In a way closely analogous to the one followed for the ellipse we can show that each line through O is a *median*.

The middle of the chord connecting the points characterized by the parameter values $u \pm q$ is (fig. 113):

$$z(M) = \left\{ \frac{a + jb}{2} \exp u + \frac{a - jb}{2} \exp(-u) \right\} \cosh q$$

the locus of which is the radius from O to the point P (u). The vector from the point $u - q$ to the point $u + q$ is:

$$z(u + q) - z(u - q) = \left\{ \frac{a + jb}{2} \exp(u) - \frac{a - jb}{2} \exp(-u) \right\} 2 \sinh q$$

and has a direction independent of q and parallel to the diameter passing through point $Q(u)$ of the conjugate hyperbola. These two directions will be called *conjugate directions*. Moreover, the conjugate direction is parallel to the tangent in point $P(u)$ of the original hyperbola. Conversely, the conjugate line is the median for all chords of the conjugate hyperbola which are parallel to the median through point $P(u)$ of the original hyperbola.

For the modulus of the line OP (fig. 113) we have:

$$|\,\mathrm{OP}\,|^2 = \left\{ \frac{a+jb}{2}\exp(u) + \frac{a-jb}{2}\exp(-u) \right\}$$

$$\left\{ \frac{a-jb}{2}\exp(u) + \frac{a+jb}{2}\exp(-u) \right\}$$

$$= \tfrac{1}{2}(a^2 - b^2) + \tfrac{1}{2}(a^2 + b^2)\cosh 2u.$$

and for the conjugate semidiameter, (computated in the same way), we find

$$|\,\mathrm{OQ}\,|^2 = -\tfrac{1}{2}(a^2 - b^2) + \tfrac{1}{2}(a^2 + b^2)\cosh 2u,$$

so that:

$$|\,\mathrm{OP}\,|^2 - |\,\mathrm{OQ}\,|^2 = a^2 - b^2,$$

in words: The difference of the squares of the moduli of two conjugate semidiameters is constant and equal to $a^2 - b^2$.

In the same way as for the ellipse, we might prove that the median is at the same time the locus of the poles of the set of parallel chords and that any tangent t is cut at equal distances from the tangent point by the two tangents drawn through the extremities of a chord parallel to tangent t.

From fig. 113 we see that the tangent in P cuts the asymptote $a - jb$ in point R in such a way that $\mathrm{OR} = \mathrm{PQ} = (a - jb)\exp(-u)$. This is twice the distance TP. By extending the line RP by the same amount we shall therefore, reach a point S situated on the other asymptote. In words: The intercept of a tangent to the hyperbola, between the asymptotes is divided into two equal parts by the tangent point.

3. *Foci*

The foci are the points situated on the real axis at distances $c = \sqrt{a^2 + b^2}$ from O. The ratio c/a is called the *eccentricity* e.

Whereas for the ellipse e is smaller than 1, it is always greater than 1 for the hyperbola. In the intermediate case of the parabola $e=1$. In order to write down the formula of the hyperbola if one of the foci is the origin, we have to add $\pm \sqrt{a^2+b^2}$ to form (2) which leads to (fig. 114):

$$\begin{matrix} z_1 \\ z_2 \end{matrix} = \tfrac{1}{2}\{\sqrt{a+jb}\,\exp u/2 \pm \sqrt{a-jb}\,\exp(-u/2)\}^2 \quad . \quad . \quad (4)$$

It follows from (4) that z_2 is purely imaginary for $\cosh u = c/a = e$ and that the modulus of z_2 in this case is $p = b^2/a$. The same result

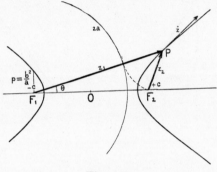

Fig. 114

was found for the ellipse, in both cases p is called the *parameter*. The absolute values of z_1 and z_2 are computed to be:

$$\begin{vmatrix} z_1 \\ z_2 \end{vmatrix} = \pm a + c \cosh u.$$

so that the difference of the two radii vectores is constant $=2a$.

The circle of radius $2a$ round one of the foci is called a *directive circle*. From fig. 114 we see that the hyperbola is the locus of the points which have equal distances to a fixed point (F_2) and to a circle provided this fixed point be situated outside the circle.

The constant difference law of the vectors to F_1 and F_2 leads to a cord construction, shown in fig. 115. A ruler is rotated round F_1; a cord, $2a$ shorter than the ruler, is fastened to the far end of the ruler and in point F_2. The cord is hold taut against the ruler by a pencil and by rotating the ruler the pencil will describe a hyperbola.

DANDELIN's proof that the ellipse is a conic can be repeated
for the hyperbola (fig. 116) with almost the same words as were

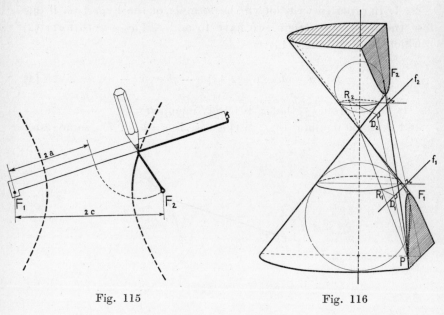

Fig. 115   Fig. 116

used for the ellipse; only, the plane of intersection is chosen in
such a way that it cuts the cone on both sides of the top. Again
the foci appear as the tangent points of the inscribing spheres
which touch the plane of intersection and the *directrices* as the
intersections of this plane with the planes passing through the
contact circles of the cone and the inscribing spheres. Referring
to fig. 116

$$PF_1 : PD_1 = PR_1 : PD_1 = R_1R_2 : D_1D_2 = \text{constant},$$

in words: the hyperbola is the locus of points for which the ratio
of the distances to a fixed point and a fixed straight line is constant
and > 1.

In the same way as for the ellipse, it can be shown that focus
and directrix are related to each other as pole and polar.

By differentiating (4) we find for the tangent:

$$\dot z = \tfrac{1}{2} \{\sqrt{a + jb}\, \exp{(u/2)} + \sqrt{a - jb}\, \exp{(-u/2)}\}$$
$$\{\sqrt{a + jb}\, \exp{(u/2)} - \sqrt{a - jb}\, \exp{(-u/2)}\}$$

showing that: $z_1/\dot{z} = \dot{z}/z_2$ which means geometrically that the tangent makes equal angles with the two vectors to the foci (mirror law, fig. 117). In the same way as for the ellipse, it can be shown that this property is not independent of the constant difference law.

Another consequence of this law is the property of isotrepency of the hyperbola (fig. 118). Hyperbola F_1F_2 will roll without sliding

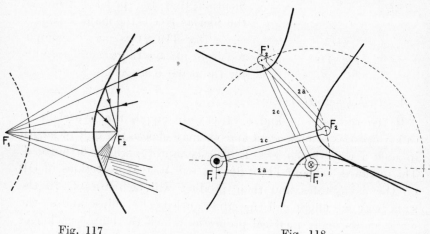

Fig. 117   Fig. 118

over hyperbola $F'_1F'_2$ if the former rotates round F_1 and the latter round F'_1. It suffices to construct only the *hyperbolic barsystem* $F_1F_2F'_2F'_1$. After what was said concerning this subject when treating the ellipse, it will not be necessary to elucidate this point further.

Again, as was the case for the ellipse, it can be shown that the hyperbola is a Kepler orbit, characterized by

$$1/r = 1/p \, (1 - e \cos \theta). \quad \ldots \ldots \quad (5)$$

(See fig. 104 of Ch. VII). Indeed, taking a focus as origin we saw already that:

$$r = a \, (1 + e \cosh u).$$

and from (4) we find for the argument θ:

$$\exp (j\theta) = \frac{\sqrt{a + jb} \exp (u/2) + \sqrt{a - jb} \exp (-u/2)}{\sqrt{a - jb} \exp (u/2) + \sqrt{a + jb} \exp (-u/2)}$$

from which: $\cos\theta = \dfrac{\cosh u + e}{1 + e \cosh u}$ with $e = c/a = \dfrac{\sqrt{a^2 + b^2}}{a}$.

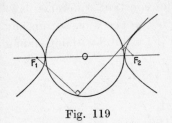

Fig. 119

This r and this $\cos\theta$ satisfy indeed the equation (5) with $1/p = b/a^2$.

As a last property of the foci, we mention that the pedal for one of the foci as pole is the major auxiliary circle (fig. 119); this may be computed from (4) by the general formula for the pedal (Ch. XI).

4. *Orthogonal Hyperbola*

If the constants a and b of (1) are equal, the hyperbola is called *isosceles* or *orthogonal* and we may choose the unit of length in such a way that $a = b = 1$. The asymptotes will be orthogonal. The distances OT and TP of fig. 113 will be the projections of OP on the asymptotes and their product will be constant. In the same way we might call the circle an isosceles ellipse and as the circle shows many metrical properties which the ellipse no longer possesses, the isosceles hyperbola will likewise show more regularities than the general hyperbola.

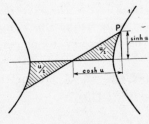

Fig. 120 a

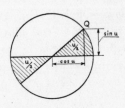

Fig. 120 b

Among these properties there is only one that we shall treat here: we shall try to find the area enclosed by the real axis, the hyperbola and the radius to point P(u) (fig. 120a). We borrow from Ch. XII the general formula for areas:

$$A = -1/2 \int Im\,(z\,\dot{z}^*)\,du.$$

Now for the unit isosceles hyperbola:

$$z = \cosh u + j \sinh u \ \} $$
$$\dot{z}^* = \sinh u - j \cosh u \ \} \quad \cdot \quad \cdot \quad \cdot \quad \cdot \quad \cdot \quad \cdot \quad (7)$$

and $\qquad \operatorname{Im} z\dot{z}^* = - \cosh^2 u + \sinh^2 u = -1,$

so that the area $A = \frac{1}{2} u$.

This reminds us of the area of a sector of the circle

$$z = \cos u + j \sin u$$

(fig. 120b), which is $A = \frac{1}{2} u$. The factor $\frac{1}{2}$ disappears in both cases if we take the two opposite sectors together. The parameter u therefore is called the *area*.

As shown in fig. 120a and 120b the hyperbolic functions are defined from P in exactly the same way as the goniometric functions are defined from Q.

On p. 4 we found for the isosceles hyperbola the formula:

$$z = \sqrt{1 + jv} \quad \cdot \quad \cdot \quad \cdot \quad \cdot \quad \cdot \quad \cdot \quad \cdot \quad (8)$$

and by the transformation:

$$v = \sinh 2u$$

this is transformed into:

$$z = \sqrt{1 + j \sinh 2u} = \sqrt{\cosh^2 u - \sinh^2 u + 2j \sinh u \cosh u}$$
$$= \cosh u + j \sinh u.$$

The form. (8) is found for the electric impedance of homogeneous electric transmission lines or for the acoustical impedance of channels with resistance. For the electrical case:

$$z = \sqrt{L/C} \cdot \sqrt{1 - j \, R/\omega L}$$

where L, C and R are the selfinductance, capacity and resistance per unit of length respectively, ω the angular frequency and this formula is brought into the form (8) by putting $R/\omega L = -v$.

5. *Cartesian ovals*

We shall now proceed to find the locus of the points for which the sum or the difference of the distance to one point (F_1) and

n times the distance to a second point (F_2) is constant. These curves are called *Cartesian ovals* and obey the formulae:

$$|z_1| + n|z_2| = C \;;$$
$$|z_1| - n|z_2| = C \;;$$
$$-|z_1| + n|z_2| = C \;.$$

For each value of C only two of these curves are possible. It will, for instance, be clear that if C is smaller than the distance between the foci, the first curve cannot exist, assuming $n > 1$.

These curves occur as boundary-lines between crystals or between bacteria colonies which grow with different velocities. In order to obtain images without spherical aberration lenses should have surfaces of which the sections are Cartesian ovals. They can easily be drawn by cord-constructions if n is a whole number. We can show that the projection of the intersection curve of two circular cones with parallel axes on a plane perpendicular to these axes is a set of Cartesian ovals (fig. 121, 122).

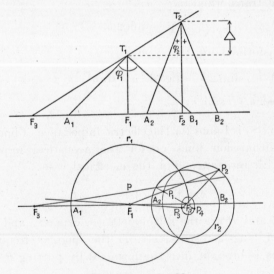

Fig. 121 and 122

For, let the foci F_1 and F_2 be the projections of the tops, then the radii z_1 and z_2 are the horizontal projections of generating lines of the cones. The projections of two intersecting generating lines on the cone axes differ by a constant amount, this being the difference $\triangle$ in heights of the tops, which can be formulated:

$$|z_1| \cot \varphi_1 - |z_2| \cot \varphi_2 = \triangle,$$

where φ_1 and φ_2 are the semitopangles of the two cones. But this formula is essentially the same as the defining formula of Cartesian's ovals.

A synthetic way of generating the ovals, which are fourth order curves, is the following (fig. 122). Cut two circles by a ray pencil, the carrier point of which is situated on the line connecting the centres of the circles. Project the point involutions obtained on the two circles from their centres. The intersection of these two ray involutions is a set of conjugated Cartesian ovals.

The circles can be considered as the bases of two cones, their centres F_1 and F_2 as the projections of the tops and the third point F_3 on their connecting line as the point where the straight line passing through the two cone tops T_1 and T_2 cuts the basic plane. A plane through T_1 and T_2 cuts the basic plane by a straight line, p, the cones by generating lines, which are projected on the basic plane as radii form F_1 and F_2 and the construction of the projection of the intersecting curve comes down to the above mentioned synthetic generation of the oval. The ratio

$$\frac{\cot \varphi_2}{\cot \varphi_1} = n = \frac{T_2 F_2}{T_1 F_1} \cdot \frac{A_1 F_1}{A_2 F_2} = \frac{F_2 F_3}{F_1 F_3} \cdot \frac{r_1}{r_2}.$$

In fig. 122 the smaller oval $P_3 P_4$ is the curve

$$|z_1| - \tfrac{5}{2} |z_2| = \text{Const.}$$

the larger one $P_1 P_2$ the curve

$$\tfrac{5}{2} |z_2| - |z_1| = \text{Const.}$$

The constant C is found by the calculation to be:

$$C = \frac{\triangle}{\cot \varphi_1} = \frac{\triangle}{T_1 F_1} \cdot r_1 = \frac{F_1 F_2}{F_1 F_3} \cdot r_1.$$

In order to arrive at an oval $|z_1| + n |z_2| = C$, it is necessary to choose the tops T_1 and T_2 on different sides of the basic plane.

CHAPTER IX

THE PARABOLA

1. *Introduction*

The parabola is generated as a conic (fig. 123) if we choose the plane cutting the circular cone parallel to one of the generating lines of the cone. Applying again Dandelin's method we find in this case only one focus and one directrix. The focus is the

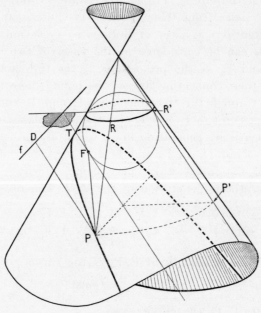

Fig. 123

point where the inscribing sphere touches the plane, the directrix is the line of intersection of the plane mentioned above and the plane through the contact circle of the inscribing sphere. Again focus and directrix belong together as pole and polar of the curve. The distance of P to f equals P'R' = PR = PF (fig. 123), so that the parabola is the locus of points at equal distances from a fixed point and a fixed straight line.

Fig. 124 shows a cord construction based on this principle. The ruler is fixed, the triangle slides along the ruler. The length of the cord equals that of the base of the triangle.

Denoting the distance of the focus F to the directrix f by p ($=$ parameter), we have for any point of the parabola (fig. 126), if the origin is in F:

$$x + p = \sqrt{x^2 + y^2}$$

Now put $y = pu$, then $x = \tfrac{1}{2} p (u^2 - 1)$ and the complex equation is:

$$z = \tfrac{1}{2} p (u^2 - 1) + jpu = \tfrac{1}{2} p (u + j)^2. \quad . \quad . \quad . \quad (1)$$

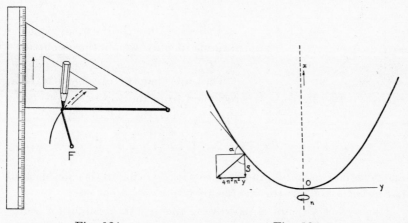

Fig. 124   Fig. 125

The level of a liquid contained in a vessel rotating round a vertical axis with constant velocity assumes the form of a parabola (fig. 125), for if the level shall be normal to the resultant force tan $a = dx/dy$ must be proportional to y, or $dx/dy = $ Const. y.

Integrated: $x = $ Const. $y^2 + C_2$,

and this corresponds to the equation derived above for the parabola.

By differentiating we find:

$$\dot{z} = p (u + j). . \quad . \quad . \quad . \quad . \quad . \quad . \quad (2)$$

Differentiating once more we find:

$$\ddot{z} = p$$

and this means that any material point moving with an acceleration, constant in value and direction (e.g. in the gravity field), will describe a parabola. Hence the application of the parabola in ballistics.

The parabola belongs also to the family of Kepler orbits, characterized by (fig. 126):

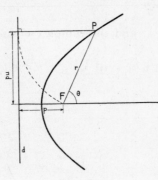

$$1/r = 2/p\ (1 - e\ \cos\ \theta)$$

for:

$$r = |z| = \tfrac{1}{2}\,p\,(u^2 + 1)$$

and:

$$\exp\,(j\theta) = \frac{u + j}{u - j}\ \therefore\ \cos\,\theta = \frac{u^2 - 1}{u^2 + 1}$$

and these values tally with Kepler's formula, if only we put the eccentricity $e = 1$.

The arc length of the parabola, reckoned from the top $(u = 0)$ to point $P(u)$ is, with the aid of (2):

Fig. 126

$$s = p \int \sqrt{1 + u^2}\ du = \tfrac{1}{2}\,p\,[u\,\sqrt{1 + u^2} + \log\,(u + \sqrt{1 + u^2})]$$

and gives no reason to important remarks. Owing to the complicated nature of $s = f(u)$, the evolvente is not a simple curve.

The area of a sector is, borrowing the general formula for sector area's from Ch. XII

$$A = -\tfrac{1}{2} \int \text{Im}\,(z\dot{z}^*)\,du.$$

This gives, with the aid of (1) and (2):

$$A = -\tfrac{1}{4}\,p^2 \int (u^2 + 1)\,du = \tfrac{1}{4}\,p^2\,(u^3/3 + u).$$

The cap cut off by the vertical line through F has an area:

$$A = \tfrac{1}{4}\,p^2 \int_{-1}^{+1} (u^2 + 1)\,du = 2p^2/3.$$

For the radius of curvature we find:

$$\varrho = p\,(1 + u^2)^{3/2},$$

giving the value $\varrho = p$ for the top $(u = 0)$.

2. *Right angles in the parabola*

Measuring $\dot{z}$ on the normal we come to the point (fig. 127)

$$z - j\dot{z} = \tfrac{1}{2}\, p\, (u + j)^2 - j p\, (u + j) = \tfrac{1}{2}\, p\, (u^2 + 1)$$

and this is a point on the real axis, lying a constant amount p to the right of point $P(u)$, in other words: The subnormal is constant $= p$.

Equ. (2) of the tangent can also be written:

$$\dot{z} = \sqrt{2p} \cdot \sqrt{z} \quad . \quad . \quad . \quad . \quad . \quad . \quad (3)$$

which means that the slope of the tangent is half the slope of the radius vector. If this changes by π (fig. 127), the slope of the

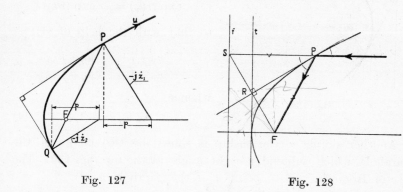

Fig. 127   Fig. 128

tangent will change by $\pi/2$, in words: the tangents in the extremities of a cord through F will be orthogonal.

Another consequence of (3) is (fig. 128) that a horizontal light ray will be reflected towards the focus.

This reflection law combined with the equal distance law leads to fig. 128 which shows that the base R of the perpendicular let down from F on the tangent, must lie on a vertical straight line halfway between F and the directrix f, but this line is the top tangent. In other words: The top tangent is the pedal of the parabola for the focus as origin.

If we construct a semi circle on FP it will be tangent to the top tangent in point R.

Extend the tangent beyond the top tangent to point U of the

Zwikker

9

directrix (fig. 129). The two triangles PUS and PUF are congruent
and as the angle at S is right, the angle at F must also be right:
The part of a tangent comprised between the directrix and the
tangent point subtends a right angle at the focus.

Let Q be the point on the parabola opposite to P. QU is
also seen under a right angle at F. $\angle$ PUQ must be right as
follows from fig. 127. Therefore:
The directrix is the orthoptic
curve of the parabola.

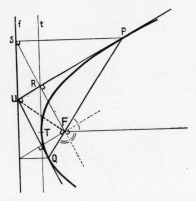

The opposite points P and Q
show a simple u-relationship. As
the arguments, θ, differ by π:

$$\exp (j\,\theta_{\mathrm{P}}) = - \exp (j\,\theta_{\mathrm{Q}})$$

so that with the help of (1):

$$\frac{u_{\mathrm{P}}+j}{u_{\mathrm{P}}-j} = - \frac{u_{\mathrm{Q}}+j}{u_{\mathrm{Q}}-j}$$

Fig. 129

whence:

$$u_{\mathrm{P}}\,u_{\mathrm{Q}} = -1. \quad . \quad . \quad (4)$$

Another simple u-relationship is shown by two points of the
parabola which subtend a right angle at the top (fig. 130). The
vector from the top to point u of the parabola is

$$z = \tfrac{1}{2}\, p\, (u^2 + 2\,ju).$$

The right angle at T requires that

$$\sqrt{\frac{u_1^2 + 2\,ju_1}{u_1^2 - 2\,ju_1}} = j \sqrt{\frac{u_2^2 + 2\,ju_2}{u_2^2 - 2\,ju_2}},$$

from which: $u_1\,u_2 = -4$.

Take point S on the real axis at $2p$ from the top. The vectors
$z_1 - \mathrm{S}$ and $z_2 - \mathrm{S}$ are respectively:

$$\tfrac{1}{2}\, p\, (u_1^2 + 2\,ju_1 - 4) \quad \text{and} \quad \tfrac{1}{2}\, p\, (u_2^2 + 2\,ju_2 - 4).$$

As $u_1\,u_2 = -4$, the latter is:

$$\tfrac{1}{2}\, p\, (16/u_1^2 - 8\,j/u_1 - 4) = -\tfrac{1}{2}\, p \cdot (u_1^2 + 2\,ju_1 - 4)\, 4/u_1^2,$$

and appears to have the same direction as $z_1 - S$. The three points z_1, z_2 and S are therefore collinear, so that we find, that S lies on all chords connecting two points for which $u_1 u_2 = -4$. Conversely we may say that the vertices of all triangles that have a right angle in T and the hypothenusa of which shall pass through a fixed point S lie on a parabola.

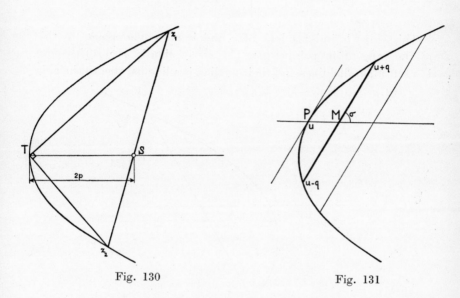

Fig. 130   Fig. 131

We may extend these considerations to any point on the axis lying $ap/2$ from T. This point will be collinear with any two points for which $u_1 u_2 = -a$. The proof will be exactly the same as that given for $a = 4$.

3. *Medians, pole and polar*

Draw the chord connecting the two points $u \pm q$ (fig. 131).

$$z(u \pm q) = \tfrac{1}{2} p (u \pm q + j)^2.$$

The centre M is

$$z_M = \tfrac{1}{2} p \{(u+j)^2 + q^2)\},$$

differing from $z(u)$ only by the real amount $pq^2/2$, so that M is

situated on a line through P parallel to the axis. The vector from
$u-q$ to $u+q$ is:

$$z\,(u+q)-z\,(u-q)=2\,pq\,(u+j)$$

with a slope defined by the argument factor:

$$\sqrt{\frac{u+j}{u-j}}.$$

This slope is independent of q and is moreover, equal to that
of the tangent in point $P(u)$. The set of chords $u\pm q$, therefore,
is a set of parallel lines and their median is a line parallel to the axis.

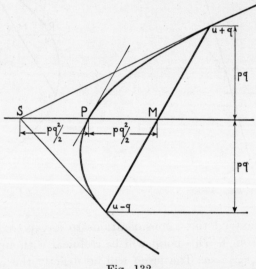

Fig. 132

Let us now draw the tangents in the extremities of the chord
(fig. 132) and calculate their point of intersection. Introducing
uniform scales s_1 and s_2 along these tangents, their point of intersection S will be

$$z_S=\tfrac{1}{2}p\,(u+q+j)^2-s_1\,(u+q+j)=\tfrac{1}{2}p\,(u-q+j)^2+s_2\,(u-q+j).$$

Separation of the real and imaginary parts yields two equations
for s_1 and s_2, from which we calculate:

$$s_1=s_2=pq,$$

and substituting these values in z_s, we find:

$$z_S = \tfrac{1}{2}\, p\,\{(u+j)^2 - q^2\}.$$

Again, as was the case for M the point S is situated on the horizontal line through P and also at a distance $pq^2/2$ from P. In words: The part of a median intercepted between a pole and the corresponding polar is cut by the parabola in two equal parts.

The vector z_s can be split into two factors:

$$\left.\begin{aligned} z_S &= \tfrac{1}{2}\, p\,(u+q+j)\ (u-q+j)\\ &= \sqrt{z\,(u+q)\,.\,z\,(u-q)} \end{aligned}\right\} \quad . \quad . \quad . \quad . \quad (5)$$

which means (fig. 133) first, that for an eye in F the parts of the tangents in the points $u+q$ and $u-q$, comprised between the tangent points and their point of intersection subtend equal angles, secondly, that the triangles FS $(u+q)$ and F $(u-q)$ S are similar, leading to equal angle relations (fig. 133).

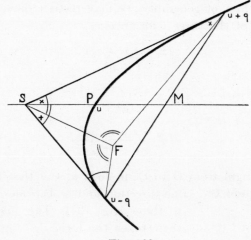

Fig. 133

(5) also indicates directly that $2p.z_s$ equals the product of the tangents in the points $u+q$ and $u-q$. As $2p$ is a vector in the direction of the real axis this means geometrically that the angle between the real axis and one tangent equals the angle between SF and the other tangent (fig. 133).

4. *Concluding remarks on conics*

The question remains whether ellipse, hyperbola and parabola are the only curves of the second order. In order to prove this, we start from the general formula for second order curves:

$$z = \frac{z_0 + z_1 u + z_2 u^2}{m_0 + m_1 u + m_2 u^2}. \quad \cdots \quad \cdots \quad (6)$$

By the transformation: $u = u' - m_1/2m_2$ the denominator assumes the form:

$$A(q + u'^2)$$

and the numerator does not change its character.

According as $q \lessgtr 0$, we shall distinguish three cases:

$q > 0$ (ellipse?, no real points at infinity)

$q = 0$ (parabola?, two coinciding points at infinity)

$q < 1$ (hyperbola?, two real points at infinity)

and without loss of generality we may restrict ourselves to the consideration of the three z-formulas:

$$z = \frac{z_0 + z_1 u + z_2 u^2}{1 + u^2};$$

$$z = \frac{z_0 + z_1 u + z_2 u^2}{u^2}$$

and

$$z = \frac{z_0 - z_1 u - z_2 u^2}{1 - u^2}.$$

Shift the origin from O to O' in such a way that the vectors z_0 and z_2 acquire the same direction and z_1 becomes orthogonal to these (fig. 134). The first equation then takes the form:

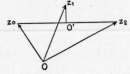

$$z = z_0 \frac{1 + jbu + cu^2}{1 + u^2}$$

where b and c are real constants.

Fig. 134

Division by z_0 only means a transformation into a similar curve and does not change its character. After this division we again apply a parallel translation by adding $-\dfrac{1+c}{2}$ to z, by which we obtain:

$$z = \frac{a + jbu - au^2}{1 + u^2}$$

which by the transformation: $u = \tan v/2$ becomes:

$$z = \frac{a+b}{2} \exp (jv) + \frac{a-b}{2} \exp (-jv),$$

which is the formula used by us for the ellipse. As through the above the character of the curve has not changed, we infer, that all curves (6), provided $q > 0$, will be ellipses and in the same way the characters of the two remaining types may be identified with those of the parabola and of the hyperbola.

CHAPTER X

INVOLUTES, EVOLUTES, ANTICAUSTICS

1. Involute and evolute

The *evolvente* or *involute* of a basis-curve z_1 is the curve described by the end of a supple cord which is unwound from the basis-curve. We shall denote this curve by z_0. Each basis-curve has many involutes depending on the starting point u_0 (fig. 135).

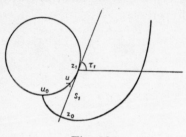

Fig. 135

The relation between z_1 and z_0 is seen from fig. 135 to be:

$$z_0 = z_1 - s_1 \exp (j\tau_1), \quad . \quad . \quad . \quad (1)$$

where we may substitute

$$s_1 = \int_{u_0}^{u} |\dot{z}_1|\, du \; ; \; \exp (j\tau_1) = dz_1/ds_1.$$

The involute of the circle is, technically speaking, the most important owing to its application to gear wheel cog-profiles: Starting from the equation for the circle

$$z_1 = \exp (ju) \text{ we find: } s_1 = u \; ; \; dz_1/ds_1 = dz_1/du = j \exp (ju)$$

and the equation of the evolvente is:

$$z_0 = (1 - ju) \exp (ju)$$

as already found before. (Ch. I, p. 5).

We shall in general use the term involute and for the sake of marking its importance reserve tbe term evolvente only for the circle involute.

As the point z_1 is the instantaneous centre of rotation, we expect s_1 to be the radius of curvature of the involute.

Let us apply the general formula:

$$\frac{1}{\varrho_0} = \frac{1}{2j} \frac{\dot{z}_0^* \ddot{z}_0 - \dot{z}_0 \ddot{z}_0^*}{(\dot{z}_0 \dot{z}_0^*)^{3/2}}$$

and let us start from (1):

$$z_0 = z_1 - s_1 \exp (j \tau_1)$$

choosing τ_1 as parameter. Evidently, as $\dot{s} \exp (j\tau) = \dot{z}$:

$$\dot{z}_0 = -j s_1 \exp (j \tau_1),$$

and

$$\ddot{z}_0 = (-j \dot{s}_1 + s_1) \exp (j \tau_1)$$

Introduction of these and their conjugate values in the formula for ϱ_0 teaches us that indeed $\varrho_0 = s_1$.

The original curve is therefore the locus of the centres of curvature of the involute, or — in a technical term — is the *evolute* of its involute.

The last formula but one is the direct analytical proof, that the direction of the involute is normal to the tangent to z_1.

We now ask: Can any arbitrary curve z_0 be considered an involute? The answer is yes. It will always have an evolute, the equation of which is:

$$z_1 = z_0 + j \varrho_0 \exp (j \tau_0) \ ; \ \varrho_0 = ds_0/d\tau_0 \ . \ . \ . \ . \ (2)$$

where ϱ_0 is the radius of curvature and τ_0 the slope of the basiscurve.

Choosing τ_0 as parameter, this may be written as

$$z_1 = z_0 + j \dot{s}_0 \exp (j\tau_0).$$

and

$$\dot{z}_1 = \dot{z}_0 + j \ddot{s}_0 \exp (j\tau_0) - \dot{s}_0 \exp (j\tau_0).$$

The first and third term cancel out, so that

$$\dot{z}_1 = j \dot{s}_0 \exp (j\tau_0)$$

which means that the direction of the evolute is the same as that of the normal to the original curve. ($\tau_1 = \tau_0 + \pi/2$). The evolute is thus tangent to all normals of the basis curve z_0.

The arc length along the evolute is

$$s_1 = \int |\dot{z}_1| \, d\tau_0 = \int \ddot{s}_0 \, d\tau_0 = \dot{s}_0 = \varrho_0$$

and we are now prepared to close the circle of our argument, as we can now apply form. (1) to determine the involute of the evolute z_1.

Executing this, the involute is:

$$z_1 - s_1 \exp (j\tau_1)$$
$$= z_0 + j \dot{s}_0 \exp (j\tau_0) - j\varrho_0 \exp (j\tau_0) = z_0$$

and this is indeed the original curve.

The radius of curvature of the evolute is:

$$\varrho_1 = \frac{ds_1}{d\tau_1} = \frac{d\varrho_0}{d\tau_0} = \frac{d^2 s_0}{d\tau_0^2}.$$

where ϱ_0 and s_0 refer to the basis curve. It is, therefore, easy to give a formula for the second evolute, that is the evolute of the evolute.

$$z_2 = z_1 + j\varrho_1 \exp (j\tau_1)$$
$$= z_0 + j \frac{ds_0}{d\tau_0} \exp (j\tau_0) + j^2 \frac{d^2 s_0}{d\tau_0^2} \exp (j\tau_0).$$

We can continue in this way and find for the nth evolute:

$$z_0 + j \frac{ds_0}{d\tau_0} \exp (j\tau_0) + \ldots + j^n \frac{d^n s_0}{d\tau_0^n} \exp (j\tau_0).$$

For the circle the first evolute is the centre, the second evolute and all higher evolutes do not exist.

2. Norwich spiral

Starting from the circle:

$$z_1 = \exp (ju)$$

we found the involute or evolvente:

$$z_0 = (1 - ju) \exp ju$$
$$\varrho_0 = s_1 = u$$
$$s_0 = \tfrac{1}{2} u^2$$

and the natural equation is

$$s_0 = \tfrac{1}{2} \varrho_0^2.$$

The involute of the circle evolvente is (fig. 136):

$$z_{00} = (1 - ju - \tfrac{1}{2}u^2) \exp(ju)$$
$$\varrho_{00} = s_0 = \tfrac{1}{2}u^2$$
$$s_{00} = \tfrac{1}{6}u^3$$

and the natural equation is: $9s_{00}^2 = 2\varrho_{00}^3$.

We may draw from any point S on the second evolvente a tangent to the circle. This tangent will have the length

$$\sqrt{|z_{00}|^2 - 1} = \tfrac{1}{2}u^2$$

and this is equal to the normal ϱ_{00} in S. See fig. 136, where $SP = SQ$.

As we remarked already, any curve has many involutes and all these involutes will be *parallel curves*, because they have the

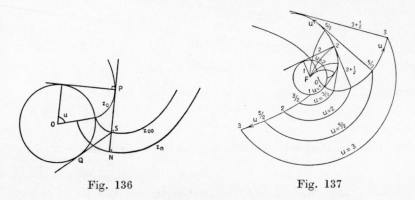

Fig. 136   Fig. 137

same normals and, measured along these normals, have constant distance apart. An interesting involute of the circle evolvente is generated as a parallel of the above mentioned curve z_{00} if we lengthen the unwounding cord by an amount equal to half the radius of the circle. The curve z_n generated in this way is called the *Norwich spiral* and its properties were discovered by *Sylvester* (1868). It follows from the way in which it is generated, that its radius of curvature is greater by $\tfrac{1}{2}$ than that of z_{00}; it is therefore $\tfrac{1}{2}(u^2 + 1)$. Its equation is, starting from z_0:

$$z_n = z_0 - \tfrac{1}{2}(u^2 + 1)\exp(ju) = \tfrac{1}{2}(1 - ju)^2 \exp(ju)$$

As $z=\frac{1}{2}(1-ju^2)$ is a parabola, the points of the spiral are found by a rotation of the points of the parabola over an angle u (fig. 137).

The absolute value of z is $\frac{1}{2}(1+u^2)$ and this equals the radius of curvature. The Norwich spiral is therefore the locus of the points for which the distance to a fixed centre equals the radius of curvature. This means that in fig. 136 ON=NP.

3. *Catenary and tractrix*

Another couple of curves mutually related as evolute and involute are the *catenary* and the *tractrix*.

The formula of the catenary (=chaincurve fig. 138) is:

$$z = u + j \cosh u.$$

it is the graphic representation of the cosh function.

The tangent is

$$\dot{z} = 1 + j \sinh u.$$

The absolute value of the velocity is

$$|\dot{z}| = \sqrt{1 + \sinh^2 u} = \cosh u.$$

The arc length, starting from the bottom of the curve is:

$$s = \int |\dot{z}|\, du = \sinh u$$

and from the formula for $\dot{z}$ we see, that the slope is determined by

$$\tan \tau = \sinh u.$$

Incidentally, $\tan \tau$ equals the arc length and this is the reason why a supple cord will hang in the shape of a catenary from which the curve has received its name. Indeed, the weight to be carried will be proportional to the length s and the vertical component of the force will be proportional to s. As the horizontal component of the force is constant, the tan of the slope will have to be proportional to s and this is what is actually found for the catenary.

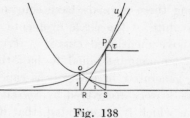

Fig. 138

The radius of curvature of the catenary is found to be:

$$\varrho = \cosh^2 u;$$

so that the natural equation of the catenary is $\varrho = 1 + s^2$.

If we measure the distance ϱ on the normal on both sides, we find the centre of curvature C and a point M, for which we have

$$z_M = z - j \cosh^2 u \cdot \exp(j\tau).$$

introducing:

$$z = u + j \cosh u$$

$$\exp(j\tau) = \frac{\dot z}{|\dot z|} = \frac{1 + j \sinh u}{\cosh u}$$

we find:

$$z_M = u + \sinh u \cosh u$$

and this is real, so that M is a point on the real axis (fig. 139).

This property is of interest in connection with capillarity. Let the catenary rotate round the x-axis, the generated surface is called *catenoid* and the two principal radii of curvature of this surface will be PC and PM, of equal length but having opposite signs; the surface being concave in the meridional planes but convex along the parallel circles. The total curvature of the

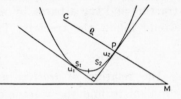

Fig. 139

surface, being the sum of the two principal curvatures is zero and this is the condition for the shape of soap films extended between two parallel circular rings.

For two points on the catenary having mutually orthogonal tangents we have the condition: (fig. 139).

$$\tan \tau_1 \cdot \tan \tau_2 = -1$$

or as

$$\tan \tau = \sinh u = s:$$

$\sinh u_1 \cdot \sinh u_2 = -1$ and $s_1 s_2 = -1$ and the sum of the curvatures in these two points is:

$$\frac{1}{\varrho_1} + \frac{1}{\varrho_2} = \frac{1}{\cosh^2 u_1} + \frac{1}{\cosh^2 u_2} = \frac{1}{1 + \sinh^2 u_1} + \frac{1}{1 + \dfrac{1}{\sinh^2 u_1}} = 1.$$

The involute of the catenary may easily be derived by means of the general formula, it is

$$z_0 = u + \frac{j - \exp(u)}{j + \exp(u)}$$

and is called the *tractrix* (fig. 138). Its principal characteristics may be calculated in the usual way; one finds:

$$\varrho_0 = \sinh u \; ; \; s_0 = ln \cosh u$$

and the natural equation: $s_0 = ln \sqrt{1 + \varrho_0^2}$.

The most remarkable property of the tractrix is that the x-axis cuts a constant piece of unit length off all tangents. For if we measure on the tangent the length $= 1$, we find the point:

$$z_0 - j \exp(j\tau),$$

which, on computation, appears to be the point u on the real axis (fig. 138). If a tug-boat should move along the x-axis (the tractor) and tug a barge by means of a rope of length 1, the barge would follow the tractrix. This explains its name.

4. *Tractrices in general*

The relation of *tractrix* and *tractor* can be extended to the problem to find the tractor curve of a given curve considered as tractrix and vice versa.

The first derivation is very simple. If the tractrix is given as $z_{ix} = f(s)$, where s is the arc length, the tractor is simply:

$$z_{or} = z_{ix} \pm \dot{z}_{ix}$$

the choice of the sign being dependent on the direction in which the tugging takes place.

The reverse problem is a bit more complicated, as any tractor may have an infinite number of tractrices. Let z_{or} be given, using an arbitrary parameter u. Take a point z_{ix} at unit distance from $z_{or}(u)$: $z_{ix} = z_{or}(u) + e^{j f(u)}$

and in such a direction that dz_{ix}/du is directed towards the point $z_{or}(u)$, in formula:

$$\dot{z}_{or}(u) + j \dot{f} e^{j f(u)} = \text{Real} \cdot e^{j f(u)}$$

or $(\dot{z}_{or} e^{-jf} + j\dot{f}) = \text{Real} = \dot{z}_{or}^* e^{+jf} - j\dot{f}$

This is to be considered as a differential equation from which $f(u)$ is to be calculated.

Example: What is the tractrix of the straight line:

$$z_{or} = u \; ; \; \dot{z}_{or} = \dot{z}_{or}^{*} = 1.$$

The differential equation is: $\sin f = \dot{f}$. Separating variables:

$$df/\sin f = d \lg \tan f/2 = du; \quad \tan f/2 = e^{u}; \quad \exp (jf) = \frac{j - \exp u}{j + \exp u},$$

and the tractrix is

$$z_{ix} = u + \frac{j - \exp u}{j + \exp u}$$

in accordance with what we expected.

5.   *The evolute of the parabola*

The evolute of the parabola (origin in the focus, fig. 140)

$$z_0 = \tfrac{1}{2}\, p\, (j + u)^2$$

is easily found to be:

$$z_1 = p\,(\tfrac{1}{2} + \tfrac{3}{2} u^2 - j\, u^3).$$

Dropping for a moment the contant $p/2$ we see, that this curve is represented in Cartesian coordinates by the equation:

$$y = \text{Const.}\; x^{3/2},$$

it is called the *semicubic parabola*. It is a curve with cusp and belongs to the cissoid class of cubics. It is also drawn in fig. 140. The cusp E is situated at $p/2$ to the right of the focus.

Fig. 140 shows the point of intersection of the parabola and its evolute. It can be calculated in the usual way and we find that it is the point $u = 2\sqrt{2}$

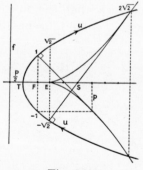

Fig. 140

of the parabola and the point $u = -\sqrt{2}$ of the evolute. This means that the tangent in this point is the parabola's normal in point $u = -\sqrt{2}$. As the product of these two u-values $2\sqrt{2}$ and $-\sqrt{2}$ equals -4, this normal passes through point S at $2p$ to the right of the parabola's top and subtends a right angle at the top T. From the general formula for the radius of curvature:

$$\varrho = p\,(1+u^2)^{3/2}$$

we find its length to be equal to $p.\ 3\sqrt{3}$.

The normal in point $u=1$ of the parabola has a length equal to $p.\ 2\sqrt{2}$; its tangent point on the evolute is situated at $p(2-j)$ with respect to the focus (fig. 140).

6.   *Anticaustics*

Suppose a cord to be slung round a polygon c (fig. 112, p. 113) and the cord stretched tight by a pencil. Now move the pencil in such a way that the cord is permanently kept taut. Repeating the argument of p. 113 we observe that the line a described by the pencil will consist of parts of ellipses, two vertices of the polygon acting temporarily as the foci of the ellipse. The curve a therefore possesses the property that its tangent always makes equal angles with the two parts of the cord leading to the pencil. When we let the number of sides of the polygon c increase indefinitely this equal angle property of the pencil curve, a will remain valid and in the limit, that is, if we sling the cord round a closed contour c of arbitrary form, the pencil curve a will still be such that the tangent in any point will make equal angles with the two tangents drawn from this point of a to the contour c.

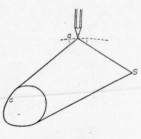

Now sling the cord round a closed contour and the fixed point S (fig. 141), manipulate the pencil in the same way, this leads again to a curve a. Again the equal angle property will occur. Any light ray coming from the source S will be reflected by the curve a (*anticaustic*) in such a way that the reflected ray will be tangent to the contour c, c therefore acting as the

Fig. 141

caustic. The length of the cord may be varied, which will lead to different anticaustics for a single choice of source S and caustic c.

In practice a light source is never a mathematical point but has finite dimensions. In fig. 142 we represent the light source by a countour s. If we wish to prevent reflected light from entering the contour c, the cord is now slung round c and s with a twist. Cases like this occur in the designing of incandescent lamps and fittings where one is anxious to keep radiation from certain lamp parts which may not reach high temperatures.

Other variations of the cord construction may be imagined dependent on the problem in hand, the cord, if required being slung with one or two twists.

In order to find an analytical formula for the curve a in the case of a point source of light S we shall suppose that the contour c is given by the formula $z = f(s)$ with respect to S as origin. We choose the arc length, s, measured along the curve, as parameter. s contains an arbitrary constant and we shall fix this constant in such a way that s will be the length of the cord CAS (fig. 143). Now reflect the point S with respect to the tangent to a in point A. The image point is E. CAE is straight and has the length s, E obviously describes an involute of the contour c, if A is moved in the prescribed way with the pencil.

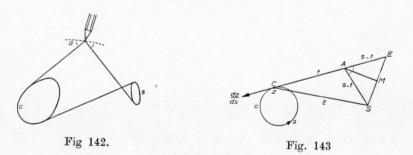

Fig 142.   Fig. 143

The „velocity" of point C along the contour c is a vector dz/ds, it has unit value and is directed along the tangent. The place of point E is therefore represented by the vector:

$$z_{\mathrm{E}} = z - s\frac{dz}{ds}$$

Zwikker

10

and for point A, situated somewhere on the tangent, we have:

$$z_A = z - t\frac{dz}{ds} \quad\cdots\cdots\cdots\quad (1)$$

where t is a real factor still to be determined.

On the other hand A is situated on the bisector of the line SE. Choosing S as the origin of coordinates, the vector SE is z_E. Point M is represented by: $z_M = \frac{1}{2} z_E$. The bisector is orthogonal to z_E, and point A on it may be represented by the formula

$$z_A = (\tfrac{1}{2} + j\,\lambda)\,z_E, \quad\cdots\cdots\quad (2)$$

where λ is a parameter, j indicating the orthogonal direction of MA with respect to SE. Now t and λ follow from equating (1) and (2):

$$z_A = z - t\frac{dz}{ds} = (\tfrac{1}{2} + j\,\lambda)\,z_E \;;\; z_E = z - s\frac{dz}{ds},$$

from which:

$$\tfrac{1}{2} + j\,\lambda = \frac{z - t\dfrac{dz}{ds}}{z - s\dfrac{dz}{ds}}.$$

For the conjugate values, denoting these by asterisks we obtain

$$\tfrac{1}{2} - j\,\lambda = \frac{z^* - t\dfrac{dz^*}{ds}}{z^* - s\dfrac{dz^*}{ds}}.$$

Addition of these two equations eliminates λ and gives an equation for t, the solution of which is:

$$t = -\frac{s^2 - zz^*}{\dfrac{dz}{ds}z^* + \dfrac{dz^*}{ds}z - 2s}.$$

Now zz^* is the square of the absolute value of the vector z (CS in fig. 143), we shall denote it by ϱ. As, furthermore, the denominator of t is the derivative of the numerator, we can write:

$$t = \frac{s^2 - \varrho^2}{\dfrac{d}{ds}(s^2 - \varrho^2)} \qquad \cdots \cdots \cdots \quad (3)$$

Measuring the distance t on the tangent of the caustic c will give us the anticaustic, so that the geometrical problem is solved.

Example: Let c be the unit circle and let S lie on the circle. If we let s start from point S (fig. 144a), s is the arc length SC; the straight distance SC$=\varrho=2\sin s/2$, hence

$$t = \frac{s^2 - 4\sin^2 \dfrac{s}{2}}{2s - 2\sin s}$$

and this has to be measured on the tangent in C for all values of s (fig. 145 curve a).

We may make s longer, for example by starting the s-scale from the bottom point of the circle (fig. 144b); in this case

$$\varrho^2 = 2(1 - \sin s)$$

$$t = \frac{s^2 - 2(1 - \sin s)}{2s + 2\cos s}.$$

The corresponding curve is shown in fig. 145 curve b.

The anticaustics have a spiral character, by mirroring an arc of the spiral with respect to the horizontal axis we may obtain symmetrical shapes.

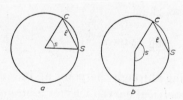

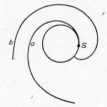

Fig. 144   Fig. 145

The formula (3) for t is simplified if the light source S is moved towards the right to infinity. For this purpose we write:

$$1/t = d/ds \; lg \, (s^2 - \varrho^2) = d/ds \; lg \, (s - \varrho) + d/ds \; lg \, (s + \varrho)$$

Now s and ϱ grow infinitely large together and as the derivative of the logarithme tends to zero for infinite value of its argument we have $d/ds\ lg\ (s+\varrho) \to 0$ for $\varrho = -x \to \infty$, so that t becomes:

$$t = \frac{s+x}{\dfrac{d}{ds}\,(s+x)}$$

and this introduced into (1) will give anticaustics for parallel rays. We may move the origin back from infinity, keeping $s+x$ constant, and as there is an arbitrary constant in s the choice of the origin is of no importance, it is only the differences in x for the various points of the caustic that will influence the shape of the anticaustic.

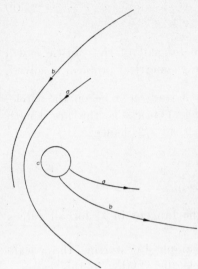

Fig. 146

Example: Let again c be the unit circle and let us make the same two choices of s as in the last example. We place the origin at the centre of the circle. For s starting in the horizontal axis, $x = \cos s$, hence:

$$t = \frac{s + \cos s}{1 - \sin s} \qquad \text{(fig. 146a)}$$

For s starting from the bottom of the circle:

$$x = \sin s, \text{ so that}$$

$$t = \frac{s + \sin s}{1 + \cos s} \qquad \text{(fig. 146b)}$$

The anticaustics are spirals passing through the point at infinity of the horizontal axis. Again symmetrical curves may be obtained by mirroring a branch of the anticaustic with respect to the horizontal axis.

In the general case the caustic is given by $z = f(u)$, where u is different from s. Take, for instance, the classical case of caustics:

the cardioid. This is the trajectory of a point of a circle (say of unit radius) rolling over an equally large stationary circle. Taking the centre of the stationary circle as origin (fig. 147) the centre M of the rolling circle may be represented by $z_M = 2 \exp(j\omega)$ and the point C of the cardioid by

$$z = 2 \exp{(j\omega)} + \exp{(2j\omega)}$$

and the formula would lose much of its lucidity if we tried to transform ω into the arc length s.

In this case it is appropriate to rewrite (1) as follows:

$$z_A = z - t \cdot \frac{dz}{d\omega} \cdot \frac{d\omega}{ds} \quad . \quad (4)$$

with

$$t \cdot \frac{d\omega}{ds} = \frac{s^2 - \varrho^2}{\dfrac{d}{d\omega}(s^2 - \varrho^2)}$$

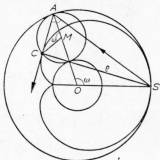

Fig. 147

and the difficulties encountered are not greater than before.

Let us work out the case of the cardioid; we take the light source S on the cardioid where it cuts the horizontal axis ($z_S = 3$). The chord ϱ is found from:

$$\varrho^2 = (z-3)(z^{\ast}-3) = 20 - 8 \cos\omega - 12 \cos^2\omega.$$

The arc-length element is:

$$ds = \sqrt{\frac{dz}{d\omega} \cdot \frac{dz^{\ast}}{d\omega}} \cdot d\omega = 4 \cos\frac{\omega}{2} \cdot d\omega.$$

and the total arc length:

$$s = \int ds = 8 \sin \omega/2 \;;\; s^2 = 32\,(1 - \cos\omega) \therefore s^2 - \varrho^2 = 12\,(1 - \cos\omega)^2,$$

hence:

$$t \cdot \frac{d\omega}{ds} = \frac{1 - \cos\omega}{2 \sin\omega}.$$

This introduced into (4) gives $z_A = 3e^{j\omega}$, and this is the circle of radius 3 (point A in fig. 147).

CHAPTER XI

PEDALS AND OTHER DERIVED CURVES

1. *Pedal and contrapedal*

The *pedal* of a curve is the locus of the bases of the perpendiculars

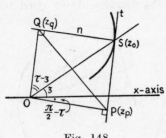

Fig. 148

let down from a fixed point on to all tangents of the curve. As the fixed point is arbitrary, each basis-curve has many pedals. We shall always take the fixed point as the origin of coordinates (fig. 148), the basis curve will be denoted by z_0 (point S) and the pedal by z_p. From fig. 148 we see that

$$|z_p| = |z_0| \sin (\tau - z)$$

and the argument function of P is $- j \exp (j\tau)$, so that

$$z_p = - j z_0 \sin (\tau - z) \exp (j\tau - z). \quad \ldots \quad (1)$$

Introducing $\exp (j\tau) = \sqrt{\dot{z}/\dot{z}^*}$, this can be transformed into:

$$z_p = \tfrac{1}{2} \frac{z_0 \cdot \dot{z}_0^* - z_0^* \dot{z}_0}{\dot{z}_0^*} . \quad \ldots \ldots \quad (2)$$

a general formula, easy to handle.

Examples: a. The circle coincides with its pedal if we choose the centre as pole. If we choose the pole on the circle itself, its formula is:

$$z_0 = 1 + \exp (ju)$$

with the pedal: $z_p = \tfrac{1}{2} (1 + \exp (ju))^2$, being a cardioid.

(Compare Ch. XX).

b. Circle evolvente, pole in centre of circle.

$$z_0 = (1 - ju) \exp (ju)$$
$$z_p = - ju \exp (ju).$$

This curve is a spiral, the modulus of which is proportional to the argument. This is *Archimedes' spiral*.

The modulus of the vector $z_0 - z_p = \exp (ju)$ is 1 and as z_p is on the tangent of z_0, Archimedes' spiral is a tractor for the evolvente as tractrix.

The *contrapedal* is the locus of the bases of the perpendiculars let down from a fixed point (which we always choose in the origin O) on to the normals of a basis curve.

We shall denote the contra pedal by z_q. (fig. 148). As

$$|z_q| = |z_0| \cos (\tau - \mathfrak{z})$$

and the argument function is simply $\exp(j\tau)$, the contrapedal is represented by:

$$z_q = \tfrac{1}{2} \frac{z \dot{z}^* + \dot{z} z^*}{\dot{z}^*}$$

which we can apply at once to any example that may occur.

Theorem I: The contrapedal of z_0 is the pedal of the evolute z_1 of z_0.

This follows from the fact that the normal SQ of the curve z_0 is tangent to its evolute. It is equivalent to stating that the contrapedal of the involute is the pedal of the basis curve.

Example: As the Norwich spiral is an involute of the circle-evolvente, its contrapedal is the pedal of the evolvente, that is Archimedes' spiral.

The tangent to the pedal is obtained by differentiating (2):

$$\dot{z}_p = \tfrac{1}{2} \frac{\dot{z}_0 \ddot{z}_0^* - \dot{z}_0^* \ddot{z}_0}{\dot{z}_0^{*2}} z_0^*.$$

Dividing this expression by z_p gives:

$$\frac{\dot{z}_p}{z_p} = \frac{\dot{z}_0 \ddot{z}_0^* - \dot{z}_0^* \ddot{z}_0}{z_0 \dot{z}_0^* - z_0^* \dot{z}_0} \cdot \frac{z_0^*}{\dot{z}_0^*}.$$

The first factor to the right hand side is the quotient of two imaginary functions and thus real. The argument of the second factor equals that of the quotient $\dot{z}_0/z_0$ and this is by the reality of the first factor also the argument of $\dot{z}_p/z_p$. In words:

Theorem II: The angle between radius vector and tangent at a point of the pedal equals the angle between radius vector and tangent at the corresponding point of the basis curve: $(\tau - \mathfrak{z})_p = (\tau - \mathfrak{z})_0$.

It means that in fig. 148 PQ is the normal to the pedal z_p.

Now as z_p/z_0 according to (1) is only a function of $\tau - \mathfrak{z}$ the quotient of the second pedal (that is the pedal of the pedal) to the first z_{2p}/z_p will equal z_p/z_0 and so on:

Corollary I: The n-th pedal z_{np} is:

$$z_{np} = \left(\frac{z_p}{z_0}\right)^n \cdot z_0.$$

If specially we ask for the negative pedal, that is the curve of which the basiscurve is the pedal we find:

Corollary II: The negative pedal z_{-p} is:

$$z_{-p} = \left(\frac{z_p}{z_0}\right)^{-1} z_0 = \frac{z_0^2}{z_p}.$$

2.   *The pedal inversion theorem*

By comparing the general formule of the pedal (p. 150) with the formula for the polar transform (p. 40) we find immediately:

Theorem III.   The pedal is the inversion of the polar transform. And we shall add

Theorem IV: The inversion is the pedal of the polar transform. Proof: Introduce the z-value of the polar transform

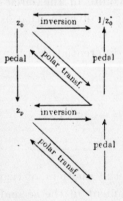

$$2 \frac{\dot{z}_0}{z_0^* \dot{z}_0 - z_0 \dot{z}_0^*}$$

into the formula for the pedal

$$z_p = \tfrac{1}{2} \frac{z \dot{z}^* - z^* \dot{z}}{\dot{z}^*}$$

and we find by figuring out indeed the value $1/z_0^*$, q.e.d.

The theorems III and IV together may be represented by the annexed scheme from which we read

Corollary III.   Pedal and basis curve exchange roles by inversion.

Corollary IV: Pedal and basis curve exchange roles by polar transformation.

The pedal of the logarithmic spiral:

$$z = \exp\,(ja + 1)\,u$$

is the curve:

$$z_p = \frac{a}{a + j}\,\exp\,(ja + 1)\,u$$

again a logarithmic spiral. The inversions are:

$$\frac{1}{z^*} = \exp(ja - 1)\, u \quad ; \quad \frac{1}{z_p^*} = \frac{a - j}{a}\exp(ja - 1)\, u$$

and the pedal of the last will be obtained from $1/z_p^*$ by multiplying by $\dfrac{a}{a - j}$, exactly reproducing $1/z^*$.

The problem of the *negative pedal*, that is the reversed problem of finding the base curve z_0 for which a given curve z_p shall be the pedal, can also be solved by making use of the inversion theorem. First find the pedal of $1/z_p^*$ and this pedal will be the inversion of the curve z_0 to be found. In this way we are led to:

$$z_0 = 2\,\frac{z_p^2\,\dot{z}_p^*}{z_p\,\dot{z}_p^* - z_p^*\,\dot{z}_p}.$$

3. *Limaçon, conchoid*

The circle pedal for arbitrary position of the pole is called the limaçon (PASCAL, 1623—1662). The equation of the circle is:

$$z_0 = a + \exp(ju)$$

and with the well-known prescription we find for the pedal:

$$z_p = (1 + a\cos u)\exp(ju).$$

Fig. 149 shows the limaçon for O outside of the circle, fig. 150 for the case where O is inside the circle. It is the inversion of a conic with respect to a focus, compare p. 107.

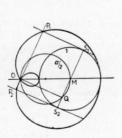
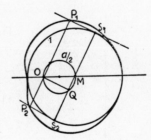

Fig. 149   Fig. 150

If O is on the circle, $a = 1$, and the limaçon merges into the cardioid.

The formula of the circle's contrapedal is:

$$z_q = -ja\sin u\exp(ju)$$

which is a circle of radius $a/2$ passing through O $(u = 0)$ and
through the centre of the basis circle $(u = \pi/2)$. The circle z_q is
described twice, when u increases from 0 to 2π. It is called the
directrix of the limaçon. The normals P_1Q and P_2Q of two points
of the limaçon, lying diametrically opposite each other with respect
to O, intersect on the directrix.

The point of the directrix for the parameter value $u + \pi/2$ is:

$$z_q\,(u + \pi/2) = a\,\cos u\,\exp\,(ju)$$

and is seen from O in the direction of $z_p(u)$, the moduli differing
by the constant value 1. The limaçon can therefore be derived
from the circle by measuring a constant length on all rays of a
pencil of which the carrier point O is situated on the circle, starting
at the second point of intersection of the rays with the circle.
This way of generating a new curve is called the ' *conchoidal*
transformation and the limaçon is the conchoidal transform of
the circle with respect to a pole on the circle.

The most general circle conchoid (O not on the circle) has no
special name but plays just as the limaçon a role in the theory of
gear wheel cog profiles (Ch. XXI).

The simplest conchoid is *Nicomedes'* conchoid (270 BC), being
the conchoidal transform of the straight line. Let (fig. 151) the
directrix be the straight line

$$a\,(1 + ju)$$

The argument function of which is:

$$\exp\,(j\varphi) = \sqrt{\frac{1 + ju}{1 - ju}}.$$

The conchoid has the equation:

$$z = a\,(1 + ju) \pm c\,\sqrt{\frac{1 + ju}{1 - ju}}$$

and the general formula for all conchoidal transforms is:

$$z_c = z_0 \pm c\,\sqrt{\frac{z_0}{z_0^*}}.$$

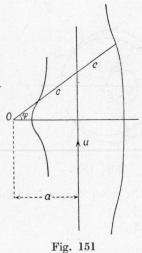

Fig. 151

4. *Pedals derived from the parabola*

Interesting examples of pedals are supplied by the parabola as base curve. If first, we choose the pole in the focus, the equation of the parabola is:

$$z_0 = \tfrac{1}{2}\, p\, (u+j)^2$$

with the pedal:

$$z_p = \tfrac{1}{2}\, p\, (ju - 1)$$

which is the tangent in the top of the parabola.

Secondly, shifting the origin to the top, the equation of the parabola becomes:

$$z_0 = \tfrac{1}{2}\, p\, u^2 + j\, p\, u$$

and that of the pedal:

$$z_p = -\tfrac{1}{2}\, p\, \frac{u^2}{1+ju}$$

which we shall call the *cissoid* (DIOCLES, 100 B.C.), fig. 152.

Thirdly, if we shift the origin to the intersection of the axis and the directrix, the equation of the parabola is:

$$z_0 = \tfrac{1}{2}\, p\, (u+j)^2 + p$$

and the pedal is:

$$z_p = \tfrac{1}{2}\, p\, \frac{1-u^2}{1+ju}$$

this curve being the *strophoid* (DE ROBERVAL, 1602—1675), fig. 152.

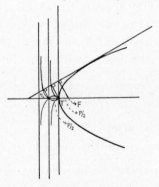
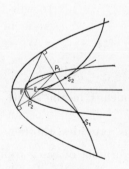

Fig. 152   Fig. 153

The pedal of the evolute is the contrapedal of the parabola. We find for this curve the formula (fig. 153):

$$z_q = \tfrac{1}{2}\, p\, (u^2 + ju) = \tfrac{1}{8}\, p\, \{(2u)^2 + 2j\, (2u)\}$$

and this ,again, is a parabola with its top in F and a parameter $p/4$.

If we choose on the parabola two points, which are the extremities of a chord through F (fig. 153), we have $u_1 u_2 = -1$. The corresponding points of the contrapedal will have parameters $2u_1$ and $2u_2$ and their product is -4, so that the two points on the contrapedal subtend at F a right angle and the line connecting them goes through point E at $4 . p/8 = p/2$ from F.

5. *Cissoid and strophoid*

Both cissoid and strophoid are cubics, so that they show all the properties, discussed in Ch. VI. The cissoid has a cusp, the strophoid a double point.

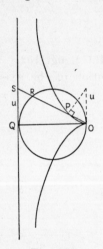

Fig. 154

The cissoid may be generated in the following way. Take a vertical line (fig. 154) QS: $z(S) = -1 + ju$ and the circle on OQ as diameter $z(R) = \dfrac{1}{-1-ju}$.

Plot the distance RS from OP on each radius.

$$z(P) = z(S) - z(R) =$$
$$= -1 + ju - \frac{1}{-1-ju} = -\frac{u^2}{1+ju} .$$

and the locus of P appears to be the cissoid. It will be clear that the cissoid will cut the circle in the highest and in the lowest points. We can write the last equation as follows:

$$\frac{z(P)}{ju} = \frac{ju}{1+ju}$$

which means in the figure that

$$\triangle \, OPU \sim \triangle \, SQO$$

and this provides another construction for the cissoid.

The formula of the strophoid can better be handled by shifting the origin from the double point to the top, which is equivalent to subtracting $p/2$ from the formula found on p. 155. Leaving the factor $p/2$ out, its formula is:

$$z = ju \frac{ju-1}{ju+1} \quad ; \quad |z| = u. \quad . \quad . \quad . \quad . \quad (3)$$

If we write this as follows:

$$\frac{z}{j\,u-1} = \frac{j\,u}{j\,u+1}$$

we arrive at the construction of fig. 155, the triangles OPM and OBC being similar, even congruent. We see from this construction, that the strophoid is the locus of the tangent points of the circles of unit radius, lying between and tangent to two parallel lines with the rays of a pencil from O, O lying on one of the parallel lines. On each ray there are two such tangent points, P_1 and P_2.

DE ROBERVAL, when introducing the strophoid (1640), had a mental picture of balls moving up and down in a cylindrical vessel.

If in (3) we pass from u to $-1/u$, the place of the point (P_2) becomes:

$$z_2 = \frac{j}{u}\frac{j\,u-1}{j\,u+1} \;\; ; \;\; |z_2| = 1/u$$

and this differs from (3) only by the real factor $1/u^2$. This means that the two points of the strophoid on one ray are related in such a way that the product of their parameters equals -1 and the product of the moduli equals 1.

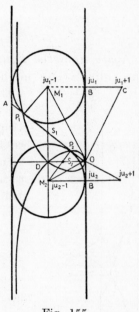

Fig. 155

By elementary methods one can prove that the quadrangle $P_1 DOM_1$ is an isosceles trapezium, from which we conclude that $P_1 S_1 = S_1 D$. But as S_1 is in the middle of $P_1 P_2$, we have also $P_2 S_1 = S_1 D$, so that the strophoid may be constructed by measuring the height of S_1 on each ray starting from the middle S_1 towards the two sides.

The angle φ between the radius vector and the tangent of the strophoide at the point P_1 is found from the quotient

$$\frac{\dot z}{z} = \frac{1+u^2-2\,j\,u}{u\,(1+u^2)} = \cos\varphi + j\,\sin\varphi.$$

As tan φ is the quotient of the imaginary and the real parts, we find

$$\tan \varphi = \frac{-2u}{1+u^2}$$

and to find the angle at P_2 we have to change u into $-1/u$, giving:

$$\tan \varphi_2 = \frac{2u}{1+u^2}.$$

Apart from the sign, the strophoid makes equal angles with the radius vector in the two points of intersection.

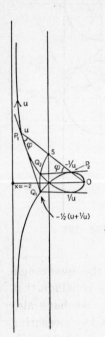

The two tangents in P_1 and P_2 do not intersect on the strophoid itself, but they cut the strophoid again in two points Q_1 and Q_2 which, as we shall see, lie in one vertical line (fig. 156).

Suppose Q_1 to have the parameter value u_0 and draw the tangents from Q_1 to the strophoid. If the tangent point P has the parameter value u, the vector PQ is

$$z_Q - z_P = j u_0 \frac{j u_0 - 1}{j u_0 + 1} - j u \frac{j u - 1}{j u + 1}.$$

If this is to be a tangent, it must have the direction of $\dot{z}(u)$, this is:

$$\dot{z}(u) = - j \frac{u^2 - 2 j u + 1}{(j u + 1)^2}.$$

The quotient of these two vectors must be real, in equation (criterion for parallelism):

$$\dot{z}(u) \{ z^*(u_0) - z^*(u) \} - \dot{z}^*(u) \{ z(u_0) - z(u) \} = 0.$$

Fig. 156

Figuring out leads to the condition:

$$(u - u_0)^2 (u^2 + 2 u u_0 - 1) = 0,$$

which gives two trivial solutions $u = u_0$ (the tangent in Q_1 itself) and two more roots of which the product is 1. The second tangent, therefore, touches the strophoid in the point $1/u$. See fig. 156. The sum of the roots is $-2u_0$, so that the parameter value in Q_1 is:

$$u_0 = -\tfrac{1}{2}\left(u + \frac{1}{u}\right); \quad |z_Q| = u + \frac{1}{u} = |z_S|.$$

For reasons of symmetry the tangent in $P_2(-1/u)$ must cut the strophoid in a point Q_2 lying straight above Q_1.

We have in this way found quite a number of metrical properties which must be added to the projective properties already discussed for all cubics in Ch. VI.

6.   Orthoptic curves

The orthoptic curve of a basis curve z is the locus of the points from where two mutually orthogonal tangents can be drawn to the curve.

Let the tangent points on z, giving rise to two mutually orthogonal tangents, be u_1 and u_2 (fig. 157). The vectors $\dot{z}(u_1)$ and $\dot{z}(u_2)$ will be mutually orthogonal. Their quotient is purely imaginary and they must therefore fulfill the condition for orthogonality:

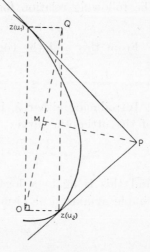

$$\dot{z}(u_1)\,\dot{z}^*(u_2) + \dot{z}^*(u_1)\,\dot{z}(u_2) = 0$$

which is an equation from which the functional relation between u_1 and u_2 must be calculated. This relation once known the point of intersection of the two tangents may be determined in the usual way, for instance as a function of u_1.

Fig. 157

For example: The logarithmic spiral is $z = \exp\{(j+1)u\}$ $\dot{z} = (j+1)\exp\{(j+1)u\}$. The condition of orthogonality is:

$$\exp(j+1)u_1 . \exp(-j+1)u_2 + \exp(-j+1)u_1 . \exp(j+1)u_2 = 0$$

or: $\cos(u_1 - u_2) = 0.$

That is $u_1 - u_2 = \pi/2.$

The two tangent points lie on radii which make a right angle

with each other. We might have deduced this same result from
the property of constant inclination, which states that the angle
between two tangents equals the angle between the corresponding
radii vectors.

The tangent in point u is represented by

$$z = z(u) + \dot{z}(u) \cdot \lambda$$

where λ is a parameter measured from the tangent point.

The two tangents in the points u_1 and u_2 may be written down as:

$$z_1 = \{1 + (j + 1)\lambda_1\} \exp (j + 1) u_1$$
$$z_2 = \{1 + (j + 1)\lambda_2\} \exp (j + 1) u_2.$$

In the point of intersection $z_1 = z_2$. Equating the two and
considering that $\exp (j + 1) u_2 = \dfrac{\exp (-\pi/2)}{j} \exp (j + 1) u_1$, we find
the following relation for λ_1 and λ_2:

$$\{j + (j - 1)\lambda_1\} e^{\pi/2} = 1 + (j + 1)\lambda_2.$$

From this and the conjugate equation we calculate:

$$\lambda_1 = \frac{-1 - \exp(-\pi/2)}{2} \quad ; \quad \lambda_2 = \frac{-1 + \exp(\pi/2)}{2}.$$

Introducing either λ_1 in z_1 or λ_2 in z_2 gives us as the point P
of the orthoptic curve:

$$z_{\text{orth}} = \frac{(1 - j)}{2}\{1 - j \exp(-\pi/2)\} \exp (j + 1) u_1.$$

and this is again a logarithmic spiral. We can write it in the
simple symmetrical form:

$$z_{\text{orth}} = \frac{1 - j}{2}\{z(u_1) + z(u_2)\}.$$

This point is constructed as follows fig. 157. Complete the rectangle
O $z(u_2)$ Q $z(u_1)$. Draw the diagonal OQ and halve it (point M).
Draw the perpendicular in M and make MP = OP, then P is the
point of the orthoptic curve.

Circles are found as orthoptic curves in the case of the conics
as basic curves, the circle degenerating to a straight line in the
case of the parabola. Dual to this, e.g.: the chords of the ellipse
subtending a right angle at the centre envelop a circle. More dual
theorems are found by different choices of the location of the origin.

CHAPTER XII

AREAS AND OTHER INTEGRALS

1. *Areas*

If u increases by du the radius vector $z(u)$ covers a sector, the area of which can be calculated as if this sector were a triangle with base $|\dot{z}|\,du$ and a height $|z|\sin(\tau-\varphi)$. (fig. 158). The area therefore is:

$$dA = \tfrac{1}{2}|z|.|\dot{z}|\sin(\tau-\varphi)\,du$$

$$= \tfrac{1}{2}|z|.|\dot{z}|\,\frac{\exp(j.\overline{\tau-\varphi})-\exp(-j\ \overline{\tau-\varphi})}{2j}\,du$$

$$= \frac{1}{4j}\,(z^{*}\dot{z}-\dot{z}^{*}z)\,du$$

$$= \tfrac{1}{2}\operatorname{Im}(z^{*}.\dot{z})\,du$$

and by integration between the limits u_1 and u_2 do we find the area bounded by the curve itself and the two radii vectores at the values u_1 and u_2.

Examples: a. Circle: $z = \exp(ju)$;
$\dot{z} = j\exp ju$, so that $\operatorname{Im}(z^{*}.\dot{z}) = 1$, and the area of the complete circle is

$$A = \tfrac{1}{2}\int\limits_{0}^{2\pi} du = \pi.$$

b. Ellipse: $z = a\cos u + jb\sin u$;
$\dot{z} = -a\sin u + jb\cos u$;

$$\operatorname{Im}(z^{*}\dot{z}) = ab.$$

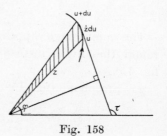

Fig. 158

The area of the complete ellipse is:

$$A = \tfrac{1}{2}\int\limits_{0}^{2\pi} ab\,du = \pi\,ab.$$

c. Hyperbola. $z = a\cosh u + jb\sinh u$; $\dot{z} = a\sinh u + jb\cosh u$,

$$\operatorname{Im}(z^{*}\dot{z}) = ab$$

and the area, starting from $u = 0$, is $A = \tfrac{1}{2}.ab.u$.

Zwikker

d.   Cardioid. (Ch. XX): $z = 2 \exp{(ju)} + \exp{2\, ju}$

$$\text{Im}\,(z^{\bullet}\dot{z}) = 6 + 3 \cos u\,.$$

The area of the complete curve is:

$$A = \tfrac{1}{2} \int\limits_{0}^{2\pi} (6 + 3 \cos u)\, du = 6\pi.$$

e.   Lemniscate (Ch. XVII): $z = \dfrac{1}{\sqrt{1 - ju}}$

$$\text{Im}\,(z^{\bullet}\dot{z}) = \frac{1}{2\,(1 + u^2)^{3/2}}\,.$$

The area of the complete curve is:

$$A = \tfrac{1}{2} \int\limits_{-\infty}^{+\infty} \frac{du}{2\,(1 + u^2)^{2/3}} = \tfrac{1}{2} \left. \frac{u}{\sqrt{u^2 - 1}} \right|_{-\infty}^{+\infty} = 1.$$

f.   Cycloid. (Ch. XVIII): $z = j\,(1 - \exp{(-ju)}) + u$

$$\text{Im}\,(z^{\bullet}\dot{z}) = 2\,(\cos u - 1) + u \sin u$$

and the area of the complete arc is:

$$A = \tfrac{1}{2} \int\limits_{0}^{2\pi} \{2\,(\cos u - 1) + u \sin u\}\, du = -3\pi.$$

The minus sign appears, because the curve turns clockwise round the origin instead of anti-clockwise as was assumed in fig. 158.

g.   Strophoid (fig. 159) (Ch. XI).

$$z = ju\,\frac{ju - 1}{ju + 1}\,.$$

$$\text{Im}\,(z^{\bullet}\dot{z}) = -\frac{2u^2}{1 + u^2}$$

$$A = -\tfrac{1}{2} \int\limits_{0}^{u} \frac{2u^2}{1 + u^2} = u - \operatorname{arc\,tan} u.$$

The area of the loop is found by substituting -1 and $+1$ for the limits of the integration; we find $2 - \pi/2$, which equals the area of the two corners cut off from the square in fig. 159 by the unit circle.

To find the area, hatched in fig. 160 we take the integral from $-1/u$ to u and subtract the area of the loop, giving $u+1/u-2$, which is proportional to the sum of the thick parts of the line OA in fig. 160.

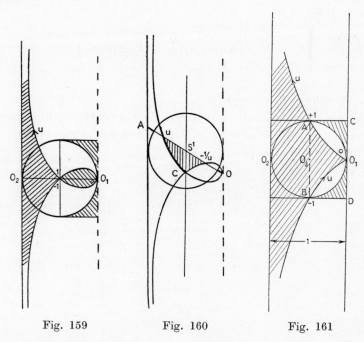

Fig. 159   Fig. 160   Fig. 161

In order to find the area of the infinitely long strip along the asymptote we shift the origin to O_2 (fig. 159), by which the equation is changed into:

$$z = ju \frac{ju-1}{ju+1} + 2$$

and we find an area π (= area of unit circle).

h. Cissoid. (Ch. XI). To find the area of the infinitely long strip along the asymptote we choose the origin in O_2 (fig. 161).

$$z = \frac{u^2}{ju-1} + 1.$$

Integrating between $u = -\infty$ and $u = +\infty$ we find for this area: $\frac{3}{4}\pi$ ($= 3$ times the circle drawn in fig. 161).

To find the area of the „ivy leaf" AO_2BO_1 we lay the origin in O_3 and determine the area of the part of the ivy leaf to the right of O_3 by integrating from $u = -1$ to $u = +1$. Adding the area of the semicircle to the left of O_3 gives as the total area of the ivy leaf:

$$\pi/2 - 1$$

The area of the lens-shaped figure AO_1 appears to be $\frac{1}{2}(1 - \pi/4)$, that is twice the corner ACO_1.

2. *Surfaces of revolution*

Simple formula's can be deduced for the areas of the surfaces generated by the rotation of a plane curve round the imaginary- or round the real axis.

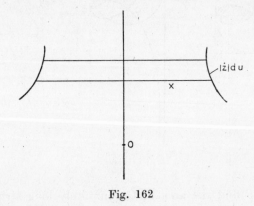

Fig. 162

The line element $|\dot{z}|\,du$, rotating round the imaginary axis will describe an area: $2\pi\,x.|\dot{z}|\,du$
and the total area of the surface will be the integral:

$$S_i = 2\pi \int x\,|\dot{z}|\,du. \quad . \quad . \quad . \quad . \quad . \quad . \quad (2a)$$

The area of the surface generated when the curve rotates round the real axis will be:

$$S_r = 2\pi \int y\,|\dot{z}|\,du. \quad . \quad . \quad . \quad . \quad . \quad . \quad (2b)$$

Examples: a. Unit sphere: $z = \exp(ju)$; $x = \cos u$; $y = \sin u$.

The sphere, if described by a rotation of the circle round the imaginary axis will have an area:

$$S = 2\pi \int\limits_{-\pi/2}^{+\pi/2} \cos u \, du = 4\pi$$

and if described by a rotation of the circle round the real axis:

$$S = 2\pi \int\limits_{0}^{\pi} \sin u \, du = 4\pi.$$

b. Torus. If the centre of the circle is not in the origin, but at the point $x = a$ on the real axis, $|\dot{z}|$ will again be 1, but $x = a + \cos u$ and the area of the torus described by a rotation of the circle round the imaginary axis will be (fig. 163)

$$S = 2\pi \int\limits_{0}^{2\pi} (a + \cos u) \, du = 4\pi^2 a.$$

For a torus that is just closed $(a = 1)$ this becomes $4\pi^2$.

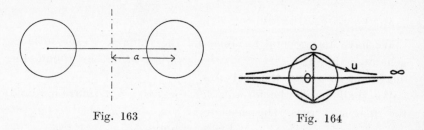

Fig. 163   Fig. 164

c. Negative sphere. Let the tractrix rotate round the real axis. The formula of the tractrix is:

$$z = u + \frac{j - \exp u}{j + \exp u}$$

$$y = \frac{2 \exp u}{\exp (2u) + 1};$$

$$\dot{z} = \pm \frac{\exp (2u) - 1}{\exp (2u) + 1} \quad (\pm \text{ for } u \lessgtr 0).$$

The area of the trumpet-shaped surface to the right is:

$$S_r = 4\pi \int \frac{\exp (2u) - 1}{(\exp (2u) + 1)^2} \, d\,(\exp u) = 4\pi \left| \frac{- \exp u}{\exp 2u + 1} \right|_{0}^{\infty} = 2\pi$$

and together with the trumpet to the left the surface has an area 4π equal to that of the unit sphere.

A second property which this surface has in common with the sphere is the constancy of the product of the two principle radii of curvature. Whereas this product amounts to $+1$ for the sphere it is -1 for the two-trumpet surface and this explains the name „negative sphere". The property referred to is shown in fig. 138, p. 140. One principle radius of curvature is the intercept on the normal from the tractrix to the evolute ($=\sinh u$), the second radius of curvature for the surface of revolution is the intercept on the same normal from the tractrix to the real axis. By an elementary geometrical property of right angled triangles the product of these two distances equals the square of the perpendicular let down on the hypothenusa and in this case the square equals 1. As the two radii of curvature have opposite directions we have to add the minus sign.

3. *Volumes of revolution*

We have also general formulas for the volumes of the surfaces generated by a rotation of the curve $z(u)$ either round the imaginary or round the real axis.

We shall derive the formula for the case of a rotation round the imaginary axis. The elementary cone shell hatched in fig. 165 has a volume:

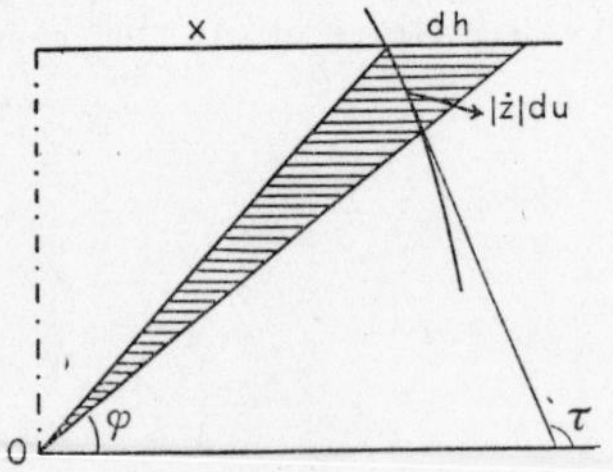

Fig. 165

$$dV_i = {}^1/_3\, y \cdot 2\pi x \cdot dh$$

with

$$y = |z| \sin \varphi$$

$$dh = |\dot z|\, du \cdot \frac{\sin (\tau - \varphi)}{\sin \varphi}$$

which gives, after substitution and integration:

$$V_i = \tfrac{2}{3}\,\pi \int x\,\mathrm{Im}\,(\dot z z^{\!*})\,du \ . \qquad (3a)$$

and in the same way we find for the volume of the surface generated by a rotation of the curve $z(u)$ round the real axis:

$$V_r = \tfrac{2}{3}\,\pi \int y \cdot \mathrm{Im}\,(\dot z z^{\!*})\,du \ . \quad \cdots \quad (3b)$$

Examples: a. Sphere: $z = \exp (ju)$; $\dot{z} = j \exp (ju)$

$$\mathrm{Im}\,(\dot{z} z^{*}) = 1 \;\; ; \;\; x = \cos u$$

$$V_i = \tfrac{2}{3}\,\pi \int\limits_{-\pi/2}^{+\pi/2} \cos u \, du = 4\pi/3.$$

b. Torus: $z = a + \exp (ju)$; $\mathrm{Im}\,(\dot{z} z^{*}) = 1 + a \cos u$

$$V_i = \tfrac{2}{3}\,\pi \int\limits_{0}^{2\pi} (a + \cos u)\,(1 + a \cos u)\, du = 2\pi^2 a.$$

c. Negative sphere: Starting from the equation of the tractrix we figure out by elementary integrals that the volume of the negative sphere amounts to $2\pi/3$; this is half the volume of the positive sphere.

4. *Center of gravity*

The center of gravity of a surface is the point of application of the resulting force of gravity, assuming that the weight is evenly distributed over the surface. From the theorems on the combination of forces it follows that the coordinates of the center of gravity G are fixed by the conditions:

$$\int \{x\,(G) - x\}\, dA = 0$$
$$\int \{y\,(G) - y\}\, dA = 0$$

which two conditions can be combined to:

$$z\,(G) = \frac{\int z\, dA}{\int dA} \quad . \quad (4)$$

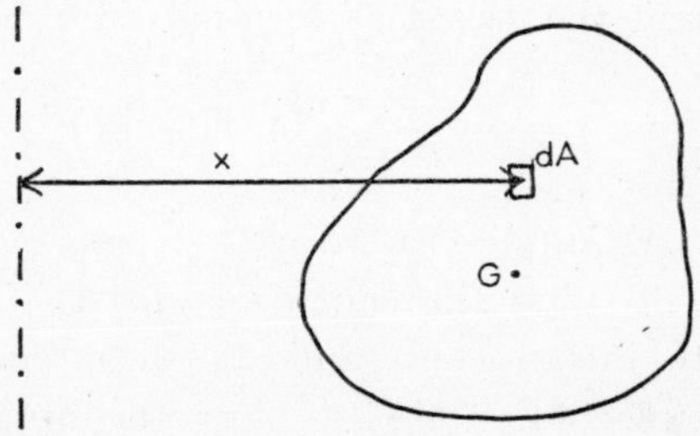

Fig. 166

and we may ask whether there exists a general formula which teaches us how to calculate $z\,(G)$ if the contour $z\,(u)$ is given. We shall find the answer by a detour, making use of GULDIN's *second rule* (named after GULDIN 1577—1643, although it was already known to PAPPOS) stating that the volume of a surface of revolution equals the product of the area of the cross-section and the length of the path described by the centre of gravity during the rotation. We prove this rule as follows. (Fig. 166). An element dA of the cross-section lying at a distance x from the axis of rotation describes a volume element:

$$d V_i = 2 \pi x . d A = 2 \pi d A \{x \mathrm{G}) - x + x \,(\mathrm{G})\}$$

and the total volume is obtained by integrating over the whole cross-section. But, as by definition:

$$\int \{x \,(\mathrm{G}) - x\} \, d A = 0$$

the volume will be:

$$V_i = 2 \pi x \,(\mathrm{G}) \int d A = 2 \pi x \,(\mathrm{G}) . A \quad \text{q.e.d.}$$

We obtained already explicit expressions for V_i and A so that for $x \,(\mathrm{G})$ we can now write at once:

$$x \,(\mathrm{G}) = \tfrac{2}{3} \frac{\int x \, \mathrm{Im} \,(z^* \dot z) \, du}{\int \mathrm{Im} \,(z^* \dot z) \, du}$$

and in the same way, by applying GULDIN's rule to a rotation round the real axis, we arrive at:

$$y \,(\mathrm{G}) = \tfrac{2}{3} \frac{\int y \, \mathrm{Im} \,(z^* \dot z) \, du}{\int \mathrm{Im} \,(z^* \dot z) \, du}$$

and the two last formulas can be taken together, giving

$$z \,(\mathrm{G}) = \tfrac{2}{3} \frac{\int z \, \mathrm{Im} \,(z^* \dot z) \, du}{\int \mathrm{Im} \,(z^* \dot z) \, du} \cdot \quad . \quad . \quad . \quad . \quad (5)$$

Examples: a. Circle $z = \exp (ju)$; $\mathrm{Im} \,(z^* \dot z) = 1$

To find the centre of gravity for the complete circle, we have to introduce 0 and 2π as integration limits and find, as was expected, $z \,(\mathrm{G}) = 0$. For the upper half of the circle separately, after introducing 0 and π for the integration limits, we find $z(\mathrm{G}) = j \ 4/3\pi$.

b.   The upper half of the ellipse $z = a \cos u + jb \sin u$ has its centre of gravity in $z \,(\mathrm{G}) = \tfrac{4}{3} j \pi b$.

c.   From the parabola $z = \tfrac{1}{2} p \,(u + j)^2$ a cap can be cut off by the vertical line through the focus, connecting the points $u = -1$ and $u = +1$. Introducing these as integration limits into the formula for $z \,(\mathrm{G})$ yields:

$$z \,(\mathrm{G}) = - p/5.$$

If we consider $z\,(G)$ as a function of the upper integration limit, keeping the lower limit constant, we obtain, what we shall call the *centroid* or the G-curve. For the circle, choosing $u=0$ as the lower integration limit, (5) yields for the G-curve (fig. 167):

$$z\,(G) = \tfrac{2}{3}\,\frac{\exp\,(ju) - 1}{ju}.$$

It is a spiral, starting from the point $z = \tfrac{2}{3}$ of the real axis for $u = 0$.

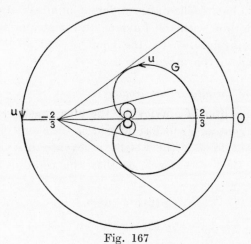

Fig. 167

This line ,,pursuits" the curve $2/3\ z$, by which we mean that the tangent in point u of the G-curve is directed towards the point $2/3\ z(u)$, because that is the centre of gravity of the elementary sector which is added to the already existing area. This can also be seen from (5) by differentiation:

$$\dot{z}\,(G) = \frac{I}{\int I\,du}\left\{\frac{2}{3}\,z - z\,(G)\right\} \quad \text{with } I = \operatorname{Im}\,(z^{*}\dot{z})$$

from which we see that the direction of $\dot{z}\,(G)$ is from the point o (G) of the G-curve to $2/3\ z$.

The ,,natural" centre of gravity will be obtained by integration z over a complete turn; we shall denote this point by G_0:

$$z\,(G_0) = \frac{2}{3}\,\frac{\oint z\,I\,du}{\oint I\,du},$$

the circle through the integral sign denoting a complete turn along the contour.

If we choose the origin in the centre of gravity of the closed curve, $z(G_0) = 0$ by definition and from (5):

$$\oint z \, \mathrm{I} \, du = 0.$$

The numerator of (5) then assumes the same complex value each time we return to the point u, but the denominator (which is real) is changed and all points G belonging to the same point of the z-curve, but reached after different numbers of circulations, will lie on one line with the fundamental center of gravity. This is illustrated in fig. 167 for the point $u = \pi$; all corresponding G-points lying on the imaginary axis.

5. *Center of gravity of the contour.*

Besides the center of gravity for the area, we have a center of gravity of the contour g which is defined as the point of application of the resultant force if the weight is evenly distributed along the contour. Mechanics teach us that the coordinates of g are determined from:

$$\int \{x\,(\mathrm{g}) - x\} \, ds = 0$$

$$\int \{y\,(\mathrm{g}) - y\} \, ds = 0$$

or combined:

$$z\,(\mathrm{g}) = \frac{\int z \, ds}{\int ds} = \frac{\int z.|\dot{z}|\,du}{\int |\dot{z}|\,du}, \quad \ldots \quad \ldots \quad (6)$$

so that we arrive at once at a formula for the computation of $z\,(\mathrm{g})$ if $z\,(u)$ is a given function.

Another derivation of (6) can be given ,starting from GULDIN's first rule (also already known to PAPPOS), stating that the area of a surface of revolution equals the product of the length of the contour of the cross-section and the length of the path described by g during the rotation. This rule can be proved along much the same lines as was done in the last section for $z\,(\mathrm{G})$.

Again we may apply (6) to a closed circuit, giving the ,,natural'' centre of gravity, g_0:

$$z\,(\mathrm{g}_0) = \frac{\oint z\,|\dot{z}|\,du}{\oint |\dot{z}|\,du}$$

or we may consider (6) as a function of the upper integration limit. In this case $z(g)$ is a so called g-curve. For the unit circle it is

$$z\left(g\right) = \frac{\exp\left(ju\right)-1}{ju},$$

a spiral which in this special case is similar to the G-curve.

Let us as a second example give the g-curve of the logarithmic spiral $z = \exp\left(ja + 1\right)u$. It is

$$z\left(g\right) = \frac{z}{ja+2}$$

that is, the same spiral, multiplied by a constant number. Its G-curve is

$$z\left(G\right) = \frac{4}{3}\frac{z}{ja+3},$$

which represents again the original curve, multiplied by a constant.

The g-curve ,,pursuits'' the point z for the same reason as the G-curve ,,pursuits'' the point $2z/3$.

All points $z(g)$ belonging to the same point z but being reached after different numbers of turns along a closed contour, will lie in one line with g_0. Furthermore it will be clear that in the point $u = 0$ the curves z and $z(g)$ touch each other and it may be proved in general that in this point of contact the curvature of the g-curve is $4/3$ times that of the $z(u)$-curve.

6. *Inertia moments*

Four different inertia moments of closed plane surfaces are used in the theory of elasticity, viz.:

$$\text{polar inertia moment} \qquad : J_0 \ = \int r^2\, dA$$
$$\text{Binet's inertia moments} \quad : J_x \ = \int y^2\, dA$$
$$J_y \ = \int x^2\, dA$$
$$\text{centrifugal inertia moment} : J_{xy} = \int xy\, dA$$

Obviously, as $r^2 = x^2 + y^2$, J_0 can be found from J_x and J_y by addition:

$$J_0 = J_x + J_y.$$

Let us calculate J_x by dividing the surface in elementary sectors and let us calculate J_x for a sector $d\varphi$ (fig. 168):

As: $y = r \sin \varphi$; $dA = r \, dr \, d\varphi$

$$dJ_x = \int r^3 \, dr \, \sin^2 \varphi \, d\varphi = \left| \frac{r^4}{4} \sin^2 \varphi \, d\varphi \right|_0^{|z|} = \tfrac{1}{4} y^2 \, zz^* \, d\varphi$$

where now y is the imaginary part of point z on the curve.

We have furthermore:

$$\exp (j\varphi) = \sqrt{\frac{z}{z^*}} \quad \therefore \quad d\varphi = \frac{1}{2j} \frac{z^* \dot{z} - z \dot{z}^*}{zz^*} \, du = \frac{\mathrm{Im} \, (z^* \dot{z})}{zz^*} \, du$$

and for simplification denoting $\mathrm{Im} \, (z^* \dot{z})$ by I, we have for Binet's moment J_x

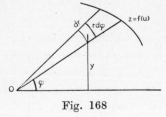

Fig. 168

$$J_x = \tfrac{1}{4} \int y^2 \, I \, du$$

In the same way we find:

$$J_y = \tfrac{1}{4} \int x^2 \, I \, du$$

$$J_0 = \tfrac{1}{4} \int zz^* \, I \, du$$

$$J_{xy} = \tfrac{1}{4} \int xy \, I \, du$$

in which expressions x, y and I refer always to point $z(u)$ of the boundary contour.

For the unit circle we know that $I = 1$; so that:

$$J_x = \tfrac{1}{4} \int_0^{2\pi} \sin^2 u \, du = \frac{\pi}{4}$$

$$J_y = \tfrac{1}{4} \int_0^{2\pi} \cos^2 u \, du = \frac{\pi}{4}$$

$$J_0 = J_x + J_y = \frac{\pi}{2}$$

$$J_{xy} = \tfrac{1}{4} \int_0^{2\pi} \sin u \cos u \, du = 0.$$

For circles of radius r all these values are to be multiplied by r^4.

We shall next calculate Binet's moment with respect to an inclined axis. Let us define the position of this axis by the angle a

which it makes with the real axis and call this Binet moment J_a. In this case the moment of an elementary sector is:

$$dJ_a = \frac{|z|^4}{4} \sin^2 (\varphi - a) \, d\varphi.$$

As $\sin^2 (\varphi - a) = (\sin \varphi \cos a - \cos \varphi \sin a)^2$, J_a can be expressed in J_x, J_y and J_{xy}:

$$J_a = J_x \cos^2 a + J_y \sin^2 a - 2 J_{xy} \sin a \cos a.$$

If we measure $1/\sqrt{J_a}$ on the radius of argument a, we come to a point

$$x = \frac{\cos a}{\sqrt{J_a}} \quad ; \quad y = \frac{\sin a}{\sqrt{J_a}}$$

and the locus of these points will be given by:

$$1 = J_x x^2 + J_y y^2 - 2 J_{xy} xy$$

which is the equation of an ellipse. It is called the *momental ellipse* (CAUCHY 1827). In general we find two orthogonal directions for one of which J_a is a maximum and for the other one J_a is a minimum.

If we construct the dual curve of this momental ellipse we shall obtain an ellipse for which the lengths of the perpendiculars from O to the tangents is equal to $\sqrt{J_a}$, and this is called the *ellipse of gyration*. (J. MAC CULLAGH, 1844)). The ratios between the principle axes of the momental ellipse and between those of the ellipse of gyration are the same, viz. $\sqrt{J_{max}/J_{min}}$, so that the ellipses are similar. If we turn the ellipse of gyration over an angle $\pi/2$ it becomes homothetic with the momental ellipse. This new ellipse is called *Culmann's ellipse*, it is the envelope of the lines running parallel to all axes a on both sides at a distance $\sqrt{J_a}$.

J_a is often put equal to $A\varrho_a^2$, where A is the area of the surface and ϱ the so-called *radius of gyration*. Instead of plotting $\sqrt{1/J_a}$ or $\sqrt{J_a}$ in order to obtain the three ellipses mentioned above, we might plot $1/\varrho_a$ and ϱ_a respectively and we should find again similar ellipses.

Culmann's ellipse for an equilateral triangle will for reasons of symmetry be a circle. The radius of gyration is $\sqrt{2}/4$ times the radius of the circumscribed circle as may be figured out in an

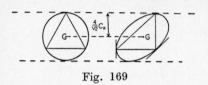

elementary way. Shift the top so that the triangle becomes scalene but leave the height the same. J_x for an axis going through the centre of gravity will not change and the horizontal line through

Fig. 169

the top will remain a tangent to $4/\sqrt{2}$ Culmann's ellipse. Generalizing: Culmann's ellipse for a scalene triangle is homothetic to the ellipse circumscribing the triangle in such a way, that the tangents to the ellipse in the three vertices of the triangle are parallel to the opposite sides of the triangle. This special circumscribing ellipse is called STEINER's *ellipse*; the momental ellipse will also be homothetic with it.

This was a case of parallel projection and from this example it may be generalized that Culmann's ellipse of the parallel projection of a plane figure is the parallel projective of CULMANN'S ellipse of the original figure. [1])

Finally we wish to mention HUYGENS' *theorems* which concern the relations between the moments of inertia with respect to an

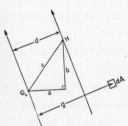

arbitrary axis and the same moments with respect to a parallel axis through the centre of gravity. Let the two axes be separated by a distance d (fig. 170)

$$J_a = \int p^2 \, dA = \int (g-d)^2 \, dA$$
$$= \int g^2 \, dA + d^2 \int dA - 2d \int g \, dA.$$

The third term is zero by virtue of the definition of the centre of gravity. The first term is the moment with respect to the axis

Fig. 170

through G, the second term is d^2A, so that

$$J_a = J_{G,a} + d^2 A$$

As the last term is essentially positive we see that the moments

¹)   J. F. CUSELL, Ingenieur, 59, nr. 265 (1947).

have a minimum for axes passing through the centre of gravity and as a rule the axes are chosen so as to pass through this point.

Comparing the moments with respect to G and to an arbitrary point H (fig. 170) of the plane we have:

$$J_{H,x} = J_{G,x} + a^2 A$$

$$J_{H,y} = J_{G,y} + b^2 A$$

by addition: $\qquad J_{H,0} = J_{G,0} + c^2 A \quad \text{(polar moment)}$

Instead of the inertia moments of the area we may try to find the inertia moments of the contour, assuming uniform distribution of mass along this contour. Their definitions will be:

Polar: $\qquad K_0 \;\; = \int r^2 ds = \int z z^* |\dot{z}|\, du$

Axial: $\qquad K_x \;\; = \int y^2 ds = \int y^2 |\dot{z}|\, du$

$\qquad\qquad\quad K_y \;\; = \int x^2 ds = \int x^2 |\dot{z}|\, du$

Centrifugal: $\quad K_{xy} = \int xy\, ds = \int xy\, |\dot{z}|\, du.$

For the unit circle, for which $|\dot{z}| = 1$, we find:

$$K_0 = 2\pi \;\; ; \;\; K_x = \pi \;\; ; \;\; K_y = \pi \;\; ; \;\; K_{xy} = 0 .$$

These moments will have minimum values if we choose the axes through g or — in the case of the polar moment — the pole in g.

CHAPTER XIII

ENVELOPES

1. *Definition of the envelope*

The *envelope* of a set of curves is the curve tangent to all curves of the set, the individuals of this set being distinguished from each other by the value of a parameter occurring in the equation of each individual curve. We say for example, that all tangents to a curve are enveloped by that curve. A classic case of an envelope is the curve touched by all positions of a ladder sliding down a wall, having always one extremity on the floor, the second on the vertical wall. This envelope is the astroid.

Two neighbouring curves of the set intersect in a point close to the two tangential points of these curves with the envelope, and as the two curves draw nearer to each other, their point of intersection will approach the envelope and in the limit it will fall on the envelope. We shall use this criterion as the definition of the envelope: The envelope is the locus of the limits of the points of intersection of two curves of the set, if we let the difference of the corresponding values of the parameter decrease to zero. We shall prove, starting from this definition, that the envelope is tangent to the individual curves of the set.

Let, in general, the set be represented by:

$$z = f(u, v) \quad . \quad . \quad . \quad . \quad . \quad . \quad . \quad (1)$$

where u is the running parameter along the curve and v is a parameter characterizing the particular member.

A point of a neighbouring curve $v + \triangle v$ will be represented by:

$$z + \triangle z = f(u + \triangle u, v + \triangle v),$$

from which

$$\triangle z = \frac{\partial f}{\partial u} \triangle u + \frac{\partial f}{\partial v} \triangle v.$$

For a point of intersection of two neighbouring curves this

vector $\triangle z$ must be zero, so that the ratio of $\triangle u$ to $\triangle v$ is found from

$$\frac{\partial f}{\partial u}\triangle u + \frac{\partial f}{\partial v}\triangle v = 0$$

or in the limit, if $\triangle v \rightarrow 0$:

$$\left(\frac{\partial z}{\partial u}\right)_v \cdot \left(\frac{\partial u}{\partial v}\right)_z + \left(\frac{\partial z}{\partial v}\right)_u = 0 \quad . \quad . \quad . \quad . \quad . \quad (2)$$

This is an equation with complex coefficients in u, v and $(\partial u/\partial v)_z$. It is equivalent to two equations with real coefficients, so that v and $(\partial u/\partial v)_z$ can be calculated as functions of u. Substitution in (1) of the relation between u and v obtained in this way furnishes the equation of the envelope, either expressed in u or in v as running parameter. From this same relation between u and v a differential quotient du/dv may be derived, which is not identical with $(\partial u/\partial v)_z$.

If $(\partial u/\partial v)_z$ turns out to be different from zero it means, that the envelope is touched by the individual curves of the set at varying values of u and, as we shall see later, this is a measure for the speed with which the individual glides over the envelope, at the same time changing its shape, during the variation of v.

As $(\partial u/\partial v)_z$ is real we deduce from (2) that for any point of the envelope $(\partial z/\partial u)_v$ and $(\partial z/\partial v)_u$ are parallel vectors. Now $(\partial z/\partial u)_v$ is the tangent to the individual curve of the set and the tangent to the envelope itself is

$$\left(\frac{\partial z}{\partial u}\right)_v + \left(\frac{\partial z}{\partial v}\right)_u \frac{dv}{du},$$

but this vector is also parallel to $(\partial z/\partial u)_v$.

We have proved herewith that the individual curves of the set are tangent to the envelope.

Owing to the symmetry as regards u and v, equation (1) can also be considered to represent a set of curves u-constant with running parameter v and we arrive at exactly the same condition (2) if we try to find the envelope of this second set. And considering the last alinea, we may say that the envelope of both sets is the locus of the points where the individual curves of one set touch the individual curves of the second set.

Zwikker

12

2. *Astroid*

Let us treat as a concrete case the problem of the sliding ladder. The straight line AB of constant length, moving with its ends along the vertical and the horizontal axis (fig. 171) can be represented by:

$$z = (1-u) \cos v + j u \sin v. \quad . \quad . \quad . \quad . \quad (3)$$

from which:

$$\frac{\partial z}{\partial u} = -\cos v + j \sin v \; ; \; \frac{\partial z}{\partial v} = -(1-u) \sin v + j u \cos v$$

$\partial z / \partial u$ and $\partial z / \partial v$ will be parallel, if

$$\frac{\sin v}{\cos v} = \frac{u \cos v}{(1-u) \sin v} \; \therefore \; u = \sin^2 v, \quad 1-u = \cos^2 v. . \quad (4)$$

and the envelope will be:

$$z = \cos^3 v + j \sin^3 v \, . \quad . \quad . \quad . \quad . \quad . \quad (5)$$

The astroid is the hypocycloid described by a point of a circle of radius $1/4$ rolling inside a circle of radius 1 (Cf. Ch. XIX):

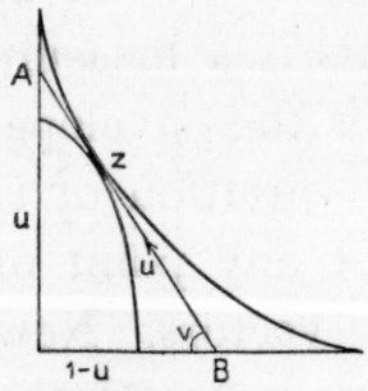

$$z = \tfrac{3}{4} \exp (jv) + \tfrac{1}{4} \exp (-3jv)$$

and this is identical with (5).

(3) is also to be considered as a set of ellipses -u- constant with semiaxes $(1-u)$ and u, and all these ellipses are also enveloped

Fig. 171

by the astroid. Each ellipse is the path that a fixed point of the ladder describes during the sliding of the ladder. The middle of the ladder describes a circle of radius $1/2$.

Applying equation (2) to any point of the envelope we find:

$$\left(\frac{\partial u}{\partial v} \right)_z = -\tfrac{1}{2} \sin 2v. \quad . \quad . \quad . \quad . \quad . \quad (6)$$

whereas from (4) we find:

$$\frac{du}{dv} = \sin 2v \, . \quad . \quad . \quad . \quad . \quad . \quad (7)$$

and we may well inquire into the geometrical meaning of these two equations.

Equation (6) states that of the two intersecting neighbouring lines the one with the greater v-value (steeper) has the lower u-value at the point of intersection. Equation (7) states that a line of greater v-value touches the astroid at a greater u-value, that is to say, more towards the upper end of the moving ladder.

If $(\partial u / \partial v)_z$ should be zero, the straight line would roll over the astroid without sliding and in general $(\partial u / \partial v)_z$ is connected with the slip and in this case, where u is the length measured on the straight line, $(\partial u / \partial v)_z$ would be the speed of the slip if v should change uniformly with time. The total slip of the line is $\int (\partial u / \partial v)_z \, dv = \int_{\pi/2}^{0} -\sin . v \cos . v \, dv = 1$ and, indeed, the point of contact lies at $u = 1$ if $v = \pi/2$ and at $u = 0$ if $v = 0$, in the meantime having moved over the whole length of the line.

If there were no slip du/dv would be equal to ds/dv, where ds is the arc length of the astroid. Owing to the slip however, the arc length of the astroid is greater:

$$\frac{ds}{dv} = \frac{du}{dv} - \left(\frac{\partial u}{\partial v} \right)_z$$

in our case: $ds/dv = \frac{3}{2} \sin 2 v$, giving by integration a length $3/2$ for the length of one arc of the astroid.

In general the parameter u will not represent the arc length along the moving curve. Let this be denoted by s'. The more general formula will then be:

$$\frac{ds}{dv} = \frac{ds'}{dv} - \left(\frac{\partial s'}{\partial v} \right)_z . \quad \cdots \quad \cdots \quad (8)$$

As we might take v proportional to time, this equation can be written as follows in terms of the velocities of the point of contact: velocity along the envelope = velocity relative to carrier curve
—slip velocity of carrier curve.

In the special problem in hand the slip velocity was negative.

We may choose another parameter, for example the real part of z. The straight line is then represented by:

$$z = x + j \, (\sin v - x \tan v)$$

Applying equation (2) gives:

$$\left(\frac{\partial x}{\partial v}\right)_z = 0 \quad ; \quad x = \cos^3 v.$$

The last result, introduced into the formula for z gives as envelope:

$$z = \cos^3 v + j \sin^3 v$$

as before. We now have the additional result that

$$\left(\frac{\partial x}{\partial v}\right)_z = 0$$

and this is trivial as two intersecting lines will have the same x-value in their point of intersection. But it does not mean that there is no slip, for now the parameter x is no longer identical with s'.

For the determination of the envelope itself, it is not necessary to introduce s'. It is however appropriate, if possible, to identify u with s'.

3.   Caustics

Other examples of envelopes are the caustics, which are the envelopes of light rays reflected by a mirror.

a.   A classical case is supplied by the light rays emerging from a point A situated on a circle of radius $3p$ and reflected on the inside of this circle. Let the point B of the circle where the ray is reflected be characterized by the angle v (fig. 172), the reflected ray has a slope $\frac{3}{2}v - \pi$ and if u is the distance on the reflected ray, the equation of the latter will be:

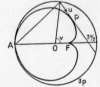

Fig. 172

$$z = 3p \exp (jv) - u \exp (\tfrac{3}{2}jv) \quad . \quad . \quad . \quad . \quad (9)$$

Carrying out the recipe for finding the envelope, we find that

$$\left(\frac{\partial u}{\partial v}\right)_z = -3p \sin \frac{v}{2} \quad ; \quad u = 2p \cos \frac{v}{2} .$$

Introducing the latter result into the equation for z, we find for the envelope:

$$- z = 2p \exp (jv) + p \exp (2jv)$$

and this is the cardioid (Ch. XX), that is the track of a point of a circle of radius p, rolling over an equally large circle.

The length of the cardioid from A to point P is found from

$$s = \int_{\pi}^{v} \left\{ \frac{du}{dv} - \left(\frac{\partial u}{\partial v} \right)_z \right\} dv = \int_{\pi}^{v} 4p \sin \frac{v}{2} \, dv = 8p \cos \frac{v}{2}$$

and for the complete arc from A to F we find a length $8p$. It is remarkable that the arc-length $AP = 8p \cos (v/2)$ equals the length of the light ray ABP. For $AB = 6p \cos (v/2)$ and $BP = u = 2p \cos (v/2)$. By unwinding a cord wound round the cardioid fixed at both ends A and F with the aid of a leadpencil which keeps the pieces PB and BA taut, we describe the reflector (Cf the problem of the anticaustic Ch. X). All caustics show this property and it can be proved along the same lines as the equal vector sum law of the ellipse was deduced from the reflection law.

The curves u constant, represented by (9), taking v as running parameter along the curves of which the cardioid is also the envelope, are limaçons (Cf. Ch. XI) of which the circle of radius $3p$ is one ($u=0$). They are the curves obtained by plotting on all reflected rays a constant stretch u.

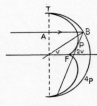

b. If the light source is at infinity the rays reflected on the circle of radius $4p$ are represented by:

$$z = 4p \exp (jv) - u \exp (2jv)$$

and the recipe for finding the envelope leads to the nephroid: (fig. 173)

$$z = 3p \exp (jv) - p \exp (3jv)$$

Fig. 173

and the length of the nephroid from the top T to the focus F is found to be $6p$.

c. Let light fall vertically on a reflecting exponential line, represented by

$$z = v + j \exp v$$

The tangent in point v is:

$$\dot{z} = 1 + j \exp v$$

The reflected ray makes the same angle with $\dot{z}$ as the imaginary axis does and is therefore proportional to

$$\frac{1}{j} \, (1 + j \exp v)^2$$

which, apart from a real factor, is:

$$1 + j \sinh v$$

so that the reflected ray may be represented by:

$$z = v + j \exp v - u \, (1 + j \sinh v).$$

$\partial z / \partial u$ and $\partial z / \partial v$ have the same direction for $u = 1$, from which we find for the envelope:

$$z = v - 1 + j \cosh v.$$

and this is the catenary.

4.   *Negative pedals*

The problem of the negative pedal, that is the problem of finding the curve of which a given curve is the pedal, has been solved in Ch. XI with the aid of the inversion-pedal-theorem. We can also solve this same problem by means of the envelope theory.

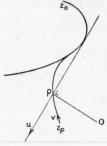

Let $z_p = f(v)$ be the given pedal and let z_0 be the required curve. The perpendicular from O on to the tangent to curve z_0 has its base P on the curve z_p. The tangent is normal to z_p and is represented by

$$z = z_p(v) + j z_p(v) \cdot u = z_p(v) \, (1 + ju).$$

Fig. 174

and we have to find the envelope of all these tangents.

$$\frac{\partial z}{\partial v} = \dot{z}_p (1 + ju) \quad ; \quad \frac{\partial z}{\partial u} = j z_p$$

and these two vectors will be parallel if:

$$\frac{\dot{z}_p\,(1+ju)}{\dot{z}_p^*\,(1-ju)}=\frac{j\,z_p}{-j\,z_p^*}$$

from which

$$ju=\frac{z_p\,\dot{z}_p^*+\dot{z}_p\,z_p^*}{z_p\,\dot{z}_p^*-\dot{z}_p\,z_p^*}$$

which value introduced into the formula of z yields for the envelope the equation

$$z_0=2\,\frac{z_p^2\,\dot{z}_p^*}{z_p\,\dot{z}_p^*-\dot{z}_p\,z_p^*}$$

in accordance with what we found on p. 153, Ch. XI.

5. *Anticaustics*

Another problem is that of the anticaustics which we have already solved in Ch. X by considering the anticaustic as the elliptical involute of the caustic. It is, however, also possible to solve it as a problem of envelopes.

Let (fig. 175) L be the light source and C be a point of the caustic. The distance LP be $2c$ Choose a length $2a$ equal to the length of the caustic from L to the point C and construct the ellipse on L and C as foci with major axis $2a$. If AC is tangent to the caustic in C, the light ray LA will be reflected towards C if A is on the ellipse and the anticaustic will touch the ellipse in A. The anticaustic is the envelope of all ellipses.

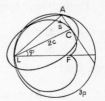

Fig. 175

Instead of making the major axis of the ellipse equal to the arc length of the caustic, we may add a constant amount. This leads to a different set of ellipses and also to a different anticaustic. We know already from Ch. X that an infinite number of anti-caustics correspond to one given caustic.

The ellipse will be represented, taking the origin of coordinates in L by:

$$z=(c+a\cos u+jb\sin u)\exp j\varphi$$

with

$$2a=s \;\; ; \;\; 4c^2=z_c z_c^* \;\; ; \;\; b^2=a^2-c^2.$$

We shall consider s as the current parameter along the caustic. The tangent point of the ellipse to the anticaustic is found by the condition that $\partial z/\partial u$ and $\partial z/\partial s$ have the same direction. Now:

$$\frac{\partial z}{\partial u} = (-a \sin u + jb \cos u)\exp j\varphi$$

$$\frac{\partial z}{\partial s} = jz\frac{\partial \varphi}{\partial s} + \left(\frac{\partial c}{\partial s} + \frac{\partial a}{\partial s}\cos u + j\frac{\partial b}{\partial s}\sin u\right)\exp j\varphi.$$

They will have the same direction if:

$$\frac{-b\sin u\dfrac{\partial \varphi}{\partial s} + \dfrac{\partial c}{\partial s} + \dfrac{\partial a}{\partial s}\cos u}{-a\sin u} = \frac{c\dfrac{\partial \varphi}{\partial s} + a\cos u\dfrac{\partial \varphi}{\partial s} + \dfrac{\partial b}{\partial s}\sin u}{b\cos u}$$

which can be simplified, because of:

$$\frac{\partial a}{\partial s} = \frac{1}{2} \quad ; \quad \frac{\partial c}{\partial s} = \frac{1}{2}\frac{a}{c} - \frac{b}{c}\frac{\partial b}{\partial s}$$

to: $$c^2 \sin u\frac{\partial \varphi}{\partial s} + \frac{b}{2}\cos u = \frac{\partial b}{\partial s}(a\cos u - c).$$

From this, together with:

$$\left(2c\frac{\partial \varphi}{\partial s}\right)^2 + \left(2\frac{\partial c}{\partial s}\right)^2 = 1$$

we find:

$$c + a\cos u = 2c - \frac{b}{\dfrac{\partial b}{\partial s}}\cdot\frac{\partial c}{\partial s} \quad ; \quad b\sin u = -\frac{bc}{\dfrac{\partial b}{\partial s}}\cdot\frac{\partial \varphi}{\partial s}.$$

Introducing these values into the equation of the ellipse we find for the anticaustic:

$$z_a = 2c\exp j\varphi - \frac{b}{2\dfrac{\partial b}{\partial s}}\left(2\frac{\partial c}{\partial s} + 2jc\frac{\partial \varphi}{\partial s}\right)\exp j\varphi =$$

$$= z_c - \frac{b^2}{\dfrac{\partial}{\partial s}b^2}\cdot\frac{\partial z_c}{\partial s},$$

which is the same result that we found in Ch. X.

If the light source is in infinity the formula will reduce to:

$$z_a = z_c - \frac{\varrho_a + s}{\dfrac{\partial}{\partial s}(\varrho_a + s)} \cdot \frac{\partial z_c}{\partial s}$$

as was shown in Ch. X, where ϱ_a is the component of z_c in the direction a from which the light comes. As an example we may reverse the problem of the reflecting exponential curve and start with the catenary

$$z_c = v - 1 + j \cosh v$$

as caustic for light coming from above. In this case

$$\varrho_a = - \cosh v \; ; \; s = \sinh v \; ; \; \frac{\partial \varrho_a}{\partial s} = - \frac{\sinh v}{\cosh v} \; ; \; \frac{\partial z_c}{\partial s} = \frac{1 + j \sinh v}{\cosh v}$$

so that

$$z_a = v + j \exp v$$

and this is the exponential curve.

CHAPTER XIV

ORTHOGONAL TRAJECTORIES

1. *General way of finding orthogonal trajectories*

The conception of conformal transformation leads almost automatically to systems of curves all of which are cut orthogonnally by a second system of curves. Any curve of one of the sets is called an *orthogonal trajectory* of the other set.

As we saw in Ch. II, any transformation

$$z = f(w)$$

(where z and w are complex numbers), the derivative dz/dw of which is a univalued function of w, is conform: the angle between two curves in the w-plane is transformed into an equal angle between the two corresponding curves in the z-plane.

Now consider w as the complex generalisation of the parameter u used up to now:

$$w = u + jv.$$

So long as we leave v constant, the function $z = f_v(w)$ represents a curve to which a u scale is attached. Passing on to a second value of v, we get a second curve and by varying v continuously we generate a set of curves which finally will cover the whole z-plane.

Now conceive, conversely, u to be constant but v variable. We generate a curve $z = f_u(w)$ and by varying u continuously we obtain another set of curves.

The network of straight lines in the w-plane consisting of the lines $v =$ constant and $u =$ constant is transformed into a network of curved lines in the z-plane consisting of the lines $z = f_v(w)$ and $z = f_u(w)$ mentioned above, and as all angles of the former network are right angles, the same will apply to the angles of the latter network. In other words we have created two sets of mutually orthogonal trajectories and both sets together may analytically be represented by one single formula:

$$z = f(w) \; ; \; z = x + jy \; ; \; w = u + jv.$$

Examples: a. $z = w^2 = (u + jv)^2$.

First let v be constant:

$$z\,(u) = v^2 \left(\frac{u}{v} + j\right)^2$$

and this is a set of parabolas, all having their focus in the origin (confocal parabolas) and all directed towards the same side of the real axis.

If we assume u to be a constant:

$$z\,(v) = -\,u^2 \left(-\frac{v}{u} + j\right)^2$$

and this, again ,is a set of confocal parabolas, but directed towards the opposite side of the real axis (fig. 176).

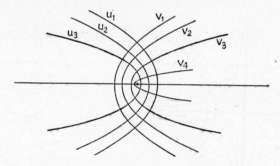

Fig. 176

The whole z-plane is covered by this network. As a check we shall verify the orthogonality. The tangent to a curve for which v is constant is:

$$\left(\frac{\partial z}{\partial u}\right)_v = \frac{dz}{dw}\left(\frac{\partial w}{\partial u}\right)_v = \frac{dz}{dw} \cdot 1$$

and the tangent to a curve u constant is:

$$\left(\frac{\partial z}{\partial v}\right)_u = \frac{dz}{dw} \cdot \left(\frac{\partial w}{\partial v}\right)_u = \frac{dz}{dw} \cdot j$$

and these two differ indeed by the factor j which means that they are orthogonal and this result is due to the fact that u and v occur in the combination $u + jv = w$.

    b. $z = \sqrt{w}$.

The lines $u = $ constant:

$$z(v) = \sqrt{u + jv} = \sqrt{u}\,\sqrt{1 + j\frac{v}{u}}$$

are isosceles hyperbolas, all with asymptotes in the 45°-directions.

The lines $v = $ constant

$$z(u) = \sqrt{jv}\,\sqrt{1 - j\frac{u}{v}}$$

are the same hyperbolas but multiplied by the factor $\sqrt{j}$, that is rotated round the origin over an angle of $\pi/4$ (fig. 177).

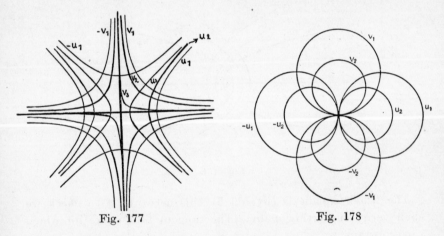

Fig. 177   Fig. 178

    c. $z = 1/w$.

This is the inversion that transforms straight lines into circles all passing through the origin (fig. 178).

    d. $z = 1/w^2$

is the inversion of case a. The two sets of curves consist of cardioids, these being the inversions of the parabolas (fig. 179).

    e. $z = 1/\sqrt{w}$

is the inversion of case b and the curves are isosceles lemniscates (fig. 180).

f. $z = \exp w = \exp (u + jv)$

(fig. 181). The lines $v = $ constant are radii emerging from the origin, the lines $u = $ constant are the set of concentric circles round the origin.

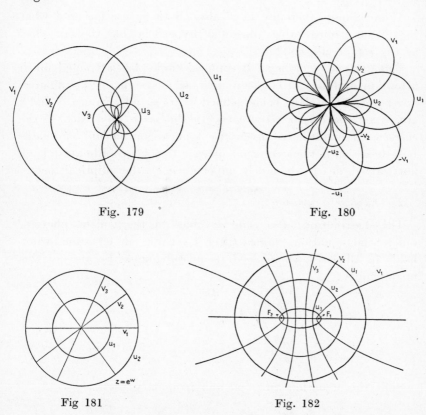

Fig. 179   Fig. 180

Fig 181   Fig. 182

g. $z = \cosh w = \cosh u \cos v + j \sinh u \sin v$.

Consider first the lines $v =$ constant, they are all hyperbolas. The lengths of the semiaxes a and b introduced in Ch. VIII are now: $a = \cos u$; $b = \sin v$

and incidentally:

$$c^2 = a^2 + b^2 = \cos^2 v + \sin^2 v = 1.$$

This means that all hyperbolas have the same foci; they are a set of confocal hyperbolas (fig. 182).

Now consider the lines $u = $ constant. These are ellipses with:

$$a = \cosh u \; ; \; b = \sinh u$$

and $$c^2 = a^2 - b^2 = \cosh^2 u - \sinh^2 u = 1.$$

These ellipses therefore have also all the same foci and what is still more remarkable, the set of hyperbolas has the same foci as the set of ellipses.

This system of orthogonal confocal conics has attracted much attention and has often been used as a system of coordinates, any point of the plane being defined by its u and v values; u and v are called the *elliptic coordinates*. In the same way, each of the cases a — f might have given rise to new curvilinear coordinates but these, with the exception of case f (polar coordinates), have not gained nearly as much importance as the elliptical ones.

2. *Laplace's equation*

The distribution of u- and v-values in the z-plane obeys a differential equation, named after LAPLACE, an equation which holds in all cases where dw/dz is unambiguous. Because of this unambiguity:

$$\frac{\partial w}{\partial x} = \frac{\partial w}{\partial jy} = \frac{dw}{dz}$$

or

$$\frac{\partial u}{\partial x} + j\,\frac{\partial v}{\partial x} = \frac{\partial u}{\partial jy} + j\,\frac{\partial v}{\partial jy}.$$

Split this equation into real and imaginary parts:

$$\frac{\partial u}{\partial x} = \frac{\partial v}{\partial y} \; ; \; \frac{\partial v}{\partial x} = -\frac{\partial u}{\partial y}$$

which are the so-called equations of CAUCHY—RIEMANN.

By differentiating once more with respect to x and y, we can eliminate either v or u and obtain Laplace's equation:

$$\frac{\partial^2 u}{\partial x^2} + \frac{\partial^2 u}{\partial y^2} = 0 \; ; \; \frac{\partial^2 v}{\partial x^2} + \frac{\partial^2 v}{\partial y^2} = 0.$$

The great importance of Laplace's equation is due to the fact that the electric and the magnetic potential in two-dimensional problems are governed by this same equation, and likewise the temperature distribution in heat-conduction problems and the velocity potential in the problem of the flow of incompressible fluids. Any of the sets of curves u-constant or v-constant which we may derive from some $z = f(w)$, may therefore represent a set of equipotential or equitemperature lines and we choose this set in such a way that one of the lines coincides with a given equipotential (equitemperature) line.

If the curves u-constant represent lines of constant potential or temperature, the lines v-constant will represent lines of force or lines of flow and the reverse, v being a measure of the so-called flow function (= the flux reckoned from an arbitrary zero streamline).

If, for instance, the potential is given on two confocal ellipses, the solution of the physical problem is simply:

$$z = \cosh w$$

by which in any point x, y both u and v are determined.

Find the two u-values for which the curves $z(v)$ coincide with the two given lines of constant potential. Let them differ by $\triangle u$. Compare this with the difference $\triangle V$ in potential and determine the factor $\triangle V / \triangle u$. With the aid of this constant factor we can change all u-values of our problem into V-values.

If, starting from a certain curve $z(u)$, we apply a transformation on u, the curve will not change its shape but we may arrive at a different set of orthogonal trajectories if we complete the new parameter u' to $w' = u' + jv'$. For example, when starting from an orthogonal hyperbola it will be possible to arrive either at a set of confocal conics (case g of p. 189) or at a set of orthogonal hyperbolas (case b of p. 188), dependent on the choice of the parameter used in the analytical formula for the original hyperbola.

In electrical problems the choice of the parameter will depend on the shape of the anti-electrode. If, for instance, in the hyperbola

$$z = a \cosh u + jb \sinh u.$$

we replace u by $u + 2 j \arctan a/b$, we find:

$$z = - a \cosh u + jb \sinh u,$$

which is the second branch of the hyperbola. This means that
the solution of the Laplace-problem:

$$z = \cosh w$$

(case g, p. 189) applies to the case where the two branches of the
hyperbola have different potential, fig. 182.

On the other hand the formula of the orthogonal hyperbola:

$$z = \sqrt{1 + ju}$$

cannot by a substitution $u + ja$ be made to coincide with
$z = -\sqrt{1 + ju}$, so that this case (case b of p. 188) applies to the
same potential for the two branches of the hyperbola, the anti-
electrode being at infinity, fig. 177.

3. The transformation $u' = lg\,u$

Most interesting is the use of the transformation

$$u' = lg\,u.$$

If u passes from 0 to ∞, u' will pass from $-\infty$ to $+\infty$, but
if u passes from $-\infty$ to 0, u' will pass from $-\infty + j\pi$ to $+\infty + j\pi$,
as $lg\,(-a) = lg\,a + lg\,(-1) = lg\,a + j\pi$.

If therefore, we complete u' to $w' = u' + jv'$, the line $v' = 0$ will
coincide with that part of the curve that carries positive values
of the u-scale and the line $v' = \pi$ will coincide with that part of
the curve that carries negative u-values. Using the u-scale, we
have to deal with the LAPLACE problem for which the u-curve is
equipotential, whereas using the u' scale, we have to deal with
the problem in which these two parts of the curve have different
potentials. This is an entirely different problem and the analytical
solution of the latter is obtained by simply substituting exp u in
stead of u in the solution of the former problem.

$z = w^2$ was the solution in the case that two parabola's are
equipotential lines. Now if the upper part of the $'z = (u + j)^2$
parabola is at one potential, the lower part at another potential,
we have to represent the parabola by the equation:

$$z = (\exp u + j)^2$$

and the LAPLACE problem will have for its solution:

$$z = (\exp w + j)^2.$$

If the break in the line has to take place not in the point $u = 0$, but in the arbitrary point $u = u_0$ we have to apply the transformation:

$$u' = \lg (u - u_0) \ ;$$

in order to obtain the result that the two parts will act as two separate equipotential lines. The solution of the new potential problem is found by first subtituting $u_0 + \exp u$ for u and then completing u to w.

Let, for example, the positive real axis be at one potential, the negative at another potential. The real axis is represented by $z = u$ so that the solution of the Laplace problem, in the case that the potential jump is at $x = 0$, will be simply: $z = \exp w$. Compare this with case f of p. 189. If the break is at $x = 1$ we shall find $z = \exp w - 1$ as the solution of the Laplace problem.

4. *Point sources*

For an electrical point source situated in the origin the solution of the potential problem is (compare case f of p. 189):

$$z = \exp w \text{ or } w = \lg z$$

and if the point source is situated in the point z_1:

$$w = \lg (z - z_1)$$

Now take

$$w = \lg \frac{z - 1}{z + 1} = \lg (z - 1) - \lg (z + 1)$$

This set of orthogonal trajectories consists of two series of orthogonal circles. w is the superposition of two point source fields, a unit source being placed in $z = + 1$ and a unit sink at $z = - 1$.

Generalizing we may say, that the field of a number of sources of strengths s_i at the points a_i together with a number of sinks of strengths σ_i at the points β_i will be:

$$\exp w = \frac{(z - a_1)^{s_1} (z - a_2)^{s_2} \ldots}{(z - \beta_1)^{\sigma_1} (z - \beta_2)^{\sigma_2} \ldots}$$

a few examples of which will be dealt with presently.[1])

---

[1]) E. L. MORGAN. Jl. Frankl. Inst. **243**, 309, (1947).

a.   Two sources; one in $z = +1$, one in $z = -1$.

$$\exp w = z^2 - 1.$$

A special line of constant potential is the line $u = 0$, for which

$$z^2 = 1 + \exp (jv).$$

The right hand side of this formula represents a circle, passing

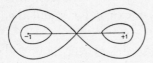

through O and the square root of this is the isosceles lemniscate (fig. 183).

b.   Distribute n equal sources evenly over a circle. We may consider this circle as the unit circle round the origin and the locations a_i of the sources are the n-th roots of 1. The solution of the electrical problem therefore is:

Fig. 183

$$\exp w = z^n - 1.$$

The equipotential-line $u = 0$ is represented by:

$$z^n = 1 + \exp (jv)$$

Fig. 184

and z is the n-th root of a circle through O, that means that z is a sinus spiral (Ch. XVII, p. 225). See fig. 184 for $n = 3$.[1]

5.   *Two magnetic problems*

The analytical solution of an electromagnetic problem in the form $z = f(w)$ is sometimes surprisingly simple. For instance, the simple equation

$$\exp (jw) = \sinh z$$

is the analytical expression of the field depicted in fig. 185. [2]

A wire, carrying an electric current is placed midway between two parallel surfaces of high permeability. The lines $v = $ constant are magnetic lines of force, the lines $u = $ constant are equipotential lines. Let us explore this field:

For $u = \pm \pi/2$, $\exp (jw) = \pm j \exp (-v)$.

---

[1]   A method for illustrating these fields by experimental means is described by A. D. MOORE, Jl. of Applied Physics **20**, 790 (1949).

[2]   B. HAGUE. Electromagnetic problems in electrical engineering, p. 167.

Hence sinh z is purely imaginary, but this means that

$$z = \pm j \cdot \frac{\pi}{2} + \text{real}$$

and this represents the two horizontal lines at $y = \pm \pi/2$.

If z is small sinh $z \approx z$ and we have the field of case f, p. 189: that is to say circular lines of force and radial equipotential lines in the neighbourhood of the origin.

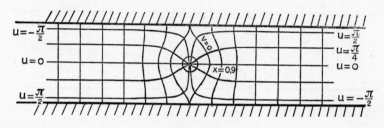

Fig. 185

Now let x be large and positive, then sinh $z \approx \frac{1}{2} \exp z.$, and the field is:

$$jw = \lg \tfrac{1}{2} + z,$$

splitting up in real and imaginary parts:

$$u = y \ ; \ -v = \lg \tfrac{1}{2} + x,$$

so that the equipotential lines ($u = $ constant) are horizontal and the lines of force ($v = $ constant) vertical straight lines; the field is homogeneous.

Now, what is the value of v in the points $z = \pm j \cdot \pi/2$? For these points:

$$\sinh z = \pm j$$

so that $v = 0$.

Another point of the line $v = 0$ can be calculated on the real axis, for which $u = 0$. Along this axis the v scale is determined by:

$$\exp(-v) = \sinh x$$

and the point $v = 0$ is found where sinh $x = 1 \therefore x = 0.9$.

196   XIV.   Orthogonal trajectories

Fig. 186 shows the case where two wires carrying currents in opposite directions lie on a surface of infinite permeability, a second surface of infinite permeability being present at a distance $\pi/2$ above the first surface. This field results from the superposition of two fields of the kind of fig. 185 and will be represented by:

$$\exp (jw) = \frac{\sinh (z + s)}{\sinh (z - s)}.$$

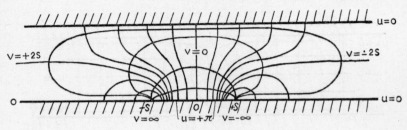

Fig. 186

In the immediate neighbourhood of one of the wires, say the one at $- s$, we have

$$\sinh (z + s) \approx z + s = r \exp (j\varphi)$$
$$\sinh (z - s) \approx \tfrac{1}{2} \exp (2s)$$

and we calculate

$$u = \varphi \; ; \; v = 2s - \lg (2r)$$

which represents again a radial field.

Where x is large and positive,

$$\sinh (z + s) \approx \tfrac{1}{2} \exp (x + s + jy) \; ; \; \sinh (z - s) \approx \tfrac{1}{2} \exp (x - s + jy)$$

from which follows:

$$u = 0 \; ; \; v = - 2s = \text{constant}$$

and this means that at great distances there is no field left.

In the point $z = 0$ we have $\exp (jw) = - 1$ that means: $u = \pm \pi$; $v = 0$.

For the upper boundary plane, $z = x + j\pi/2$, the righthand side of the equation is real, therefore $u = 0$ and the v-scale along this plane is fixed by:

$$\exp (- v) = \frac{\cosh (x + s)}{\cosh (x - s)}.$$

6. *Non-Laplacian orthogonal trajectories*

It is not difficult to find sets of mutually orthogonal curves that are no solutions of Laplace's equation and therefore are not represented by $z = f(w)$.

Consider, for instance, all evolventes of the unit circle. They are all cut orthogonally by the tangents to that same circle. The set of evolventes may be represented by:

$$z = (1 - ju) \exp\{j(u + v)\} . \quad . \quad . \quad . \quad . \quad (1)$$

from which we can now verify that $\partial z/\partial v$ is not equal to $j \partial z/\partial u$ as was the case in all the examples so far dealt with in this chapter.

Nevertheless, we may ask how we can calculate the orthogonal trajectories in those cases, where z is a function of u and v but not a function of the combination $(u + jv)$

Jump from point u on curve v to a neighbouring point $u + du$ on curve $v + dv$; this jump will be represented by:

$$dz = \frac{\partial z}{\partial u} du + \frac{\partial z}{\partial v} dv$$

If this jump is to have the direction of the normal, it must be equal to $\partial z/\partial u$, multiplied by an imaginary number:

$$dz = j \cdot \frac{\partial z}{\partial u} \cdot dp .$$

By equating the two expressions for dz, we obtain a relation between du, dv and dp. A second relation is obtained by a transition to conjugate values. From these two equations dp may be eliminated and what remains is a relation between u and v, which by introduction into the original equation $z = f(u, v)$ leads to the equation of an orthogonal trajectory.

As an arbitrary constant of integration occurs in the relation between u and v, we find as a rule an infinite set of orthogonal trajectories.

Let us, as an example, find the orthogonal trajectories of the set of evolventes of the unit circle, given above:

$$\frac{\partial z}{\partial u} = u \exp\{j(u + v)\} \; ; \; \frac{\partial z}{\partial v} = (j + u) \exp\{j(u + v)\}.$$

The condition for orthogonal direction is:

$$u \, du + (j + u) \, dv = ju \, . \, dp$$

from which

$$du = - \, dv \; ; \; (udp = dv)$$

integrated:

$$u + v = \text{Const.} = \psi$$

and introduced into (1):

$$z = (1 - ju) \exp{(j\psi)}$$

and this is indeed a tangent to the unit circle.

CHAPTER XV

KINKED CURVES

1. *Discontinuous functions*

Discontinuities and kinks will occur in curves if their formula contains a function which is itself discontinuous. Such functions have come into general use in this century in connection with operational calculus. [1])

The *staircase function* $y = \mathrm{Sc}\, x$ equals the greatest whole number comprised in x. Each time that x, during its continuous growth, goes through a whole number, $\mathrm{Sc}\, x$ jumps up by unity.

The *sawtooth function* $y = \mathrm{St}\, x = x - \mathrm{Sc}\, x$ grows liniarly from 0 to 1 if x grows continuously from n to $n + 1$. The moment x passes through $n + 1$, $\mathrm{St}\, x$ falls down to 0 again.

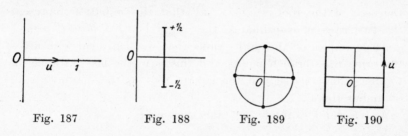

Fig. 187   Fig. 188   Fig. 189   Fig. 190

Heaviside's *step-function* $y = \mathrm{Sk}\, x$ is equal to zero for all values of x from $-\infty$ up to k and is equal to unity for all values of x beyond k.

The *meander function* or *signum function* $y = \mathrm{Sg}\, x$ is ± 1, the sign being the one $\sin x$ would adopt for the same value of x.

Fig. 187 shows the curve $z = \mathrm{St}\, u$; it is described periodically from 0 to 1.

Fig. 188 represents

$$z = \tfrac{1}{2} + j\,(\mathrm{St}\, u - \tfrac{1}{2})$$

the vertical line is again periodically described.

[1]) R. V. Churchill. Modern operational mathematics in Engineering, New York en London 1944.

The four points of fig. 189 can be represented by

$$z = \exp\left(j \cdot (\pi/2)\,\mathrm{Sc}\,u\right) = j^{\mathrm{Sc}\,u}$$

and the square shown in fig. (190) by a combination of fig. 188 and 189:

$$z = \left\{ \tfrac{1}{2} + j\,(\mathrm{St}\,u - \tfrac{1}{2}) \right\} . \, j^{\mathrm{Sc}\,u} \,.$$

These functions may occasionally be useful; one gets however the impression that all these things are merely witticisms when compared with what we shall deal with in the following sections.

2. *Irrational functions*

Of much more importance are kinks that are not introduced deliberately by the introduction of discontinuous functions. A simple example is

$$z = \sqrt{u}.$$

The curve follows the real axis as long as $u > 0$, but for $u < 0$ it follows the imaginary axis and because of the ambiguity of the sign of the root we may say that this equation represents the two axes of coordinates, the origin being a *branch point*.

All examples of „natural" kinks that we shall deal with are at the same time branch points and this is in the last instance due to the ambiguous sign of the square root or the manifold value of higher roots.

As a second example we take the curve:

$$z = \mathrm{arc}\,\cos u$$

which follows the real axis as long as $-1 < u < +1$; the function is multivalued with the period 2π. And what if u has values beyond these limits? Let us calculate z:

$$u = \cos z = \cos (x + jy) = \cos x \cosh y + j \sin x \sinh y.$$

As u is real, either $\sin x$ or $\sinh y$ must be zero. The latter supposition means that $y = 0$ and z is real, but that is the case we met already for $|u| < 1$. The former supposition means that

$$x = 0 \ (\pm\, n.\pi) \ ; \quad \cos x = 1 \ ; \quad \cosh y = u.$$

This case applies to $u > 1$ and:

$$z = \pm\, j \ \text{area cosh } u \ (\pm\, n.2\pi j).$$

We see, therefore, that the curve starts at $z = \pi/2$ for $u = 0$ (fig. 191), follows the real axis up to $x = 0$ where $u = 1$. Then it branches off and goes up or down in vertical direction towards infinity.

Apart from the angle $\pi/2$ which the curve possesses in point $u = 1$, it makes an angle π in the point $u = \pm \infty$.

A similar behaviour shows the curve $z = \text{arc sin } u = = \text{arc cos } (u + \pi/2)$.

It is congruent to the former one, but shifted in the direction of the real axis by the amount $\pi/2$.

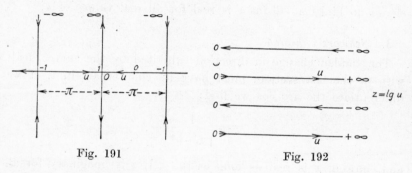

Fig. 191   Fig. 192

If we turn the figure for $z = \text{arc cos } u$ over an angle of $\pi/2$, we obtain the figure for:

$$z = \text{area cosh } u$$

which is real for all values of $u > 1$, but assumes purely imaginary values for $u < 1$. The congruency with fig. 191 follows directly from:

$$u = \cosh z = \cos (jz)$$

$$\therefore z = \text{area cosh } u = (1/j) \text{ arc cos } u.$$

The function: $z = \lg u$ is represented by a set of parallel horizontal lines, because:

$$u = \exp (z + n.2\pi j) \quad , \quad \text{as } \exp (2\pi j) = 1$$

and for any real value of u, z is multivalued with a period $2\pi j$. If u goes from 0 to ∞, z not only moves along the x-axis, but also along all horizontal lines at heights $n.2\pi j$ (fig. 192)

$$\lg (-u) = \pi j + \lg u \quad , \quad \text{because } \lg (-1) = \pi j.$$

The values of $z = lg\, u$ for negative values of u are, therefore, found from the values of z for the corresponding positive u-values by adding $\pi j + n \cdot 2\pi j$. If therefore, u goes from $-\infty$ to 0, z moves from right to left along a set of horizontal lines at heights $\pi j + n \cdot 2\pi j$ above the x-axis (fig. 192). We may express the results of fig. 192 by stating, that the function $lg\, u$ shows kinks over angles π at infinity.

Before closing this section we wish to remark, that the function

$$z = \text{area sinh } u$$

shows no kinks at all, as z is real for all real values of u.

3. *Schwarz's theorem*

The sudden change in direction exhibited by the curves dealt with in the last section, must have its counterpart in $\dot{z}$. If we differentiate the arc cos we find:

$$\dot{z} = \frac{1}{\sqrt{1-u^2}}$$

and, indeed, $\dot{z}$ is real as long as $|u| < 1$, $\dot{z}$ is imaginary for all values of $|u| > 1$. Integrating again:

$$z = \int \frac{du}{\sqrt{1-u^2}} = \text{arc cos } u$$

and we conclude that the kinks are found much more easily if we write z in the form of an integral than in the form of a closed function.

Now take the function:

$$z = \int \frac{du}{\sqrt[3]{1-u}} \;;\; \dot{z} = \frac{1}{\sqrt[3]{1-u}} \quad \cdot \quad \cdot \quad \cdot \quad \cdot \quad \cdot \quad (1)$$

$\dot{z}$ is real for all $u < 1$, beyond this value $\dot{z}$ is a third root of a negative number. As $\sqrt[3]{-1} = \exp\left(\pm j\,\pi/3\right)$

$$\sqrt[3]{1-u} = \sqrt[3]{u-1} \cdot \exp\left(\pm j \cdot \pi/3\right),$$

from which we see that the curve changes its direction at $u = 1$ by an angle $\pm \pi/3$, at the same point it branches again.

Generalizing, we find Schwarz's theorem: The curve:

$$z = \int \frac{du}{(u-u_1)^{\mu_1}(u-u_2)^{\mu_2}\ldots} \quad \ldots \quad \ldots \quad (2)$$

will show abrupt changes in direction, viz. at u_1 over an angle $\mu_1\pi$, at u_2 over an angle $\mu_2\pi$ etc.

4. *Triangles and rectangles*

According to Schwarz's theorem a triangle will be generated by:

$$z = \int u^{-\mu_1}(1-u)^{-\mu_2}\,du$$

with vertices at $u=0$, $u=1$ and $u=\infty$, (fig. 193) If, more in particular, we choose $\mu_1 = \mu_2 = 2/3$, an equilateral triangle will be generated, or, rather, a network of equilateral triangles.

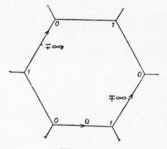

Fig. 193   Fig. 194

The length of the sides of the triangle are found with the aid of Euler's Beta-functions, defined by:

$$B(p,q) = \int_0^1 u^{p-1}(1-u)^{q-1}\,du$$

This integral gives at once the side from $u=0$ to $u=1$, if we put $p=1-\mu_1$; $q=1-\mu_2$; sidelength $= B(1-\mu_1 ; 1-\mu_2)$.

In order to calculate the side $u=1$ to $u=\infty$ we introduce the new parameter $u'=1/u$, running from 1 to 0 and this side will be:

$$\int_0^1 u'^{-\mu_3}(1-u')^{-\mu_2}\,du' \quad \text{(with } \mu_1+\mu_2+\mu_3=2\text{)}$$

which equals $B(1-\mu_2 ; 1-\mu_3)$.

The side from $u = -\infty$ to $u = 0$ is expressed in a Beta-function by introducing $1 - 1/u$ as new parameter and will be:

$$B\left(1 - \mu_3 \; ; \; 1 - \mu_1\right).$$

These values of the Beta-functions are as a rule computed with the help of Γ functions, making use of Binet's formula:

$$B\left(p, q\right) = \frac{\Gamma\left(p\right) . \Gamma\left(q\right)}{\Gamma\left(p + q\right)} \quad \text{with:} \quad \Gamma\left(p\right) = \int\limits_0^\infty x^{p-1} e^{-x} dx.$$

In the case of an equilateral triangle $\mu_1 = \mu_2 = \mu_3 = 2/3$ and all three sides have the length:

$$B\left(\tfrac{1}{3} \; ; \; \tfrac{1}{3}\right) = \frac{\Gamma^2\left(1/3\right)}{\Gamma\left(2/3\right)} = 5.35.$$

Hexagons will be generated by (fig. 194):

$$z = \int u^{-1/3} \left(1 - u\right)^{-1/3} du$$

and the length of each side will be $B\left(\tfrac{2}{3} \; ; \; \tfrac{2}{3}\right) = 2.0$.

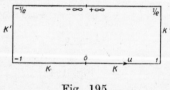

Fig. 195

A rectangle is described by the „elliptic integral":

$$z = \int \frac{du}{\sqrt{\left(1 - u^2\right)\left(1 - e^2 u^2\right)}},$$

with e (eccentricity) < 1, or, written inversely, by $u = sn\ z$ (sine amplitude z), the rectangle having corners at $u = \pm 1$ and at $u = \pm 1/e$.

The length of the semibase is the integral from 0 to 1, which is called the complete elliptic integral, $K(e)$, and which is tabulated (e.g. in Jahnke-Emde's Funktionentafeln) for all values of e. One can prove by transformation of the variable u that the integral from $1/e$ to ∞ also equals $K(e)$ and that the integral from 1 to $1/e$ equals $K\left(\sqrt{1 - e^2}\right) = K'$.

For $e = 1/\sqrt{2}$, $K\left(\sqrt{1 - e^2}\right) = K(e)$ and the base of the rectangle is twice the height. In order to obtain a square, one has to take $e \approx 0.17$, because, as may be seen from the tables, $K\left(\sqrt{1 - e^2}\right) = 2 K(e)$ in this case.

For relatively small values of e the following approximate relation exists between e and the ratio between the rectangle-sides, n:

$$e = 4 \exp(-\pi n) \quad ; \quad n = \frac{K(\sqrt{1-e^2})}{2\,K(e)},$$

so that we are in a position to choose e in accordance with the shape of the rectangle to be analytically represented.

We have seen in Ch. VI that a rectangle can also be represented by Weierstrass' integral:

$$z = -\int\limits_{\infty}^{u} \frac{dx}{\sqrt{4\,(x-\mathsf{p}_1)\,(x-\mathsf{p}_2)\,(x-\mathsf{p}_3)}}$$

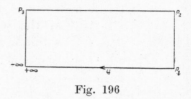

Fig. 196

or, inversely, by Weierstrass' function $u = \mathsf{p}(z)$ with corners, where $u = \mathsf{p}_1$, p_2, p_3 respectively (fig. 196).

5. *Application to potential and streamline problems*

Many potential- and streamline problems are connected with boundary contours which show corners and in connection with what we said in Ch. XIV concerning the solutions of these problems, it is of the utmost importance to be able to express these boundaries by analytical forms.

If, for example, a right-angled corner is a line of constant potential we may infer that, as the right angle is represented by $z = \sqrt{u}$, the solution of Laplace's differential equation in this case will be:

$$z = \sqrt{w}$$

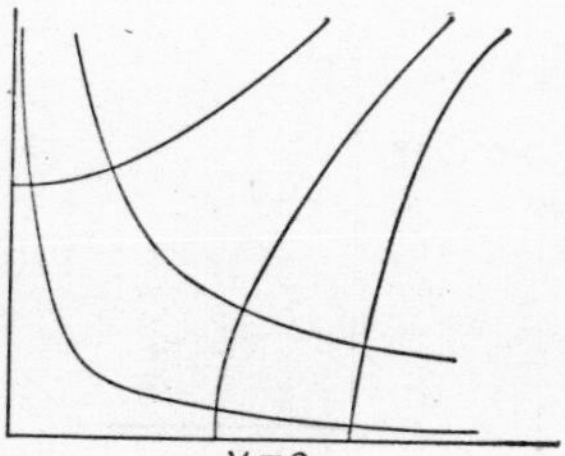

Fig. 197

where the lines $v = \text{constant}$ will be equipotential lines and the lines $u = \text{constant}$ lines of force or conversely, if the lines $v = \text{constant}$ are streamlines, the lines $u = \text{constant}$ will be equipotential lines (fig. 197). The line $v = 0$ is the corner itself; for $v > 0$ we write the solution:

$$z(u) = \sqrt{jv}\,\sqrt{1 - j\,u/v}$$

and we find a set of orthogonal hyperbolas. Compare fig. 177 p. 188.

A boundary like that in fig. 198 is represented by:

$$z = \text{arc cos } u \quad \text{or} \quad u = \cos z \ . \ . \ . \ . \ . \ (3)$$

and the Laplace-probleem will be solved by: $w = \cos z$ and can be analyzed along the lines of Ch. XIV.

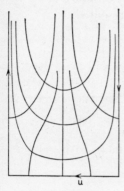

We are led to

$$w = sn\, z \quad \text{or} \quad w = \mathsf{p}(z)$$

as the solutions of the Laplace problem within a rectangle as an equipotential contour and to

$$z = \int^{\cdot} \frac{dw}{w^{2/3}\,(1-w)^{2/3}} \quad \text{or} \quad z = \int^{\cdot} \frac{dw}{w^{1/3}\,(1-w)^{1/3}}$$

if triangular, resp. hexagonal boundaries come into play.

Fig. 198

In order to find x and y for certain given values of u and v, it is necessary to split the integral into real and imaginary parts:

$$z = \int (U + jV)\,(du + jdv) = x + jy \ . \ . \ . \ . \ . \ (4)$$

from which: $x = \int U\, du - \int V\, dv \ ; \ y = \int V\, du + U\, dv.$

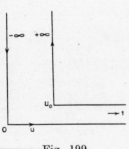

Although the problem is solved as far as its principle is concerned, the mathematical difficulties encountered in the practical construction of the lines of force may still be considerable.

What is the formula for the figure composed of the two right-angled corners, shown in fig. 199? We note an angle $\pi/2$ at $u = 0$, an angle π at the infinite point of the real axis, say, at $u = 1$, an angle $-\pi/2$

Fig. 199

at, say, $u = u_0$ and again an angle π at the infinite point of the imaginary axis. The formula:

$$\dot{z} = \frac{\sqrt{u_0 - u}}{(1 - u)\sqrt{u}}$$

will comply with all these kinks. It can be integrated:

$$z = 2 \arc \sin \sqrt{\frac{u}{u_0}} + \sqrt{u_0 - 1} \, \lg \frac{\sqrt{u_0 - u} + \sqrt{u_0 - 1} \cdot \sqrt{u}}{\sqrt{u_0 - u} - \sqrt{u_0 - 1} \cdot \sqrt{u}}, \quad . \quad (5)$$

an integral which fixes the location of the point u_0 at

$$z = \pi + j \pi \sqrt{u_0 - 1}$$

so that the widths of the two channels appear to be π and $\pi \sqrt{u_0 - 1}$ respectively. If, conversely, these widths are given, their ratio determines the value of u_0.

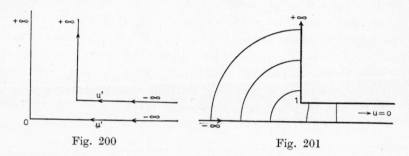

Fig. 200   Fig. 201

Completing u to w gives us the solution of Laplace's problem in case both corners are at the same potential. It is more likely however, that each corner has its own potential or is formed by separate streamlines (fig. 200). We have to make a break at $u = 1$ and we know from what was said concerning this subject in Ch. XIV, that the solution of Laplace's equation in this case is obtained by substituting $\exp w + 1$ for u in *equ.* (5) of the boundary line. An analysis of the field may be made in the way, shown in Ch. XIV.

The curve of fig. 201 may be represented by:

$$\dot{z} = j \frac{\sqrt{u - 1}}{u}$$

integrated:

$$z = j \{ \sqrt{u - 1} - \arc \tan \sqrt{u - 1} \}. \quad . \quad . \quad . \quad (6)$$

For $u = 1$, $z = 0$, so that the origin is situated in the corner; for all negative values of u, $z = -j \pi/2 + \text{real}$ and this gives the bottom line of the figure.

If the two parts are at different potentials or are different streamlines, we have to make a break in the u scale at $u = 0$ by the substitution $u' = \lg u$ and the field will be represented by (6) after passing from u to exp w:

$$z = j \left\{ \sqrt{\exp w - 1} - \text{arc tan} \sqrt{\exp w - 1} \right\}.$$

For large values of $|w|$ this reduces to

$$z = j \exp (w/2)$$

and this is the simple configuration of fig. 181, p. 89, namely a set of circular lines of force.

The reader may find more examples in: L. M. MILNE-THOMSON. Theoretical Hydrodynamics (1938) and R. V. CHURCHILL. Introduction to Complex Variables (1948). For the application to turbine blades shaped as logarithmic spirals we may refer to KÖNIG: Zeitschr. f. angewandte Mathem. und Mechanik 2, Heft 6 (1922) and to SÖRENSEN in the same periodical, vol. 7, Heft 2 (1927).

CHAPTER XVI

SPIRALS

1. *Archimedes' spiral and hyperbolic spiral*

The two classical spirals are Archimedes' spiral and the hyperbolic spiral. The former is the locus of points for which the radius vector is proportional to the argument and the latter is the locus of points for which the radius vector is inversely proportional to the argument. In formula:

Archimedes' spiral : $z = u \exp (ju)$.

Hyperbolic spiral : $z = 1/u \exp (ju)$.

We encountered already Archimedes' spiral (p. 151) as the tractor of the circle evolvente. The heart-shaped disc used on sewing machines in connection with the coiling of the spool consists of two spirals of Archimedes' (fig. 202). A pin in contact

Fig. 202

with the disc performs a uniform motion backwards and forwards if the disc rotates with constant angular velocity. A property of

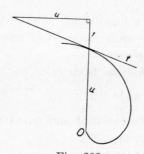

Fig. 203

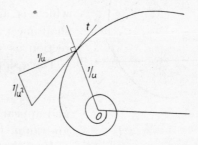

Fig. 204

this disc is that all secants through O have the same length. This property is shared with the circle and with the cardioid (Ch. XX).

Archimedes' spiral and the hyperbolic spiral are mutual inversions. The tangent construction of both curves is simple and may be read from the formula for the tangent:

Archimedes' spiral : $\dot{z} = (ju + 1)\exp ju$ (fig. 203)

Hyperbolic spiral : $\dot{z} = \dfrac{ju - 1}{u^2} \exp ju.$ (fig. 204)

The „slope", that is the angle between radius vector and tangent is in both cases arc tan u, although with opposite signs.

2. *Logarithmic spiral*

Much more important than the two spirals considered in the last section, is the *logarithmic spiral*, being the locus of points for which the radius vector is an exponential function of the argument:

$$z = \exp\{(ja + 1)u\}. \qquad \cdots \qquad (1)$$

a curve which has been studied intensively by DESCARTES (1640), OLE RØMER (1735) and JACOB BERNOULLI (1654—1705). The last-named geometer remarked on behalf of the logarithmic spiral: „although changed I always come back the same", by which is meant that many of the derived curves are again logarithmic spirals. We encountered already as examples of this peculiar behaviour the pedal, the centroid and the orthoptic curve.

Another example is the inversion:

$$z = \exp\{(ja - 1)u\}$$

which is again a logarithmic spiral. We shall meet with more examples of resurrection as we proceed.

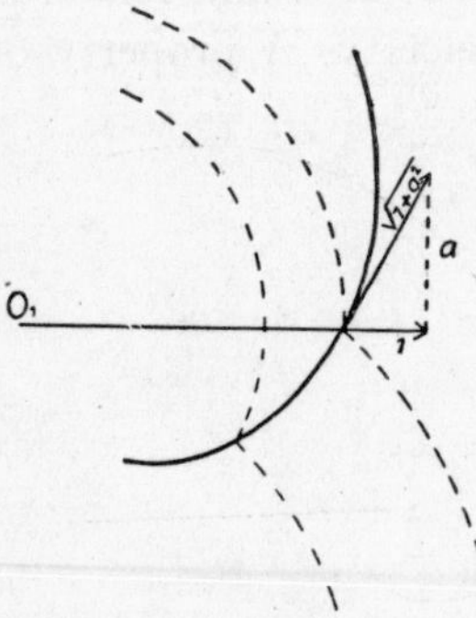

The „slope" follows from (1):

$$\dot{z} = (ja + 1)z$$

and appears to be constant and equal to arc tan a. (comp. fig. 205).

Fig. 205

It is said that insects approach a burning candle along a logarithmic spiral because they try to see the light at a constant angle with the direction they fly in just as they do when they fly in the sunshine along a straight line.

The boundary of two crystals which grow with different velocities will be a logarithmic spiral for that part of the boundary, where the growth of the slower crystal is rectilinear, and of the faster one curvilinear .The velocity of the latter is $\sqrt{1 + a^2}$ times that of the former (fig. 205). The same is observed to hold for the boundary line between two bacteria colonies spreading with different velocities.

Apply all tangents to the spiral from a fixed point R. From all tangent points the line OR is seen to subtend the fixed angle $\pi -$ arc tan a, so that all these points are situated on a circle (fig. 206).

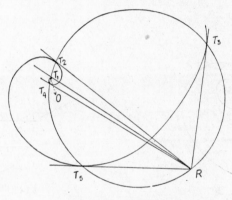

Fig. 206

The normal let down from O on the tangent in point u has the length (fig. 208) $n = \dfrac{a \cdot \exp (u)}{\sqrt{1 + a^2}}$.

Application of two equal constant forces P to cords wound over two logarithmic spirals as shown in fig. 207 will produce a moment proportional to $\exp(u)$, if u is the angle of rotation of the system. Inversely, the rotation u is proportional to the logarithm of the moment and this property is used in the construction of measuring devices with logarithmic scales.

We calculate in the usual way the arc-length s and the radius of curvature ϱ and find:

$$s = \sqrt{1 + a^2} \cdot \exp (u) \; ; \; \varrho = \sqrt{\frac{1 + a^2}{a}} \cdot \exp (u)$$

from which we obtain as the natural formula of the logarithmic spiral:

$$s = a \cdot \varrho$$

and from the standpoint of natural geometry the logarithmic spiral is the simplest curve.

The radius vector itself, Oz (fig. 208) has a length $\exp(u)$ and the projection of ϱ on this radius vector is also $\exp(u)$. The centre of curvature, z_1, which is a point of the evolute, is therefore found by drawing the perpendicular to Oz in the point O and the formula for the evolute is simply: $z_1 = j\,z/a$.

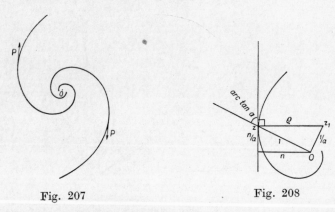

Fig. 207   Fig. 208

All evolutes are logarithmic spirals, similar to the original one, the n-th evolute being:

$$z_n = (j/a)^n \cdot z .$$

Conversely, all involutes are also similar logarithmic spirals, the n-th involute being:

$$z_{-n} = (j/a)^{-n} \cdot z .$$

The logarithmic spiral can even coincide with its own evolute (and with all higher evolutes and all involutes), namely, if:

$$z_1 = j/a\, z(u) = z(u + \triangle u)$$

or
$$j/a = \exp\{(ja + 1)\triangle u\} .$$

Separating absolute value and argument function gives:

$$1/a = \exp(\triangle u) \ ; \ \pi/2 = a\triangle u + 2n\pi .$$

Elimination of $\triangle u$ leads to a transcendental equation for a:

$$1/a = \exp \left\{ (\tfrac{1}{2} - 2n)\, \pi/a \right\}.$$

There is a solution for each whole value of n, for $n = 1$ we find by numerical calculation (fig. 209):

$$a = 3{,}6; \text{arc tan } a = 75°.\ (= \text{,,slope''}).$$

The corresponding curve is drawn in fig. 209; if z is the original

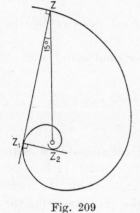

curve, z_1 is the first evolute, z_2 the second one and so on. This special spiral, called after BERNOULLI, may be called an auto-evolute.

Let us now solve the problem of the

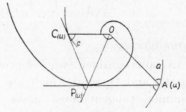

Fig. 209   Fig. 210

caustic (fig. 210). Denoting the slope by $\mu (= \text{arc tan } a)$, the lightray reflected in point P of the logarithmic spiral will be represented by

$$z = \exp (ja + 1)u \,.\, \{1 + \lambda \exp (2j\mu)\}$$

where λ is a parameter along the reflected ray, measuring the distance with $\text{OP} = \exp (ju)$ as unit of length. In order to find point C of the envelope we put

$$dz = 0$$

that is:

$$(ja + 1)\{1 + \lambda \exp (2j\mu)\} + \frac{\partial \lambda}{\partial u} \,.\, \exp (2j\mu) = 0.$$

Separating real and imaginary parts:

$$1 + \lambda \cos 2\mu - a\lambda \sin 2\mu + \frac{\partial \lambda}{\partial u} \cos 2\mu = 0$$

$$a + \lambda \sin 2\mu + a\lambda \cos 2\mu + \frac{\partial \lambda}{\partial u} \sin 2\mu = 0$$

from which we solve:

$$\lambda = 1 \; ; \; \frac{\partial \lambda}{\partial u} = -2.$$

As $\lambda = 1$, we see that $OP = PC$ and the line OC is parallel to the tangent in P. As $\exp(2j\mu) = \dfrac{1+ja}{1-ja}$, the caustic is with $\lambda = 1$:

$$z(C) = \frac{2}{1-ja} \cdot \exp(ja+1)u.$$

The caustic is again a logarithmic spiral, similar to the original one.

Inversely, the anticaustic of the same original spiral will be (fig. 210):

$$z(A) = \frac{1-ja}{2} \exp(ja+1)u.$$

3. *Syntrepency*

Let us now consider two congruent logarithmic spirals with vertices O_1 and O_2, and which are tangent in point T. Because the common tangent must make equal angles with the radii vectores, this point T must be situated on the line connecting the

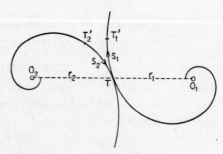

Fig. 211

two vertices. Now let each curve rotate round its own vertex but in such a way that the two remain tangent. The tangent point will move along the line $O_1 O_2$. Let T_1' and T_2' (fig. 211) become tangent points after a certain rotation. The change in length of the first radius vector, r_1 when going from T to T_1', is proportional to the distance s_1 between T and T', measured along the first curve and a similar relation applies to the second curve. Now, as the sum of the radii is constant, r_1 and r_2 change by equal, though opposite, amounts and s_1 will be equal to s_2. The two curves, therefore, will roll without sliding.

Curves showing this property, viz. rolling without sliding when rotating round two fixed points, are called syntrepent. If the two curves are congruent or if they are symmetrically congruent, they are called isotrepent. The logarithmic spiral therefore is isotrepent. Other examples of isotrepent curves are the ellipse (Ch. VII) and the hyperbola (Ch. VIII).

We may note that the angular velocities of the two wheels are different and that even the ratio of these angular velocities is not constant, so that syntrepent wheels present a means to transform uniform rotations into non-uniform rotations or, conversely, to correct for the non-uniformity of a rotation.

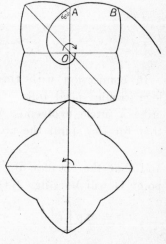

Fig. 212 shows how this gear-coupling works. Fig. 213 shows the interesting case known as Rømer's wheels. Each

Fig. 212   Fig. 213

wheel consists of eight pieces of logarithmic spirals, all with the centre of the wheel as their apex and one of the spirals is drawn more completely.

If we represent these spirals by the formula:

$$z = j^n \exp(\pm ja + 1) u$$

we have to adapt the value of a to the requirement that when going from A to B the argument difference $a \triangle u$ be $\pi/4$, if the radius vector changes in the ratio exp $(\triangle u)$ equal to $\sqrt{2}$. From this we figure:

$$\triangle u = ln\sqrt{2} \; ; \quad a = \pi/4\,ln\sqrt{2} = 2.24 \; ; \quad \text{arc tan } a = 66°.$$

Returning to fig. 211 we may observe, that if we keep the first spiral fixed and let the second spiral roll over the first one, the point O_2 will describe a circle round the point O_1.

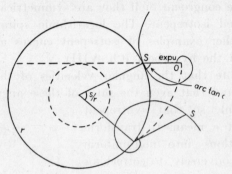

Fig. 214

In connection with this result we may remark, that if the logarithmic spiral rolls over a steady circle, the apex will describe a circle evolvente. We prove this as follows. Considering that for the spiral the arc length is:

$$s = \sqrt{1+a^2}\,\exp$$

and that the circular arc, covered by s will be s/r, the place of point O will be: (fig. 214)

$$z = \exp\left[j\,\frac{\sqrt{1+a^2}}{r}\exp u\right][r - j\exp(u + j\text{ arc tan }a)].$$

Introducing the new parameter: $v = \dfrac{\sqrt{1+a^2}}{r}\exp u$ and knowing

that $\exp(j\text{ arc tan }a) = \sqrt{\dfrac{1+ja}{1-ja}}$, the curve can be written:

$$z = r\left[1 - j\,\frac{v}{1-ja}\right]\exp j\,(v)$$

$$= \frac{r}{1-ja}[1 - j(a+v)]\exp j\,(a+v)\,.\,\exp(-ja)$$

which is, apart from the constant factor $\dfrac{\exp(-ja)}{1-ja}$, the well-known formula for the circle evolvente. The evolvente is derived from a circle with radius $r/\sqrt{1+a^2}$; the line from any instantaneous position of O to the corresponding tangent point is tangent to this circle (fig. 214).

4. *Klothoid*

The klothoid is a spiral represented by Fresnel's integral:

$$z = \int\limits_0^s e^{js^2}\, ds\,.$$

The letter s is used for the parameter as it represents the arc length. For:

$$\dot{z} = e^{js^2}\,,\quad |\dot{z}| = 1$$

and the arc length is

$$\int |\dot{z}|\, ds = s \text{ indeed.}$$

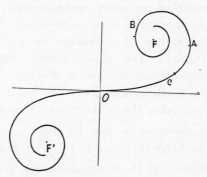

Fig. 215

The curve plays an important role in the theory of optical diffraction, and in treatises on optics it is mostly called CORNU's *spiral*.

Fresnel's integral is compiled in tables (e.g. JAHNHE-EMDE, Funktionentafeln p. 23). It converges to the values

$$z = \pm\sqrt{j} \cdot \sqrt{\pi/2} \text{ for } s = \pm\infty \text{ (points F, foci, in fig. 215).}$$

The slope of the tangent is s^2 and the tangent will be vertical for those values of s, for which

$$s^2 = (2n + 1)\,\pi/2\,.$$

We find therefore as values for s:

point A (fig. 215) : $s = \sqrt{\pi/2}$
point B   : $s = \sqrt{3\pi/2}$

and the arc length from A to B is $\sqrt{\pi/2} \cdot (\sqrt{3}-1)$.

In the same way the points where the tangent is horizontal will be found by the condition:

$$s^2 = 2n\,\pi/2\,.$$

In the usual way we calculate for the radius of curvature:

$$\varrho = 1/2s\,,$$

so that the natural equation is simply:

$$\varrho \cdot s = \text{constant.}$$

It is this property that makes the curve of importance for roadbuilders. When tracing a bend one should not change the radius of curvature discontinuously as this involves discontinuities in centrifugal forces. One must, on the contrary, try to change the radius of curvature as a continuous function of the arc length s. The most natural solution, therefore, is to take $1/\varrho$ proportional to s as is the case with the klothoid. One follows the klothoid from O to the point C where the slope is $\pi/4$ [1]) and then takes the symmetrical curve in order to cover a total change in direction to $\pi/2$. In point C, $s = \sqrt{\pi/4}$ and the total length of the bend therefore is $\sqrt{\pi}$. Fig. 216 shows a cycle track, consisting of four klothoid segments, the total length being $4 \cdot \sqrt{\pi/2}$.

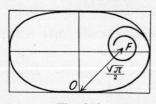

Fig. 216

Road builders might also choose a curve for which

$$1/\varrho = \text{constant } \sqrt{s}$$

or $$1/\varrho = \text{constant } s^2.$$

but these curves do not possess simple geometric properties.

The klothoid's simple natural equation makes it invariant with respect to the so-called *bimetal transformation*. A property of a bimetal is the change of its curvature to a certain amount when being heated. The curve

$$1/\varrho = f(s)$$

is transformed into:

$$1/\varrho = f(s) + \text{const.}$$

and as a rule the transform and the original curve belong to different classes of curves. The circle:

$$1/\varrho = a$$

---

[1]) Up to this point the klothoid is hardly distinguishable from the lemniscate (Ch. XVII) and road builders prefer the use of the term lemniscate bends.

is transformed into another circle: $1/\varrho = a + \text{const.}$ The klothoid:

$$1/\varrho = 2s$$

is transformed into itself:

$$1/\varrho = 2(s + s_0) \; ;$$

the new curve coincides with the old one after a shift over a distance s_0.

5. *Miscellaneous spirals*

Of importance for wave propagation theory are the *hyperbolic tangent* and the *hyperbolic cotangent:*

$$z = \tanh((ja + 1)u) \quad \text{and} \quad z = \cotanh((ja + 1)u)$$

two spirals which are mutually inverse. If a homogeneous conducting cable is shortcircuited at the far end, the entrance impedance is a hyperbolic tangent of an argument which itself is proportional to the length of the cable and is, besides, dependent on the properties of the cable. If the far end of the cable is left open the entrance impedance is a

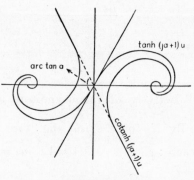

Fig. 217

hyperbolic cotangent. The same applies to acoustic or mechanic conducting devices and even to optical devices.

As $\exp\{-(ja+1)u\}$ decreases rapidly with an increasing value of the parameter u, both:

$$\tanh((ja+1)u) = \frac{\exp\{(ja+1)u\} - \exp\{-(ja+1)u\}}{\exp\{(ja+1)u\} + \exp\{-(ja+1)u\}}$$

and its inversion, the cotanh, approach very quickly to the logarithmic spiral:

$$z = 1 \mp 2\exp\{-2(ja+1)u\}$$

of which the apex lies in the point $+1$ of the real axis.

For small values of u, the tanh. starts from O, the cotanh. from infinity. Expanding the exponentials in power-series:

$$\exp x = 1 + x + \ldots$$

we find for small values of u:

$$\tanh = (ja + 1)\, u \;\; ; \;\; \cotanh = 1/(ja + 1)\, u\,.$$

from which we deduce that the slope of the tangent in O,

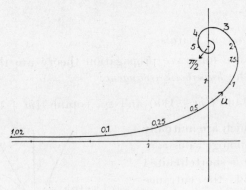

Fig. 218

respectively of the asymptote amounts to arc tan a (fig. 217).

By *Nielsen's spiral* (fig. 218) we mean:

where:
$$z = \mathrm{Ei}\,(ju) = \mathrm{Ci}\,u + j\,\mathrm{Si}\,u$$

$$\mathrm{Si}\,u = \pi/2 - \int_u^\infty \frac{\sin u}{u}\,du$$

$$\mathrm{Ci}\,u = -\int_u^\infty \frac{\cos u}{u}\,du$$

$$\mathrm{Ei}\,u = \int_\infty^{-u} (e^{-u}/u)\,du\,.$$

The functions are tabulated in JAHNHE-EMDE: Funktionen-tafeln p. 19; they are called integral sine, integral cosine and integral logarithm.

The derivative is:

$$\dot z = \frac{\cos u}{u} + j\,\frac{\sin u}{u} = \frac{\exp ju}{u}$$

and represents in itself the hyperbolic spiral. Further:

$$|\dot{z}| = 1/u \; ; \; s = \int |\dot{z}|\, du = ln\, u \, .$$

The curve is vertical where $\cos u = 0$, $u = (2n+1)\,\pi/2$ and in combination with the formula of the arc length s, we may calculate the lentgh of any arc between vertical tangents, for example the arc between $u = \pi/2$ and $u = 3\pi/2$ is:

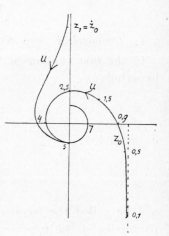

$$\triangle s = ln\, 3\pi/2 - \ln\, \pi/2 = ln\, 3 \, .$$

The slope itself τ appears to be equal to u and the radius of curvature: $\varrho = ds/d\tau = d\, ln\, u/du = 1/u$, from which follows the natural equation:

$$\varrho = \exp(-s).$$

From the theorem that $\varrho\tau = 1$ follows at once that the arc length of the osculating circle measured between

Fig. 219

the osculating point and its lowest point is constant $= 1$.

Fig. 219 shows HANKEL's spirals:

$$z_0 = H_0(u) = J_0(u) + jN_0(u) \, ;$$
$$z_1 = H_1(u) = J_1(u) + jN_1(u).$$

The properties of which may be found with the help of the properties of HANKEL, BESSEL and NEUMANN functions, tabulated in JAHNHE-EMDE, Funktionentafeln p. 90.

CHAPTER XVII

LEMNISCATE

1. *Geometrical properties*

In the first chapter of this book we dealt with the orthogonal hyperbola:

$$z = \frac{p}{\sqrt{2}} \sqrt{1+ju} \; ; \qquad \ldots \ldots \quad \text{(1a)}$$

its inversion:

$$z = \frac{p\sqrt{2}}{\sqrt{1-ju}} \qquad \ldots \ldots \ldots \quad \text{(1b)}$$

will be called the *lemniscate*. The constant p will be called the parameter of the hyperbola and of the lemniscate; it is also the radius of the inversion circle. The lemniscate (GREEK: lemniskos $=$ looped knot) is a discovery by JACOB BERNOULLI (1694). In order to distinguish it from other looped knots this particular one is often called the „isosceles" or the „orthogonal" lemniscate in the same way as its inversion, is called the orthogonal hyperbola.

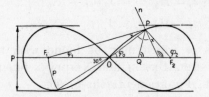

Fig. 220

The most important geometrical property of the lemniscate is the constancy of the product of the two radii vectores from any point of the curve to two fixed points. These fixed points, the foci, are the points $\pm\, p$ on the real axis. Indeed the product is:

$$(z-p)\,(z+p) = z^2 - p^2 = \frac{2\,p^2}{1-ju} - p^2 = p^2\,\frac{1+ju}{1-ju}$$

and as the last factor has an absolute value 1, the product of the moduli is constant and equal to p^2. The lemniscate therefore is a member of the family of CASSINI's ovals, compare p. 292.

The argument factor determines the sum of the arguments of the two radii vectores (fig. 220):

$$\exp j \left(\varphi_1 + \varphi_2\right) = \frac{1+ju}{1-ju} \quad \cdot \quad \cdot \quad \cdot \quad \cdot \quad \cdot \quad (2)$$

Now the argument of the vector from the origin to any point of the curve, P, is from (1)

$$\exp \left(j \varphi_0\right) = \left(\frac{1+ju}{1-ju}\right)^{1/4},$$

so that:

$$\varphi_1 + \varphi_2 = 4 \varphi_0.$$

The bisector of the angle $F_1 P F_2$ will have an inclination $2\varphi_0$ with respect to the major axis. If it cuts this axis in Q, $\triangle$ OQP will be isosceles. The line PQ not only bisects $\angle$ $F_1 P F_2$ but also the angle between OP and the normal. This is due to the fact that the normal makes an angle $3\varphi_0$ with the major axis, as is seen from the differentiation of (1).

The normal will be vertical if the argument is one third of a right angle, $\pm \pi/6$. As it follows from (2) that

$$u = - \tan 2 \varphi_0,$$

the values of u in the points with vertical normal (horizontal tangent) will be $\pm \sqrt{3}$. With this value of u we calculate for the radius vector

$$|z| = \frac{p\sqrt{2}}{\sqrt{1+u^2}} = p$$

so that these points appear to be on the inversion circle.

The tops of the lemniscate are the points $\pm p\sqrt{2}$ on the real axis, the radius of curvature in these points is found to be $\frac{1}{3} p \sqrt{2}$.

The origin is a double point, $u = \infty$ and by differentiating (1) we can show that the tangents have slopes of $\pm 45°$.

The area of the complete lemniscate (two loops together) is readily calculated in the usual way; it is $2\, p^2$.

For the length of the curve we find from (1):

$$s = \int |\dot{z}| \, du = \frac{p}{\sqrt{2}} \int (1 + u^2)^{-3/4} \, du.$$

This is an elliptical integral which can be transformed into a more familiar form by the substitution

$$u = \frac{x\sqrt{2-x^2}}{1-x^2}$$

by which:

$$s = p \int \frac{dx}{\sqrt{(1-x^2)(1-x^2/2)}}$$

and this is the elliptical integral of the first kind, the values of which are given in many collections of numerical tables (e.g. JAHNKE-EMDE: Funktionentafeln p. 57).

When u runs from 0 to ∞ we describe one half loop; x runs from 0 to 1 and we have to take the so-called complete integral, which amounts to 1.8541. The total perimeter of the double loop will be 7.4164 p.

From

$$\dot{z} = \frac{p}{\sqrt{2}} (1 - ju)^{-3/2}$$

we find

$$|\dot{z}| = ds/du = \frac{p}{\sqrt{2}} (1 + u^2)^{-3/4}$$

and for the argument function of the tangent:

$$\exp(j\tau) = \left(\frac{1-ju}{1+ju}\right)^{-3/4},$$

hence:

$$d\tau/du = \tfrac{3}{2} \frac{1}{1+u^2}$$

and

$$\varrho = \frac{ds/du}{d\tau/du} = \tfrac{1}{3} \, p\sqrt{2} \, (1+u^2)^{1/4}.$$

In the neighbourhood of the double point we may neglect 1 with respect to u^2, so that approximately:

$$s = p\sqrt{2} . u^{-1/2} \; ; \; \varrho = \tfrac{1}{3} \, p\sqrt{2} \, u^{1/2}$$

and we find that approximately the product:

$$\varrho s = \tfrac{2}{3}\, p^2 = \text{constant}$$

a property which holds strictly for the klothoid. This property accounts for the importance of both the klothoid and the lemniscate in designing the bends of roads. (cf. p. 218).

2. *Sinus spirals*

The lemniscate is a member of the family of the sinus spirals, which are defined by:

$$|z|^n = \tfrac{1}{2}\cdot(2\,p)^n \cos n\varphi$$

a definition which by the introduction of the parameter:

$$u = -\,\tan n\varphi$$

is transformed into:

$$z = \frac{2\,p}{\sqrt[n]{2}}\;\frac{1}{(1+ju)^{1/n}} \quad \cdots \cdots \quad (4)$$

The sinus spirals are a set of by pairs mutually inverse curves, the most important of which have been known to us a long time already:

$$
\begin{cases}
n=1 &:\text{ circle}\\
\;\;-1 &:\text{ straight line}\\
\;\;\tfrac{1}{2} &:\text{ cardioid}\\
\;-\tfrac{1}{2} &:\text{ parabola}\\
\;\;2 &:\text{ lemniscate}\\
\;-2 &:\text{ orthogonal hyperbola.}
\end{cases}
$$

The sinus spirals have a number of properties in common. One of them is the proportionality between the inclination of the normal and the argument, the former rotating with a speed, $n+1$ times the speed of rotation of the argument. This property follows from the differentiation of (4), for the lemniscate we found indeed in the last section the factor 3.

SERRET (1842) found two general expressions for the length and the area of sinus spirals, making use of Euler's gamma-function Γ, defined by:

$$\Gamma(x) = \int\limits_{0}^{\infty} e^{-\xi}\cdot\xi^{x-1}\,d\xi.$$

In order to avoid lengthy analytical calculations we give Serret's formulas here without proof:

Length of sinus spiral:

$$l = p\frac{\varGamma^2\,(1/2n)}{\varGamma\,(1/n)}$$

Area of sinus spiral:

$$A = 2^{\frac{2\,(n-2)}{n}} \cdot n \cdot \pi p^2 \cdot \frac{\varGamma\,(2/n)}{\varGamma^2\,(1/n)}\ .$$

Applied to the lemniscate for which n=2, and taking into account that

$$\varGamma\,(\tfrac{1}{4}) = 3.6256\ \ ;\ \ \varGamma\,(\tfrac{1}{2}) = \sqrt{\pi}\ \ ;\ \ \varGamma\,(1) = 1;$$

these formulas yield:

$$l = 7.4164\ p,$$
$$A = 2p^2.$$

As another general theorem we may mention that the pedal of a sinus spiral is again a sinus spiral, viz. of the order $n/n+1$, for example,

	Sinus spiral		Pedal
$n = 1$	circle	$n = \tfrac{1}{2}$	cardioid
$- \tfrac{1}{2}$	parabola	$- 1$	straight line
$- 1$	straight line	∞	point
$\pm \infty$	point	1	circle
$- 2$	hyperbola	2	lemniscate
2	lemniscate	$^2/_3$	
$- \,^2/_3$		$- 2$	hyperbola

The reader is invited to verify the inversion theorem of the pedal (p. 152) with the help of this table.

For the application of sinus spirals in electrical potential problems we may refer to p. 194.

3. *Lemniscate and hyperbola*

We shall see in this section that the lemniscate and the hyperbola are in many ways related to each other. We have introduced them already as inverse curves:

$$z_{\text{hyp}} = p/\sqrt{2}\,\sqrt{1+ju} \; ; \; z_{\text{lem}} = \frac{p\sqrt{2}}{\sqrt{1-ju}} . \quad . \quad . \quad . \quad (7)$$

For these curves we find:

$$z/\dot{z} = 2j\,(1 \pm ju)$$

where the $+$ sign is valid for the hyperbola, the minus sign for the lemniscate. As appears from this formula, a radius through O makes equal angles with hyperbola and lemniscate but on opposite sides (fig. 221, points P and Q).

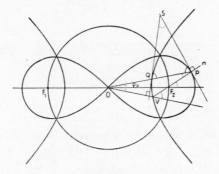

Fig. 221

We may remark in passing that this is a general property of inverse curves. It can be considered as a consequence of the conformal transformation and can be proved more directly as follows:

$$\dot{z}\,(d/du)\,(1/z^*) = -(\dot{z}\dot{z}^*/z^{*2}) = \text{Real}\,.\,z^2$$

from which the angle property can be read.

The angle at P and Q appears to be $\pi/2 - 2\varphi_0$, if φ_0 is the argument of OP. The two tangents in P and Q, therefore, meet in point S at an angle $4\varphi_0$. The slope of QS is $\pi/2 - \varphi_0$ and QS, therefore, is normal to the line OV, which has a slope $-\varphi$.

The reflection property of the hyperbola is inverted into the property of the lemniscate that the tangent to the lemniscate in P makes equal angles with the circles OF_1P and OF_2P.

By application of the general formula for the pedal to the formula (7) for the hyperbola, we find the pedal:

$$\tfrac{1}{2}\, p\, \sqrt{2}\, / \sqrt{1+ju}$$

which, apart from the factor $\tfrac{1}{2}$, is identical with the lemniscate considered up to now (fig. 222).

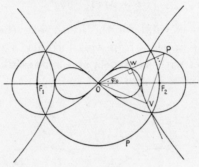

Fig. 222

Draw the tangent to the hyperbola in V (fig. 222). The base point of the normal, let down on this tangent from O be W. V and W have opposite arguments. Multiply OW by the factor 2 and we come to point P of the greater lemniscate. From congruent triangles we conclude that $OV = PV$ and that $\angle\ WPV = 2\varphi_0$. The slope of VP, therefore, equals $3\,\varphi_0$, so that VP is the normal to the lemniscate in point P. This normal obviously runs through point V of the hyperbola. Compare also fig. 221.

4. *Wave impedance and wave admittance.*

The equations (1) and (7) are connected with the wave impedance and the wave admittance of infinitely long electrical lines, containing resistance, self induction and capacity. If the current be denoted by i, the voltage by v, the electrical equations are:

$$- \partial v/\partial x = (R + jwL)\, i$$

$$v = - (1/jwC)\, . \, \partial i/\partial x,$$

where R is the resistance per unit of length, L the self-induction per unit of length, ω the angular frequency and C the capacity per unit of length. The equations are solved by:

$$v = v_0 \exp (\gamma x) \; ; \quad i = i_0 \exp (\gamma x)$$

where γ is the so called propagation constant.

Obviously $\partial/\partial x = \gamma$ and by introducing this into the electrical equations we find for γ:

$$\gamma^2 = jwC \, (R + jwL)$$

and with this value from either of the equations for the wave impedance $z = v/i$:

$$z = \sqrt{L/C} \cdot \sqrt{1 + R/jwL} \, .$$

Now writing

$$\sqrt{L/C} = p/\sqrt{2} \; ; \quad u = -R/wL$$

the wave impedance takes the form of the orthogonal hyperbola (1) or (7). The inversion, the wave admittance, will be represented by the lemniscate.

Analogous considerations apply to the impedance and admittance of mechanical or acoustical devices and the geometrical representation is of great help when working with these quantities.

5. *Straight line guides*

Generalized lemniscates are generated by JAMES WATT's hinge joint mechanism (1784). Two fixed points F_1 and F_2 (fig. 223) at a distance $2p$ carry rotary levers F_1A and F_2B, each of a length b. A and B are connected by a rod of length $2c$ which can freely

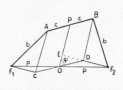

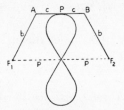

Fig. 223   Fig. 224

rotate round its ends. The path described by point P, the middle of AB, is called W*att's lemniscate* (fig. 224). In the neighbourhood of the double point we find fairly long stretches of the curve, which are practically straight and Watt designed this construction in order to transform rotary movements into straight ones. We speak of straight line guides. CATALAN (1885) gave the following derivation of the equation of Watt's lemniscate.

Complete the parallelogram ABCD (fig. 223)

$$\triangle \ F_1CO \cong \triangle \ F_2DO \ \therefore \ F_1C = F_2D$$

$$\therefore \triangle \ F_1AC \cong \triangle \ F_2BD \ \therefore \ \angle \ F_1CA = \angle \ F_2DB.$$

But as $F_1C // F_2D$, these angles must be right. This enables us to calculate $OP = |z|$ as a function of the argument φ:

$$EF_2 = p \ \sin \ \varphi \ ; \ \ ED = \sqrt{c^2 - p^2 \ \cos \ ^2\varphi}$$

$$|z|^2 = BD^2 = b^2 - (p \ \sin \ \varphi \pm \sqrt{c^2 - p^2 \ \cos^2 \ \varphi})^2 ; \quad . \quad (9)$$

the $+$ sign is valid if A and B are on opposite sides of the line $F_1 F_2$ and (9) may be considered as the lemniscate's equation in polar coordinates.

Let us now specialize by the choice $c = p$. Equ. (9) gives two different results, depending on whether we use the $-$ or the $+$ sign.

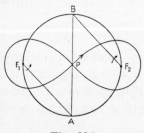

For the $-$ sign we arrive at the trivial result

$$|z| = b$$

and P describes a circle.

In the case of the $+$ sign we find:

$$|z|^2 = b^2 - 4p^2 \sin^2 \varphi.$$

and this curve is called *Booth's lemniscate*.

Fig. 225

Specializing one step further we take $b = p \sqrt{2}$. The mechanism takes the form of fig. 225 and the equation is:

$$|z|^2 = 2p^2 \ \cos \ 2\varphi$$

which we recognize as Bernoulli's lemniscate in the guise of a sinus spiral.

In connection with this subject we will mention two more straight line guides: the conchoid guide and Peaucellier's invertor.

The *conchoid guide* is illustrated in fig. 226. A lever AB rotates round A. A rod CBD can slide through a rotary sleeve at the fixed point D. The stretch BC is constant and C describes a circle conchoid; if we choose suitable conditions the path of C may be very nearly straight.

Peaucellier's invertor consists of two levers of length *a*, fig. 227, rotating round O. Between the ends A and B a rhomb is spanned, consisting of four rods of length *c*. We shall prove that

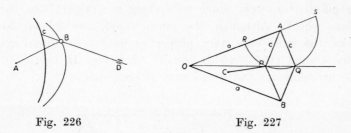

Fig. 226   Fig. 227

P and Q belong together as inversions. As they both lie on the bisector of $\angle$ AOB they are in one line with O. Draw the circle of radius *c* round A. Applying the theorem of constant power for this circle, we have:

$$OP.OQ = OR.OS = (a - c)\ (a + c) = a^2 - c^2 = \text{Const.},$$

which proves the inversion character of the two points P and Q.

If now we make P describe a circle passing through O by connecting it by a rotary lever to some appropriately chosen fixed point C, Q will describe the inversion of this circle and that is a straight line.

CHAPTER XVIII

CYCLOID

1. *Geometrical properties*

The *normal cycloid* or for short the *cycloid* is the track described by a point of a circle which rolls along a straight line. (Greek: kyklos=wheel). Although the curve itself was known to the Greeks, the most important properties have been discovered by Galileo Galilei (1564—1642) and by Christiaan Huygens (1629—1695) in connection with mechanical problems.

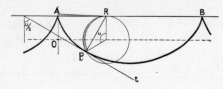

Fig. 228

We shall conceive the circle to roll underneath and against a horizontal straight line, called the *directrix*. We choose the radius of the circle equal to $p/4$, where p is called the cycloid's *parameter*. We choose, furthermore, the origin at a distance $p/4$ under the directrix. The movement of the point P can be considered as the superposition of a uniform translation of the centre of the rolling circle in a horizontal direction and a uniform rotation round this centre; in formula:

$$z = \tfrac{1}{4}\,p\,\{u + j \exp{(ju)}\}, \quad \ldots \quad \ldots \quad (1)$$

if we start the u scale at point A directly above the origin (fig. 1). This point A and all its equivalents are cusps with vertical tangents, as appears from the differentiation of (1).

The instantaneous tangent point R of the rolling circle and the directrix is given by

$$z\,(\mathrm{R}) = \tfrac{1}{4}\,p\,(u + j)$$

and hence the vector from P to R is represented by:

$$z\,(\mathrm{R}) - z\,(\mathrm{P}) = \tfrac{1}{4}\,p\,\{\,j - j\exp\,(ju)\,\}\,.$$

We may compare this result with the general equation for the tangent:

$$\dot{z} = \tfrac{1}{4}\,p\,\{\,1 - \exp\,(ju)\,\}\ \cdot\ \cdot\ \cdot\ \cdot\ \cdot\ \cdot\quad(2)$$

which differs from it only by the factor j. This means, first, that PR is normal to the tangent in P. This same result can be deduced in a kinematical way, if we realize that R is the instantaneous centre of rotation of the rolling circle, so that all points of the circle will describe infinetely small parts of circles round R so that the instantaneous direction of the moving point P must be normal to RP.

Moreover, the absolute value of $\dot{z}$ equals the length PR. The absolute value of the velocity and of PR as well is:

$$|\dot{z}| = \tfrac{1}{4}\,p\,\sqrt{\{\,1 - \exp\,(ju)\,\}\,\{\,1 - \exp\,(-ju)\,\}} = \tfrac{1}{2}\,p\,\sin\,u/2\,.\quad(3)$$

Although R is on the normal, the distance PR is not the radius of curvature. If we calculate the latter by the general formula, we find easily:

$$\varrho = p\,\sin\,u/2\ \cdot\ \cdot\ \cdot\ \cdot\ \cdot\ \cdot\ \cdot\ \cdot\quad(4)$$

which means that the radius of curvature is cut into two equal parts by the directrix. A beam of parallel light rays impinging on a reflecting cycloidal surface along the line RP would be focussed by the mirror in R. Although a cycloidical mirror would show many optical deficiencies it would form an image without plane curvature of an object, situated at infinity, the plane of the image being the plane of the directrix. This property is shared neither by the spherical nor by the parabolic mirror.

The arc length measured from the lowest point $u = \pi$ of the cycloid is:

$$s = \int_{\pi}^{u} |\dot{z}|\,du = p\,\cos\,u/2\ \cdot\ \cdot\ \cdot\ \cdot\ \cdot\ \cdot\quad(5)$$

and the total length of one arc amounts to $2p$.

Combination of (4) and (5) yields as the natural equation of the cycloid:

$$\varrho^2 + s^2 = p^2.$$

This is the equation of a circle in Cartesian coordinates. If, therefore, a cycloid rocks on a horizontal plane (fig. 229), the centre of curvature belonging to the instantaneous point of support describes a circle of radius p round the equilibrium position T_0 of the supporting point. As (fig. 229) the radius of curvature PK

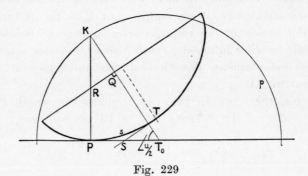

Fig. 229

equals $p \sin u/2$ and $PT_0 = s = p \cos u/2$, the angle KT_0P equals $u/2$. From the equation (2) for PR we may infer that this vector also makes an angle $u/2$ with the directrix, so that in fig. 129 T_0K is normal to the directrix.

Draw the top tangent TS parallel to the directrix. We shall prove that S is halfway between P and T_0 by the following sequence of calculations.

$$KR = \tfrac{1}{2} p \sin u/2 \; ; \; KQ = \tfrac{1}{2} p \sin^2 u/2 \; ; \; TT_0 = \tfrac{1}{2} p \left(1 - \sin^2 u/2\right) =$$
$$= \tfrac{1}{2} p \cos^2 u/2 \; ; \; T_0S = \tfrac{1}{2} p \cos u/2 = s/2 \, .$$

Take (fig. 230) two points P_1 and P_2 on the cycloid differing by π in the values of the parameter. Their normals will be mutually orthogonal and by (4) and (5) we see that s for one point equals ϱ for the other point.

We shall conclude this section with the remark that the area of the cycloid is calculated to $\tfrac{3}{16} \pi p^2$, that is, three times the area of the rolling circle.

2. *The projections of the screw, trochoids*

In defining the cycloid we made the centre of the rotating circle move with uniform velocity in the direction of the x-axis. Let it instead move now with the same velocity in the direction normal to the x-y-plane. The latter rotating circle will at any moment be projected on the former rotating circle by projecting

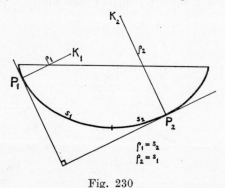

Fig. 230

rays having an inclination of $\pi/4$. As in the latter case each point of the circle describes a screw we may infer that the cycloid is the projection of the screw (fig. 231).

If the projecting rays have an inclination which differs from $\pi/4$ or if the pitch of the screw differs from $2\pi \cdot p/4$, the projected curve will be represented by the general formula:

$$z = \tfrac{1}{4}\, p\, \{ku + j \exp{(ju)}\}.$$

This curve can also be interpreted as the path of a point of a circle rolling with a certain amount of slip or, better still, as the path of a point at a distance $p/4$ from the centre of a circle of radius $kp/4$ which rolls without slip. These curves are called *trochoids* (Greek: trochos = wheel). They exhibit a double point in case $k < 1$, and maxima and minima only if $k > 1$.

3. *Brachistochrone*

JOHANN BERNOULLI found (1697), that the cycloid has the property of being the brachistochrone, with which we mean to say, that of all the curves, connecting two points A and B, the cycloid is the one along which a material point, accelerated by gravity, will move from A to B in the shortest time. As we shall presently see this mechanical property is a consequence of the geometrical property that the directrix cuts the normal into two equal parts, which fact we shall express by the formula (fig. 232):

$$y_{\mathrm{A}} - y_{\mathrm{P}} = \tfrac{1}{2}\,\varrho \sin \alpha \;.\; .\; .\; .\; .\; .\; .\quad (6)$$

(That α equals $u/2$ is of no importance for this problem).

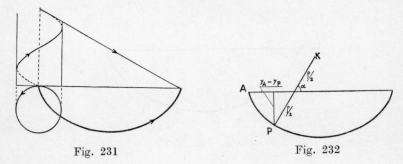

Fig. 231   Fig. 232

We can change from one kinematical track to a neighbouring one by shifting the elements of the track in the direction of the normal over a distance δn, where δn may vary along the track s. The length of the element is then varied by (fig. 233):

$$\delta\,ds = -\frac{\delta n}{\varrho}\,ds. \;.\; ,\; .\; .\; .\; .\; .\quad (7)$$

The material point will move over ds with a velocity, found from the principle of constant energy:

$$v = \sqrt{2g} \cdot \sqrt{y_{\mathrm{A}} - y_{\mathrm{P}}}$$

where y_{A} is the ordinate of the starting point, at which the velocity is supposed to be zero. As the variation in y_{P} equals $\delta n \cdot \sin \alpha$, the variation of the velocity amounts to:

$$\frac{\delta v}{v} = \tfrac{1}{2}\,\frac{\delta n \cdot \sin \alpha}{y_{\mathrm{A}} - y_{\mathrm{P}}} \;.\; .\; .\; .\; .\; .\; .\quad (8)$$

The variation in the time element necessary to cover the arc element ds will be:

$$\delta t = \delta\,\frac{ds}{v} = \frac{v\delta\,ds - ds \cdot \delta v}{v^2}.$$

Now suppose this to be negative, the original track would then not have been the track of the shortest falling time. If it were positive we could have taken δn with opposite sign and would have found a track on the opposite side of the original track with shorter falling time. If the original track is to be the brachistochrone it will be necessary that for all parts of it $\delta t = 0$, or that:

$$\frac{\delta \, ds}{ds} = \frac{\delta v}{v}.$$

Inserting here (7) and (8) we find for the condition:

$$y_A - y_P = \tfrac{1}{2}\, \varrho \sin \alpha$$

and this is just the property of the cycloid referred to above.

The energy-principle was applied, supposing that the falling body assumes no rotational energy. If now we allow it to rotate with angular velocity ω, the equation expressing the energy principle reads:

$$\tfrac{1}{2}\, mv^2 + \tfrac{1}{2}\, J\omega^2 = mg\,(y_A - y_P)$$

where J is the inertia moment. There are many cases where ω will be proportional to v, say $\omega = v/r$ and we calculate:

$$v = \sqrt{2g'}\,\sqrt{y_A - y_P} \ \text{ with } \ g' = g\,\frac{m}{m + J/r^2}.$$

The only thing that has happened is an apparent change in g; the cycloid remains however the brachistochrone.

If the motion starts without initial velocity each point of the

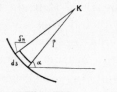

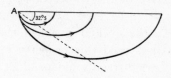

Fig. 233   Fig. 234

plane lower than the starting point A can be reached by one cycloid and the track will show a lowest point if the straight line connecting A with the endpoint has a slope smaller than arc tan $2/\pi$, that is 32.5.° (fig. 234)

4. *Tautochrone*

Let us now figure out the actual amount of the falling time for a particle moving along the cycloid. It is:

$$t = \int \frac{ds}{v} = \int\limits_{u_0}^{u} \frac{|\dot z|\, du}{v},$$

where

$$|\dot z| = \tfrac{1}{2}\, p \sin u/2 \; ; \; v = \sqrt{2g} \cdot \sqrt{y_0 - y} \; ; \; y = \tfrac{1}{4}\, p \cos u,$$

so that:

$$t = \sqrt{\frac{p}{2g}} \cdot \int\limits_{u_0}^{u} \frac{\sin \tfrac{1}{2} u\, du}{\sqrt{\cos u_0 - \cos u}}.$$

The indefinite integral is known, viz.

$$-\frac{1}{\sqrt 2}\, \text{arc sin} \, \frac{1 + 2 \cos u - \cos u_0}{1 + \cos u}.$$

as may be verified by differentiating back again. The arcsin assumes the value $\pi/2$ for the starting point $u = u_0$. A remarkable thing occurs, if we lay the end point of the integral in the bottom point of the cycloid, $u = \pi$, for now the arc sin assumes the value $-\pi/2$ irrespective of the value of u_0. The definite integral has therefore the value

$$t = \tfrac{1}{2}\, \pi \sqrt{p/g},$$

irrespective of the choice of u_0. This property of constant falling time was discovered by HUYGENS (1670) and because of this property the cycloid is called the *tautochrone* or *isochrone*.

HUYGENS used this property in order to construct a pendulum with a period strictly independent of the amplitude. As is generally known, this is only approximately the case for a circular pendulum. If a mass is allowed to slide backwards and forwards along a cycloid, the total period will be $2\pi \sqrt{p/g}$, irrespective of the amplitude HUYGENS obtained this result by suspending a mass by a cord unwound from the cycloid's evolute.

Applying the general recipe for finding evolutes to form. (1) of the cycloid, we arrive at:

$$\tfrac{1}{4}\, p\, \{u - j \exp(ju) + 2j\}$$

which, apart from a constant shift $\tfrac{1}{4}\, p\, (\pi + 2j)$, is identical with (1) and therefore represents again a cycloid. HUYGENS therefore compelled the suspending cord of his pendulum to oscillate between two cycloid arcs (fig. 235).

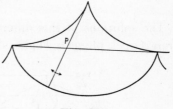

If, as is the case with the cycloid, the evolute is congruent with the original curve, all higher evolutes and also the first and the higher

Fig. 235

involutes will be congruent with the original curve.

5. *Path of electron in combined electric and magnetic fields; phygoids*

Suppose an electron to be subject to an electric field in the direction of the imaginary axis, which field imparts to it an acceleration $-g$ and at the same time subject to a magnetic field in the direction normal to the x-y-plane, this field imparting to it an acceleration in the x-y-plane normal to and proportional to the instantaneous velocity. The mechanical equation will be, denoting by dots differentiations with respect to time:

$$\ddot{z} = -jg + j\omega\dot{z} \quad [\omega \text{ is known as Larmor's frequency}]$$

which can be solved by well-known methods, with the result:

$$z = \tfrac{1}{4}\, p\, \{k\omega t + \exp(j\omega t)\}$$

where p is arbitrary, $k = 4g/p\omega^2$.

The path is obviously a trochoid, degenerating into a normal cycloid, if incidentally $k = 1$. In the cycloidal case, $p = 4g/\omega^2$, and we calculate for the velocity at the lowest point of the path $\sqrt{2} \cdot g/\omega$. If the velocity in the bottom point is greater than this amount, the path will be a trochoid with double points and loops.

Paths showing a certain resemblance with these curves are
described by an aeroplane with stopped motor and fixed elevator.
The plane is subject to the gravitational acceleration $-g$ and
to a lift normal to the velocity and proportional to the square
of the velocity. The equation of motion, therefore, is:

$$\ddot{z} = -jg + j\omega\,|\dot{z}|\,\dot{z}$$

The solutions of this differential equation are called *phygoids* [1])
from Greek phyge = flight. A number of types is given in fig. 236,

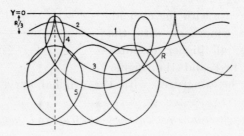

Fig. 236

where the line $y = 0$ is chosen in such a way that on it the velocity
would be zero. As in the case of trochoids, we distinghuish
phygoids with loops (tumblers); with cusps and phygoids of the
inflected type. The general formulas can be given with the aid
of elliptic functions and in order to avoid lengthy analytical
work we shall not enter into this problem here. Incidentally the
type with cusps consists of a series of semicircles of radius R,
represented by:

$$z/R = (1/e)\, sn\, u\, dn\, u + j\, cn^2 u \;\; ;\;\; u = t\sqrt{g/R} \;\;,\;\; e^2 = \tfrac{1}{2},$$

where $sn\, u$, $cn\, u$ and $dn\, u$ are the elliptic functions of eccentricity
e, which can be found in tabular collections such as JAHNKE-
EMDE's Funktionentafeln.

A few properties can be found by elementary methods. For

---

[1]) F. W. LANCHESTER. Aerodonetics, London 1908.
     W. F. DURAND. Aerodynamic Theory. Vol. 5, p. 86.
     F. WILLERS. Graphische Integration, p. 104.

the straight line solution, nr. 1, the total acceleration is zero:

$$0 = -g + \omega v^2$$

from which, together with

$$v^2 = 2gh,$$

we find for the vertical distance of this line to the dead line $y = 0$, the value $h = 1/2\omega$. The lift constant ω is an experimental datum, and cannot be made to disappear from the formulas.

The radius of the semicircles follows from the condition, that in the bottom point the total acceleration shall be v^2/R:

$$v^2/R = -g + \omega v^2.$$

As $v^2 = 2gR$ we find for $R: 3/2\omega$ that is, three times the value of h, found above.

6. *The cycloid as envelope and as caustic*

We shall now demonstrate that the cycloid can be considered as the envelope of all successive positions of the diameter of a circle of radius $p/2$ rolling over a straight line.

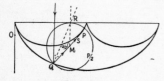
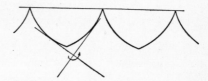

Fig. 237   Fig. 238

Choosing the position of the origin as shown in fig. 237, the centre of the rolling circle will be at $\frac{1}{4} p (u-j)$, if the circle has rotated over an angle $u/2$. The diameter can be represented by:

$$z = -js \exp (j u/2) + \tfrac{1}{4} p (u-j),$$

if s is the distance measured along the diameter. In order to find the envelope we calculate

$$\partial z/\partial s = -j \exp (j u/2) \quad \text{and} \quad \partial z/\partial u = \tfrac{1}{4} p + \tfrac{1}{2} s \exp (j u/2) ;$$

they are parallel if the ratios between the real and between the imaginary parts are equal, which leads to:

$$s = -\tfrac{1}{2} p \cos u/2,$$

This is the tangent point of the diameter to the envelope. Substituting this value into the equation of the diameter yields for the envelope:

$$z = \tfrac{1}{4}\, p \left\{ u + j \exp\left(ju \right) \right\}$$

and this again is the cycloid.

Fig. 238 shows a tooth bar and wheel transmission based on this geometrical property of the cycloid.

The extremity Q (fig. 237) of the diameter describes a cycloid, the linear dimensions of which are twice those of the envelope, and a light ray coming from above will be reflected by this larger cycloid in the direction of QP. We see, therefore, that the envelope studied above, can be considered as the caustic of the larger cycloid for a light source, at infinity.

CHAPTER XIX

EPI- AND HYPOCYCLOIDS

1. *Introduction*

The generalisation of the normal cycloid leads to the curves described by the points of a *rolling circle* which rolls on a stationary circle (the *pitch* circle). If the rolling circle rolls on the outside of the stationary circle the cycloids generated are *epicycloids*, if it rolls on the inside of the stationary circle they are *hypocycloids*. The normal cycloid may be considered as an epi- or a hypocycloid for an infinite radius of the pitch circle.

The curves described by points not situated on the circle itself but inside or outside it and moving together with the rolling circle are called *epi- and hypotrochoids*. They are also termed lenghthened or shortened cycloids according as to whether the point under consideration is situated outside or inside the rolling circle.

These curves and many of their properties were already known to the Greeks, who gave them the above mentioned names. Both kyklos and trochos mean wheel. In their geocentric conception of the universe the planets moved along cycloids and trochoids. In Western Europe OLE RØMER (1644—1710), a Dane, drew attention to these curves in connection with the problem of admissable gear wheel tooth profiles (1674) (Ch. XXI).

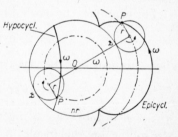

Fig. 239

The cycloids are particularly well suited for a treatment, which uses complex notation. We shall give the rolling circle a radius r and the pitch circle a radius nr. Let the point of contact of pitch circle and rolling circle move on the pitch circle with the angular velocity ω., then the centre of the rolling circle can be represented by: (fig. 239)

$$z_M = (n + 1)\, r \,.\, \exp(j\omega).$$

if we choose it on the real axis at the moment when $\omega = 0$. The angle over which a radius of the rolling circle has turned relatively to its initial direction equals $(n+1)\omega$ and point P of the cycloid therefore is given by:

$$z = (n+1)\,r\,.\,\exp\,(j\omega) + r\,.\,\exp\,(j\,(n+1)\,\omega), \quad . \quad . \quad (1)$$

a formula which holds both for epi- and hypocycloids, if only we attribute a negative value to n in the case of hypocycloids. The constant n can have any real value, even smaller than 1, which only means that the rolling circle is larger than the pitch circle. Hypocycloids with $|n| < 1$ are called *pericycloids*. However, a pericycloid is always identical with an epicycloid. Indeed, by introducing a new parameter $\omega' = (1+n)\,\omega$, the formula (1), in which in the case of a pericycloid $-1 < n < 0$, is transformed into:

$$z = (n+1)\,\{r \exp j\,(\omega'/1+n) + (r/n+1)\,\exp j\omega'\}$$

and this is, apart from the factor $(n+1)$ an epicycloid described by a circle r, rolling on a stationary circle of radius $r/(n+1)$, so that the new ratio between the radii of stationary and rolling circle is $n' = 1/n + 1$ and this a positive value.

For example, the cardioid $(n=1)$ is an epicycloid represented by

$$z = 2p \exp\,(j\omega) + p \exp\,(2j\omega)$$

but this can also be written as a pericycloid $(n = -\frac{1}{2})$

$$z = 2\,\{p \exp\,(j\,\omega'/2) + \tfrac{1}{2}\,p \exp\,(j\omega')\}$$

(with $\omega' = 2\omega$.), this being the track of a point of a rolling circle $2p$ rolling on the inside of a stationary circle p.

For n equal to 0, the rolling circle is infinitely large and the cycloid will be identical with the circle evolvente.

If n is a whole number, the cycloid will repeat itself after the centre of the rolling circle has described one complete revolution round the pitch circle. If n is a rational fraction a/b, the cycloid will consist of a arcs all of which will have been described after b revolutions of the centre of the rolling circle round the pitch circle.

In order to describe a trochoid the ratio between the two

amplitudes in (1) need not be the same as the ratio between the arguments of the two exponentials, so that any curve:

$$z = p \exp (j\omega) + q \exp \{ j (n+1) \omega \} \quad . \quad . \quad . \quad . \quad (2)$$

will be a trochoid. We see, therefore, that the ellipse (Ch. VII)

$$z = \tfrac{1}{2} (a+b) \exp (ju) + \tfrac{1}{2} (a-b) \exp (-j\omega)$$

is a trochoid, $n = -2$.

A curve:

$$z = a_0 + a_1 \exp (jn_1 \omega) + \ldots + a_i \exp (jn_i \omega)$$

will be called a trochoid of higher order or a *hypertrochoid*. The constant a_0 is of no importance for the nature of the curve as it only means a shifting of the origin.

A remarkable hypertrochoid is:

$$z = \exp (j\omega) + \tfrac{1}{3} \exp (3j\omega) + \tfrac{1}{5} \exp (5j\omega) + \ldots \text{ in inf.} = \tfrac{1}{2} \lg j \cotan \omega/2.$$

which is the same curve as $z = \tfrac{1}{2} \lg ju$, namely a set of horizontal parallel lines, compare p. 201.

We have still to prove the above equality of the series and the right-hand member. To this end we write:

$$\lg (1+z) = \quad z - z^2/2 + z^3/3 - z^4/4 \ldots\ldots\ldots \text{in inf.}$$

$$\lg (1-z) = -z - z^2/2 - z^3/3 - z^4/4 \ldots\ldots \text{ in inf.}$$

$$\overline{\hspace{9cm}} \text{ subtract}$$

$$\tfrac{1}{2} \lg (1+z)/(1-z) = z + z^3/3 + z^5/5 \ldots\ldots \text{ in inf.}$$

and for $z = \exp (j\omega)$ this is equivalent with $\tfrac{1}{2} \lg j \cotan \omega/2$.

2. *Natural equation, evolute*

The tangent of the cycloids is found by differentiation of (1):

$$\dot{z} = j (n+1) r \{ \exp (j\omega) + \exp (j (n+1) \omega) \} \quad . \quad . \quad (3)$$

from which we find for an arc length element:

$$\dot{s} = |\dot{z}| = \sqrt{\dot{z} \dot{z}^*} = 2 (n+1) r \cos (\tfrac{1}{2} n \omega)$$

and for the arc length, by integration with respect to ω:

$$s = 4 \frac{n+1}{n} r \sin (\tfrac{1}{2} n\omega).$$

The length of one arc of the curve is found by introducing the values $\pm \pi/n$ for the limits of the integral, which gives

$$l = 8\,\frac{n+1}{n}\,r$$

a formula which applies to a number of important curves, which together with their lengths are collected in the following table:

Epicycloids : $n = \infty$; normal cycloid   ; $l = 8r$
              2 ; nephroid (fig. 243)   ; $12r$
              1 ; cardioid (fig. 242)   ; $16r$
            $\frac{1}{2}$; double cardioid   ; $24r$
            0 ; evolvente   ; ∞

Hypocycloids : -1 ; contact point   ; 0
           -2 ; diameter   ; $4r$
          $-\frac{5}{2}$; sandstar (fig. 241)   ; $\frac{24}{5}r$
          -3 ; deltoid (fig. 240)   ; $\frac{16}{3}r$
          -4 ; astroid (fig. 171, p. 178) $6r$.

As to the direction of $\dot z$, it is interesting to compare it with the vector from P to the contact point B of pitch circle and rolling circle $z_{\mathrm{B}} = nr \exp (j\omega)$. This vector is: (fig. 239)

$$z_{\mathrm{P}} - z_{\mathrm{B}} = r\left\{\exp (j\omega) + \exp j\,(n+1)\,\omega\right\}$$

and differs from $\dot z$ by an imaginary constant. This vector, therefore, is the normal and this result is evident from a kinematic point of view, as the contact point B acts as the instantaneous centre of rotation of the rolling circle.

By elementary methods we can find from fig. 239 that the length of PB equals

$$2r \cos (\tfrac{1}{2}\, n\, \omega).$$

Now, by using the general formula for it, we readily find the radius of curvature of the cycloid to be:

$$\varrho = 4\,(n + 1/n + 2)\,r \cos (\tfrac{1}{2}\, n\omega),$$

from which we see that this radius is cut by the pitch circle in the ratio $(n+2)/n$. This ratio is indicated in fig. 240 to 243; for the normal cycloid $(n = \infty)$ this ratio is 1, as we saw already in the preceding chapter.

Comparing the expressions found for the arc length s and the radius of curvature ϱ we find that their relation is

$$s^2/a^2 + \varrho^2/b^2 = 1 \quad ; \quad b/a = (n/n + 2)$$

and this is the natural equation of the cycloids, which for the normal cycloid $(n = \infty)$ leads to:

$$s^2 + \varrho^2 = \text{constant.}$$

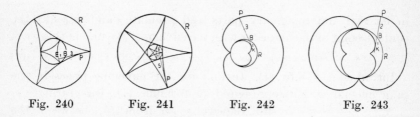

Fig. 240   Fig. 241   Fig. 242   Fig. 243

By applying the well-known recipe for finding the equation of the evolute we obtain:

$$z_{\text{evolute}} = \frac{n+2}{n} \{(n+1)r \exp j\omega - r \exp (j(n+1)\omega)\}.$$

This curve is similar to the original cycloid; the amplification factor is $(n+2)/n$. The minus sign before the second term means that the evolute is shifted over a half arc length with respect to the original curve. Compare fig. 240 to 243, where the evolutes are inserted into the figures. For $n = \infty$ (normal cycloid) the evolute is congruent to the original curve. Of course, all higher evolutes and also the first and higher evolventes are similar to the original cycloid and this is one of the most striking properties of this class of curves.

3. *The cycloids as envelopes*

Just as in the case of the normal cycloid we may ask whether the general cycloid can be considered as the envelope of the successive positions of the diameter of a rolling circle of radius $2r$. This appears indeed to be so. The centre of this rolling circle is given by (fig. 244):

$$z(C) = (n+2)r \exp (j\omega)$$

and the slope of the diameter, which was vertical in the position $\omega = 0$ will now be $\pi/2 + (1 + n/2)\,\omega$.

Introducing the parameter s along the diameter, this will be represented by:

$$z = (n + 2)\,r \exp{(j\omega)} + js \exp{(j\,(1 + n/2)\,\omega)} \quad . \quad . \quad (4)$$

where the factor j in the second term stands for $\exp{(j\,\pi/2)}$.

In order to find the envelope we split up the equation:

$$dz = 0$$

in its real and imaginary parts and calculate s and $\partial s/\partial\omega$ for the contact point of the diameter with the envelope. We find in this way:

$$s = r \sin{(\tfrac{1}{2}\,n\omega)} \;\; ; \;\; \partial s/\partial\omega = -\,(n + 2)\,r \cos{(\tfrac{1}{2}\,n\omega)}. \quad . \quad (5)$$

Introducing s into (4), we find for the envelope precisely the same cycloid as that represented by formula (1). Integrating the slip velocity $\partial s/\partial\omega$ from (5) between the limits $-\pi/n$ and $+\pi/n$ we find for the total slip:

$$4\,\frac{n + 2}{n}\,r$$

which, augmented by the length $4r$ of the diameter, gives a value

$$l = 8\,\frac{n + 1}{n}\,r$$

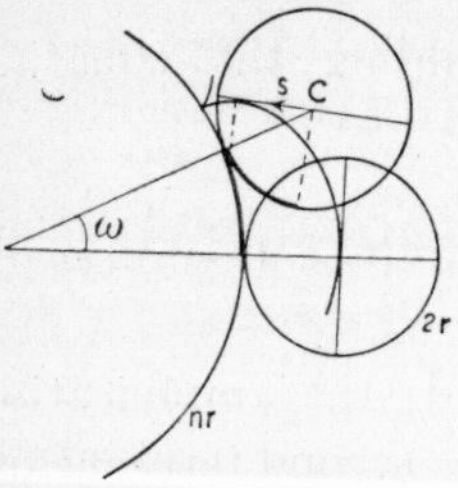

Fig. 244

for the length of the arc, in accordance with the result found in the last section.

The classical cases of the generation of envelopes, treated in Ch. XIII may all be considered as special cases of the present subject. The sliding ladder enveloping the astroid may be considered as the diameter of a circle of radius r, rolling within a circle of radius $2r$. The nephroid is enveloped by the diameter of a circle of radius r, rolling on a stationary circle of the same radius r, while the cardioid is enveloped by the diameter of a circle $2r$ rolling on a circle r.

4. Deltoid

The hypocycloid $n = -\,3$ with three cusps owes its importance to Jacob Steiner's (1796—1863) studies. We saw already in

Ch. IV that it is in a curious way connected with the triangle.
It is described by a point of a rolling circle of radius $R/2$ rolling
inside a stationary circle of radius $3R/2$. But it is also possible
to consider it as the hypocycloid of the order $n = -3/2$, in which
case it is described by a point of a rolling circle of radius R.
By this circle it is described three times (fig. 245). The opposite
points A and B of the rolling circle R
describe the same hypocycloid, but this same
hypocycloid is also generated as the envelope
of the positions of the diameter AB (tangent
point C). We see, therefore, that all tangents
of the cycloid have the same length $2R$
between the two points of intersection with
the curve and that the middles M of these
tangent chords are all situated on a circle
of radius $R/2$. This circle will be called

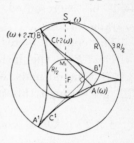

Fig. 245

Feuerbach's circle and its centre F *Feuerbach's point*. If M is
represented by $R/2 \exp (j\omega)$, the inclination of the tangent BA
will be $-\omega/2$.

If the rolling circle R proceeds over an angle $\triangle\omega$, the diameter
AB turns over an angle $-\triangle\omega/2$ and when M has arrived at the
position opposite its initial one on Feuerbach's circle, the
diameter, now in the position A'B', will be normal to AB. These
two normal tangents will intersect on Feuerbach's circle:
Feuerbach's circle is the locus of the points of intersection of
two mutually orthogonal tangents to the deltoid: Feuerbach's
circle is the orthoptic curve.

Point A is represented by the formula:

$$z (\omega) = \tfrac{1}{2} R \exp (j\omega) + R \exp (-j \, \omega/2). \quad . \quad . \quad . \quad (1)$$

Point B can be represented by a similar formula, with a minus
sign before the second term, but it can also be considered as
represented by (1) for the value $\omega + 2\pi$ of the parameter.

The direction of the tangent (argument τ) in point A can be
calculated from (1), giving:

$$\exp (j\tau) = \sqrt{\dot{z}/\dot{z}^*} = \exp j \, \omega/4 \, . \therefore \tau_A = \omega/4.$$

Obviously the direction of the tangent in point B $(\omega + 2\pi)$

will be: $\tau_B = \omega/4 + \pi/2$, which shows that these two tangents are orthogonal (and will meet on Feuerbach's circle) and, conversely, that the tangent points of two mutually orthogonal tangents are the extremities of a third tangent (e.g. points C and C' in fig. 245).

Point C, the tangent point of a tangent with slope $\tau = -\omega/2$ will be represented by form. (1) for the value -2ω of the parameter.

The contact point S of the rolling circle R and the stationary circle $\tfrac{3}{2}R$ is the instantaneous centre of rotation of the rolling circle. The normals to the hypocycloid in A, B and C will therefore all go through this point S.

5. *The deltoid and the orthogonal complete quadrangle*

Let us now take an arbitrary point z_0 inside the cycloid (O from orthocentre) and try to find the tangents passing through O. If $\dot{z}$ is a tangent to the cycloid it must have the same direction as $z - z_0$ if it is to pass through O. The condition therefore is:

$$(z - z_0)/(z^* - z_0^*) = \dot{z}/\dot{z}^*.$$

Introducing z and $\dot{z}$ from (1) this leads to:

$$\exp\left(^3/_2\,j\,\omega\right) - \frac{2z_0^*}{R}\exp\left(j\omega\right) + \frac{2z_0}{R}\exp\left(j\,\omega/2\right) - 1 = 0. \quad . \quad (2)$$

This is an equation of the third order in $\exp\left(j\,\omega/2\right)$, which means that the cycloid is of class 3. Denote the three solutions for ω by ω_1, ω_2 and ω_3, then this equation must be identical with:

$$\left.\begin{array}{c}\left(\exp j\,\omega/2 - \exp j\,\omega_1/2\right)\left(\exp j\,\omega/2 - \exp j\,\omega_2/2\right) \times \\ \times \left(\exp j\,\omega/2 - \exp j\,\omega_3/2\right) = 0\end{array}\right\} \quad . \quad (3)$$

Equating the coefficients of the corresponding powers of $\exp\left(j\,\omega/2\right)$ of (2) and (3) gives us:

$$\exp\left(j\,\omega_1/2\right) + \exp\left(j\,\omega_2/2\right) + \exp\left(j\,\omega_3/2\right) = 2\,z_0^*/R$$

$$\exp\left(-j\,\omega_1/2\right) + \exp\left(-j\,\omega_2/2\right) + \exp\left(-j\,\omega_3/2\right) = 2z_0/R$$

$$\exp j\left(\omega_1/2\right) . \exp\left(j\,\omega_2/2\right) . \exp\left(j\,\omega_3/2\right) = 1.$$

The last equation teaches us:

$$\tfrac{1}{2}\left(\omega_1 + \omega_2 + \omega_3\right) = 0 \ (\mathrm{mod.}\ 2\pi),$$

or, in words: the sum of the inclinations of three concurrent tangents, $\frac{1}{4}\Sigma\omega_i$ is zero, mod. π.

The second equation shows how z_0 is built up from three vectors e_1, e_2, e_3, each of length $R/2$ and having the directions $-\omega_1/2$; $-\omega_2/2$ and $-\omega_3/2$.

Denote the tangent points by C_1, C_2, C_3. Now, as C_1 is characterized by the value ω_1 of the parameter the point $\exp{(-j\omega_1/2)}$ will be the middle of the tangent in C_1 and will

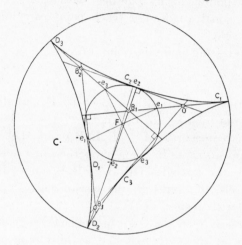

Fig. 246

lie on Feuerbach's circle and the three vectors $e_i = \frac{1}{2}R\exp{(-j\omega_i/2)}$, have simple geometric meanings. The vector FO is the vectorsum of these three vectors, (fig. 246).

Now draw the tangents orthogonal to the tangents in C_1 and C_2. They will be characterized by the ω values $\omega_1 + 2\pi$ and $\omega_2 + 2\pi$. Now again:

$$\tfrac{1}{2}(\omega_1 + 2\pi) + \tfrac{1}{2}(\omega_2 + 2\pi) + \tfrac{1}{2}\omega_3 = 0 \ (\text{mod. } 2\pi)$$

and the corresponding tangents will again be concurrent (fig. 246 point B_3). In the same way we find that:

$$\tfrac{1}{2}(\omega_1 + 2\pi) + \tfrac{1}{2}\omega_2 + \tfrac{1}{2}(\omega_3 + 2\pi) = 0 \ (\text{mod. } 2\pi)$$
$$\tfrac{1}{2}\omega_1 + \tfrac{1}{2}(\omega_2 + 2\pi) + \tfrac{1}{2}(\omega_3 + 2\pi) = 0 \ (\text{mod. } 2\pi)$$

leading to points B_1 and B_2.

As $\exp\left(-\tfrac{1}{2} j\left(\omega_i + 2\pi\right)\right) = -\exp\left(-\tfrac{1}{2} j\,\omega_i\right) =$ argument function of point $- e_i$ the location of the points will be:

$$O \; : \; (e_1 + e_2 + e_3)$$
$$B_1 \; : \; (+ e_1 - e_2 - e_3)$$
$$B_2 \; : \; (- e_1 + e_2 - e_3)$$
$$B_3 \; : \; (- e_1 - e_2 + e_3)$$

These four points form together with the six tangents a complete orthogonal quadrangle, each point carrying three sides of the quadrangle.

Another interesting point is point C:

$$C \; : \; - e_1 - e_2 - e_3$$

lying symmetrically to O with respect to F and differing from all three B-points by a vector of length $2\,|e| = R$. Point C, therefore, is the circumcentre of $\triangle\, B_1 B_2 B_3$ and the radius of the circumcircle appears to be R. As O plays the same role as the three points $B_1 B_2 B_3$ the triangles $OB_1 B_2$, $OB_2 B_3$ and $OB_3 B_1$ will also have circumcircles of radius R, the circumcentres lying opposite the points B_i with respect to F.

We have already seen that two orthogonal tangents have their tangent points at the extremities of a third tangent. The sides of the triangle $B_1 B_2 B_3$, therefore, touch the cycloid in points D_1, D_2, D_3 which lie on one tangent with C_1, C_2, C_3 respectively.

The middle of $B_1 B_2$ is represented by

$$z = \tfrac{1}{2} z_{B_1} + \tfrac{1}{2} z_{B_2} = - e_3$$

and will be a point of Feuerbach's circle. So are the middles of $B_2 B_3$ and $B_3 B_1$. The middle of OB_1 lies also on this circle, as it is represented by

$$\tfrac{1}{2} z_0 + \tfrac{1}{2} z_{B_1} = e_1$$

and the same can be said of the middles of the sides OB_2 and OB_3.

As we know already, two mutually orthogonal tangents will also intersect on Feuerbach's circle.

FEUERBACH'S circle, therefore, carries nine particular points of the quadrangle and is therefore also known by the name of „nine points circle". (fig. 246).

The centre of gravity of $\triangle\, B_1 B_2 B_3$ is given by

$$z_G = 1/3\ (z_{B_1} + z_{B_2} + z_{B_3}) = -\,{}^1/_3\ (e_1 + e_2 + e_3)$$

so that it lies on the line OC and divides it in the ratio 2 : 1; the distance CF is also divided in the same ratio.

Conversely, it is possible to start from any triangle $B_1 B_2 B_3$ for the construction of the corresponding cycloid. First find Feuerbach's point F in the triangle and the three vectors from F to the middles of the three sides. Let these vectors be $\frac{1}{2}\,R \exp\,(j\,\omega_1/2)$; $\frac{1}{2}\,R \exp\,(j\,\omega_2/2)$ and $R/2 \exp\,(j\,\omega_3/2)$ respectively. Then turn the triangle round F, in other words, add an equal amount to all ω_i's until $\varSigma\omega_i = 0$. The corresponding cycloid will then be the curve represented by (1).

6. *Projective properties of the deltoid*

The condition $\omega_1 + \omega_2 + \omega_3 = 0$ for the concurrency of the tangents in three points characterized by the parameter values ω_1, ω_2 and ω_3 reminds us of the condition

$$u_1 + u_2 + u_3 = 0$$

for the collinearity of three points on a cubic (Ch. VI).

Indeed, the deltoid being of the third class and fourth order is the dual transform of a cubic of the fourth class.

All projective properties found for third order curves in Ch. VI will be valid for the deltoid in the dual translation.

For example: the deltoid will occasionally be enveloped by the lines connecting a linear point series with a projective point involution on an other straight line, the two carrier lines being tangents to the cycloid. For let point O describe the tangent ω_1. Draw in each position of O the two remaining tangents ω_2 and ω_3 passing through O. ($\omega_1 + \omega_2 + \omega_3 = 0$) (mod. 4π). The points of intersection of these two tangents with an arbitrary fourth tangent ω_4 will cut out an involution on ω_4, if O describes ω_1 and this involution will be projective to the point series O on ω_1. The double points of the involution correspond to the points of intersection of ω_1 with the cycloid, the two ,,double rays'' therefore are mutually orthogonal. The points of intersection of ω_2 and ω_3 with ω_4 lie harmonically with respect to these two points; the double points being characterized by: ω_4, $-\frac{1}{2}\omega_1$, $\frac{1}{2}\omega_1 - \omega_4$ and by ω_4, $2\pi - \omega_1/2$, $\omega_1/2 - 2\pi - \omega_4$.

Through each point of ω_4 belonging to a pair of the involution, passes a third tangent. These tangents are respectively characterized by

$$-\omega_2 - \omega_4 \quad \text{and} \quad -\omega_3 - \omega_4$$

and will be concurrent (point O') with the tangent.

$$\omega' = \omega_2 + \omega_3 + 2\omega_4 = 2\omega_4 - \omega_1$$

which is independent of the choice of ω_2 and ω_3. As $\omega' - \omega_4 = \omega_4 - \omega_1$, the tangents ω' and ω_1 make equal angles with ω_4. The point series O' on ω' and O on ω_1 will be projective; they are even congruent because the extremities of ω' correspond to the extremities of ω_1 and because ω' and ω_1 have equal lengths.

Another theorem: Choose three concurrent tangents (point O), the tangent points being C_1, C_2, C_3. Draw from all points C_i the remaining tangent, these three are concurrent.

We may consider this theorem to be proved by the dual theorem of Ch. VI. We can, however, prove it also directly as follows. For the three concurrent tangents we have:

$$\omega_1 + \omega_2 + \omega_3 = 0.$$

For the tangents in points C_1, C_2 and C_3, we have respectively:

$$2\omega_1 + \omega_1' = 0$$
$$2\omega_2 + \omega_2' = 0$$
$$2\omega_3 + \omega_3' = 0$$

and on adding we see that also

$$\omega_1' + \omega_2' + \omega_3' = 0$$

and this means that these three tangents are concurrent. Let the point be O', it is characterized by:

$$\omega_1' = -\tfrac{1}{2}\omega_1 \ ; \ \omega_2' = -\tfrac{1}{2}\omega_2 \ ; \ \omega_3' = -\tfrac{1}{2}\omega_3$$

and it can be constructed along the lines found earlier for O.

7. *Roses*

The curves represented by

$$z = 2r \cos n\omega \exp (j\omega)$$

are called *roses*. The modulus changes sinussoidically if the argument ω increases at an uniform rate, so that the curve consists of a number of leaves. By writing $\cos n\omega$ as a sum of two exponentials the formula takes the form:

$$z = r\{\exp (j(1+n)\omega) + \exp (j(1-n)\omega)\}$$

which shows that the roses are trochoids; they are often called *star-trochoids*. As n is arbitrary and $m\omega'$ may be substituted for ω, any trochoid:

$$z = A\{\exp (jv_1 \omega) + \exp (jv_2 \omega)\}$$

will be a rose, $n = (v_1 - v_2)/(v_1 + v_2)$.

Examples:

$n = 1.$ $z = r\{\exp (2j\omega) + 1\}$

Fig. 247

This is a circle.

$n = 2.$ $z = r\{\exp (3j\omega) + \exp (-j\omega)\}$

This curve is called the fourleaved clover (fig. 247).

$u = 3.$ $z = r\{\exp (4j\omega) + \exp (-2j\omega)\}$

Fig. 248

and this is the three-leaved clover or trefoil (fig. 248).

The clover curves are of frequent occurrence when plotting tensor properties of ternary or quaternary cristals, for example the piezo-electric characteristic of quartz is represented by a three-leaved clover.

$n = 1/3.$ $z = r\{(\exp (\tfrac{4}{3}j\omega) + \exp \tfrac{2}{3}(j\omega)\}$

and this is a limaçon. Indeed, the limaçon in general is the conchoidal transform of a circle for a pole lying on the circle. If, therefore, this circle is represented by:

$$z = 2r \cos \omega \exp (j\omega)$$

the equation for the limaçon will be:

$$z = (2r \cos \omega + l) \exp j\omega .$$

Now, shift the origin to the centre of the circle, that is to say, subtract r, then the equation of the limaçon becomes:

$$z = r \exp (2j\omega) + l \exp (j\omega)$$

and if, finally, we choose $l = r$, this represents a rose, as the change of the parameter from ω to $2\omega/3$ does not change the shape of the curve (fig. 249).

Theorem: The roses are the pedals of the cycloids. Let the cycloid be given by

$$z = (\mu + 1) r \exp (j\omega) + r \exp (j(\mu + 1) \omega).$$

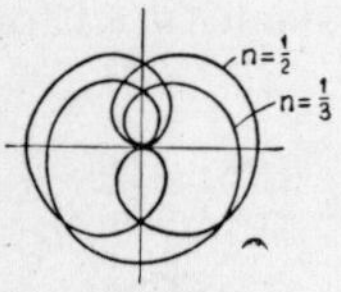

By applying the general formula of the pedal we find:

Fig. 249

$$z_p = (\mu/2 + 1) r \{\exp j\omega + \exp j\,(\mu + 1)\,\omega\}$$

and this represents a rose with $n = \mu/(\mu + 2)$; tabulated for the various cycloids:

Cycloid		*Pedal*	
circle	$\mu = 0$	$n = 0$	circle
nephroid	1	$\frac{1}{3}$	limaçon
caustic	2	$\frac{1}{2}$	two ears (fig. 249)
deltoid	-3	3	threeleaved clover
astroid	-4	2	fourleaved clover

CHAPTER XX

CARDIOID AND LIMAÇON

1. *Various properties and applications of the cardioid*

One of the most important epicycloids is the cardioid to which we shall now devote a separate chapter. This curve was discovered in the seventeenth century, HUYGENS (1629—1695) being one of the scientists who was particularly interested in its proporties.

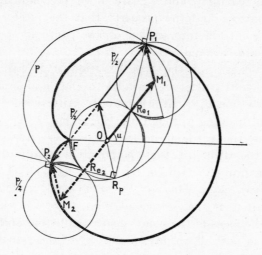

Fig. 250

The cardioid is described by a point of a circle rolling on a stationary circle, the pitch circle, of the same radius $(p/2)$ as the rolling circle (fig. 250); p will be called the parameter of the cardioid. The curve has one cusp, which we shall call the focus (F in fig. 250). Choosing the origin in the centre of the pitch circle, the equation is:

$$z = p \exp (ju) + \tfrac{1}{2} p \exp (2ju) \quad . \quad . \quad . \quad . \quad (1)$$

If we commute the two terms and try to interpret z again as representing a cycloid this leads to the conception of the cardioid as the pericycloid described by a point of a rolling circle of radius p, rolling along the inside of a stationary circle of radius $p/2$. The instantaneous tangent point of both circles is denoted by R_p in fig. 250, while R_e is the tangent point corresponding to the same point P if we consider the cardioid as an epicycloid. As R_e and R_p act as instantaneous centres of rotation, they must both be situated on the normal to the cardioid in point P.

As the circle p travels twice completely round the pitch circle during the generation of the cardioid, we find two points, P_1 and P_2 corresponding to the same tangent point R_p and these points lie diametrically opposite each other on the circle p. The two normals, erected in P_1 and P_2, are in R_p perpendicular to each other, so that we find the property that the pitch circle is the locus of the points of intersection of two mutually perpendicular normals to the cardioid.

From the fact that the arcs FR_{e_2} and $P_2R_{e_2}$ are equal we conclude that FP_2 must be parallel to OM_2 and must therefore be part of the line P_1P_2. In other words: Any chord drawn in the cardioid and passing through the focus has a constant length $2p$ and cuts the cardioid in two points so situated that the tangents to the cardioid in these points are mutually perpendicular.

One more property can be read from fig. 250. The chord P_1P_2 is cut into two equal parts by the pitch circle and this leads to the formulation of the *conchoidal property* of the cardioid: The cardioid is the locus of the points generated by measuring constant distances p in both directions on any ray of the pencil F, starting from the second point of intersection of the ray with a circle of radius $p/2$, F being situated on the circle.

The direct analytical proof of this conchoidal property is given by shifting the origin to the focus:

$$z = \tfrac{1}{2}\,p + p \exp\,(ju) + p/2 \exp\,(2ju) \quad . \quad . \quad . \quad . \quad (2)$$

$$= (p \cos u + p) \exp ju. \quad . \quad . \quad . \quad . \quad . \quad . \quad . \quad (3)$$

See fig. 251, where $p \cos u$ is the intercept of the ray cut off by the pitch circle; p is the prolongation of constant length beyond the pitch circle.

We speak of *cardioid microphones* or *cardioid aerial* systems, if their sensitivity distribution in space is represented by a cardioid. For a monopole microphone or aerial this distribution is uniform: $p \exp ju$, for a dipole system it obeys the cosine law: $p \cdot \cos u \cdot \exp ju$. The combination of the two produces a cardioidal curve according to equ.3.

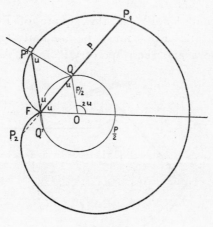

Fig. 251

In general we find for the tangent to the cardioid form. (1):

$$\dot{z} = jp\{\exp(ju) + \exp(2ju)\}$$

the argument factor of which is:

$$\exp(j\tau) = \sqrt{\frac{j\{\exp(ju) + \exp(2ju)\}}{-j\{\exp(-ju) + \exp(-2ju)\}}} = j\exp(j\tfrac{3}{2}u),$$

which means that the slope of the normal in point $P(u)$ amounts to $\tfrac{3}{2}u$.

The interpretation of equ. (1) that z is the addition of the vector $p \exp ju$, drawn from O to M (fig. 250) and the vector $\tfrac{1}{2} p \exp 2ju$ from M to point P of the cardioid is once again shown in fig. 252. If, now, we take into account that the normal in P has the slope $\tfrac{3}{2} u$ we may infer that a light ray incident horizontally from the right hand side will be reflected, as shown in fig. 252, towards the point F. This use of the cardioid for the production of an anastigmatic image was invented by SIEDENTOPF (1908). He called this apparatus the *cardioid condensor*.

Equ. (3) shows that the argument of the vector FP equals u; by measuring in fig. 251 the angle $2u$ at F we come to point $P'(2u)$ of the cardioid.

From (2) we find for P':

$$z\,(2u) = \tfrac{1}{2}\,p\,\{\,1 + \exp\,(2\,ju)\,\}^2.$$

which shows that $\tfrac{1}{2}\,p.\mathrm{FP'}$ is the square of FQ, so that the triangles FP'Q and FQO must be similar. The angle FP'Q, therefore, is also u and the slope of QP' is $3u$. As this is $\tfrac{3}{2}$ times

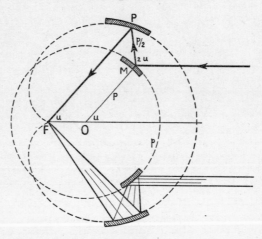

Fig. 252

the value of the parameter in P', $P'Q$ must be a normal to the cardioid.

Two points of the cardioid have mutually orthogonal tangents (or mutually orthogonal normals) if their parameters differ by $\pi/3$. As the argument of the vector FP equals the parameter, three rays through F making angles $\pi/3$ with each other will cut the cardioid in six points where the normals are either parallel or mutually orthogonal (fig. 253). Two special cases are represented in fig. 255 and 256, showing remarkable regularities. From fig. 253 we deduce that the three rays passing through F and making angles of $\pi/3$ with each other cut the pitch circle in three points, lying $2\pi/3$ arc degrees apart and forming an equilateral triangle. So do the three points R, where two mutually orthogonal normals intersect and which are situated on the pitch circle opposite to the three points mentioned above. Fig. 254 may be illustrative in this repect.

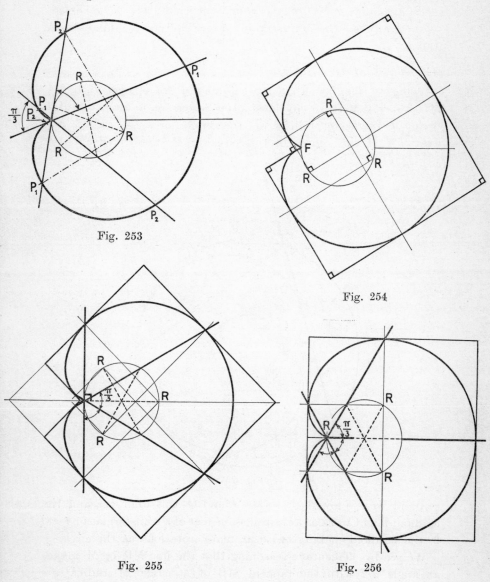

Fig. 253

Fig. 254

Fig. 255

Fig. 256

Various properties of the cardioid have already been mentioned in earlier chapters. Its evolute is similar and three times as small, whereas the involute is also similar but three times as large. The total perimeter is $8\,p$, the area is $3/2\;\pi\;p^2$, that is, six times the area of the pitch circle. Owing to the fact that the cardioid is an algebraic curve of the fourth order it can be generated synthetically as the intersection of two projective involutions. And so on.

2.   *The cardioid as caustic*

Owing to the fact that the cardioid is an epicycloid it has the property that it envelops all positions of a diameter of a circle of radius p, rolling on the pitch circle of radius $p/2$. Fig. 257. If the centre of this circle p, M, were fixed and the

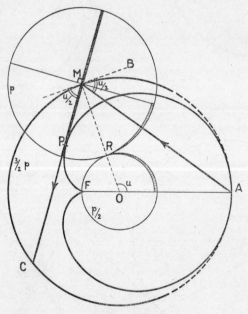

Fig. 257

cardioid were allowed to rotate round O ,this diameter and the cardioid might work as a transmission gear of a transformation ratio 2, the cardioid making twice as many rotations as the circle p.

We see by elementary reasoning that the line MP in M makes an angle $u/2$ with the tangent MB of a circle of radius $\tfrac{3}{2}\,p$ having O as centre and this tangent makes the same angle with the line AM, where A is the top of the cardioid. If this circle $\frac{1}{2}\,p$ is a mirror, all rays coming from A will be reflected tangent to the cardioid, so that the cardioid is the caustic of the circle. This was proved already in Ch. XIII.

If two mutually perpendicular rays start from A they will be reflected at points B and D, situated diametrically opposite each other on the circle $\frac{1}{2}\,p$ (fig. 258) and after reflection meet again in a point C, again on the circle $\frac{3}{2}\,p$. The circle $\frac{3}{2}\,p$ is part of the orthoptic curve.

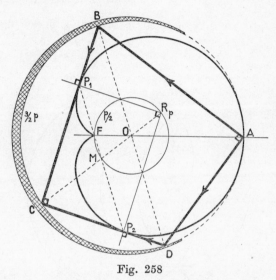

Fig. 258

The normals in the tangent points to the cardioid, P_1 and P_2 will also be mutually perpendicular and intersect in point R_p of the pitch circle (compare fig. 250). Again by comparing fig. 250 we know that P_1P_2 passes through the focus F and that $P_1M = MP_2$. M is, therefore, the centre of the rectangle $P_1R_pP_2C$ and lies on the diagonal CR_p. As MR_p must also be equal to p, MR_p must be the diameter of the pitch circle and contain the point O. All these interrelations are shown in fig. 258.

3. *Cardioid as inversion of parabola*

Starting from equ.(2) in the form.:

$$z = \tfrac{1}{2}\,p\,\{1 + \exp\,(ju)\}^2$$

we transform this by the parameter transformation

$$u = \tan v/2$$

into the algebraic form:

$$z = \frac{-2p}{(v+j)^2}$$

by which we discover that the cardioid is the inversion of the parabola:

$$z = -\tfrac{1}{2}\, p\, (v-j)^2$$

with respect to an inversion circle of radius p. See fig. 259. F is

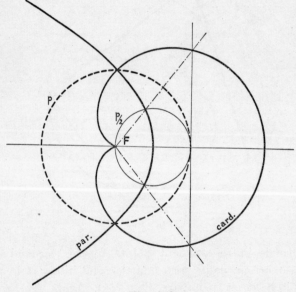

Fig. 259

focus for both parabola and cardioid. The pitch circle is inverted into the directrix of the parabola. For $v = \pm 1$ both curves assume the values $z = \pm jp$; they intersect on the imaginary axis. The slope τ in this point follows for both from

$$\exp{(2j\tau)} = \pm\, \frac{1-j}{1+j} = \pm j$$

hence $\tau = \pm \pi/4$.

By this inversion relation it is easy to find properties of one
of the two curves by simply translating known properties of
the second one. It must be kept in mind that straight lines are
inverted to circles passing through F (F-circles) and the reverse
and that angles are left unchanged by the inversion.

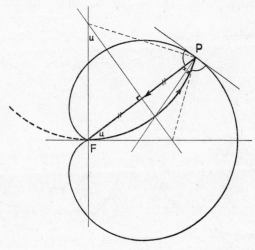

Fig. 260

Fig. 260 shows the inversion of the well-known reflection law
of the parabola. A horizontal ray is reflected by the parabola
towards the focus F. The inversion of the horizontal ray is an
F-circle tangent to the horizontal axis and the inversion of a ray
through F is again a ray through F. Circle FP and ray FP make
equal angles with the normal to the cardioid in P.

Another theorem states that two mutually orthogonal tangents
to the parabola intersect in a point of the directrix. The inversion
of this theorem is (fig. 261) that two mutually orthogonal F-
circles tangent to the cardioid intersect in a point of the pitch
circle.

A third theorem states that the base of a perpendicular let
down from the focus on a tangent of the parabola lies on the
top-tangent. Inversely (fig. 262): the diametrically opposite point
to F of any tangent F-circle of the cardioid lies on the top
tangent F-circle (of radius p).

We may note in passing that the centres M of all these circles lie on the pitch circle (radius $p/2$).

There is another relation between the cardioid and the top tangent F-circle. The cardioid is the pedal of the latter. This was already shown in Ch. XI. This property is shown separately in the lower part of fig. 262 and in the upper part it means that

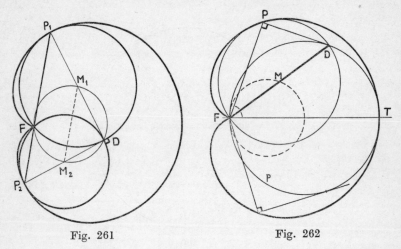

Fig. 261   Fig. 262

PD is tangent to the circle p. This may be proved in an other way by observing that $\angle\,\mathrm{TFD} = \angle\,\mathrm{DFP}$, which is the inversion of the parabola property that the perpendicular let down from F onto the tangent (FD) bisects the angle between the two lines connecting F with the top and the tangent point. Owing to this equality of angles, arc FD and $\angle\,\mathrm{PDF}$ are both complements of the same quantity and therefore PD must be a tangent to the circle p.

Let us also try to find a new theorem for the parabola by inverting the cardioid property shown in fig. 253, 254, 255 and 256. It can be put as follows: Mutually orthogonal F-circles tangent to the parabola will touch the parabola in six points which are projected from the focus by rays making angles of $\pi/3$ with each other.

4.   *Application to electrical circuit theory*

Again, by virtue of its algebraic character, the cardioid will

occur as impedance contour or as contour representing the complex
ratio of two voltages or currents, always with the angular
frequency ω acting as parameter. Take for instance, the series
connection of a resistance R, a selfinduction L and a condensor C,
connected to a voltage U of the main. The ratio of the voltage
of the selfinduction to that of the main will be:

$$\frac{U_L}{U} = \frac{j\omega L}{R + j\omega L + 1/j\omega C} = \frac{\omega^2 LC}{\omega^2 LC - j\omega RC - 1}.$$

Now give R the special value $2\sqrt{L/C}$, then:

$$\frac{U_L}{U} = \frac{-1}{(j+v)^2} \text{ with } v = \frac{1}{\omega\sqrt{LC}}$$

and this is a cardioid (fig. 263). For the voltage on the condensor
we find, again for $R = 2\sqrt{L/C}$:

$$\frac{U_C}{U} = \frac{1/j\omega C}{R + j\omega L + 1/j\omega C} = \frac{1}{2j\omega\sqrt{LC} - \omega^2 LC + 1}$$

and this is:

$$\frac{U_C}{U} = \frac{-1}{(-1/v + j)^2}$$

which is represented by the same cardioid, see fig. 263. The third
partial voltage, that of the resistance, is:

$$\frac{U_R}{U} = \frac{R}{R - jL + 1/j\omega C} = \frac{2jv}{(v+j)^2}$$

and runs through the toptangent F-circle.

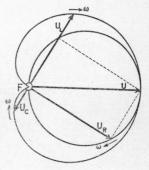

Fig. 263

U_L and U_C have opposite directions;
in general the parameter values v and
$1/v$ mark opposite points on the cardioid,
The part of the U_L vector intercepted
between the toptangent F-circle and the
cardioid has the same absolute value as
U_C, a geometrical property of the cardioid not mentioned up to now.

Another reason why the cardioid appears in electrotechnics is
its being the square of the curve

$$z = 1/(v + j),$$

which is a circle. Now the complex ratio of output- to input voltage of an amplification can often be represented by this circle. The result of the amplification by two steps in cascade is then represented by a cardioid, if there is no back coupling.

5. *Pascal's limaçon*

Pascal's limaçon is in more than one respect the generalization of the cardioid. We shall introduce the limaçon as a circle-conchoid with the conchoidal origin on the circle itself. Let the base circle again have the radius $p/2$ and denote the arbitrary constant prolongation of all rays by l. The limaçon is then represented (compare equ. 3, p. 258) by the formula:

$$z = (p \cos u + l) \exp ju$$

and the cardioid is the special case where $l = p$.

Substituting exponentials for the cosine, this can also be written in the form:

$$z = \tfrac{1}{2} p + l \exp (ju) + \tfrac{1}{2} p \exp (2ju).$$

The first term drops if we take the centre of the base circle

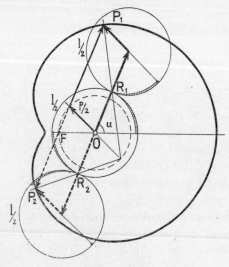

Fig. 264

as the origin and what remains is the equation of a trochoid (fig. 264). The radius of both the pitch circle and the rolling circle is $l/2$ and the limaçon is generated by a point inside the rolling circle at a distance $p/2$ from its centre. As shown in fig. 264 many properties of the cardioid are shared by the limaçon. The chord P_1P_2 passes through the focus F and all chords through F have the constant length $2l$. The normal in P goes through the instantaneous tangent point R of pitch circle and rolling circle and the normals of the two „opposite" points P_1 and P_2 intersect on the base circle of radius $p/2$, but not at a right angle as was the case for the cardioid.

A third way to consider the limaçon as a generalization of the cardioid is to conceive of it as a pedal of a circle, but now the origin does not lie on the circle itself as we assumed in the case where the cardioid turned out to be the pedal. In our case the circle is of radius l and has its centre M at a distance p from F (fig. 265).

A fourth generalization occurs if we consider the limaçon to be the inversion of a conic

$$z = \frac{\exp ju}{p \cos u + l}$$

which is a parabola if $l = p$; it will be an ellipse for $l > p$ (as in the fig. 264 and 265), and a hyperbola if we choose $l < p$.

Let us ask now, where in the figure of the limaçon we find the inversion of the second focus of the ellipse. Let F′ be the point in question. A circle through F′ and F will be the inversion of a ray through the second focus of the ellipse. It is reflected by the ellipse towards F and this reflected ray remains a straight line through F after inversion. All circles through F and F′ cut the limaçon at the same angle as does the straight line from F to the point of inter-

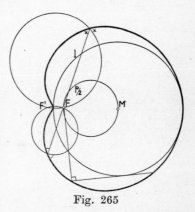

Fig. 265

section (fig. 265), and this property can be used for the construction of the point F′.

The circle l of fig. 265 is the inversion of the major auxiliary circle of the ellipse, which is the pedal of the ellipse for F as origin. We see in this way that the roles of base curve and pedal have been interchanged by the inversion. Compare the general theorem of p. 152. The circle $p/2$ in fig. 265 is the inversion of one of the directrices.

CHAPTER XXI

GEAR WHEEL TOOTH PROFILES

1. *Coupling of epi- and hypocycloids*

In Ch. XIX we found that any epicycloid can be regarded as the envelope of the positions of the diameter of a circle rolling on the fixed circle.

We shall now generalise this result in such a way, that we regard the diameter as a hypocycloid of the rolling circle and try to find the envelope of the positions of a hypocycloid with m arcs within a circle of radius mr rolling on a fixed circle nr. The result will again be an epicycloid.

We can prove this without any calculations by considering the circles nr and mr both as pitch circles, and letting them rotate round their centres O_1 and O_2 and by introducing a circle r as shown in fig. 266. This circle r when rolling on the pitch circle nr would describe an epicycloid, but if we, conversely, rotate the circle nr together with the epicycloid, this will cut the now stationary circle r in a point P that will move over this circle with constant angular velocity so long as the circle nr rotates uniformly.

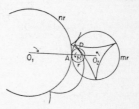

Fig. 266

Circle r would generate a hypocycloid in circle mr if it rolled on it on the inside. Conversely, if we keep circle r fixed but let circle mr rotate together with the hypocycloid, the point of intersection P of hypocycloid and circle r will move on the circle r with constant velocity.

We see in this way that the epicycloid and the hypocycloid will always have the point P in common. But as for both the direction of the normal will be from P to the contact point A, the two cycloids will always be tangent to each other.

If now we keep one of the pitch circles fixed and let the other one roll on it, it will be clear that the epicycloid envelops the consecutive positions of the hypocycloid, q.e.d.

In technical terms, we have here devised a gear wheel tooth coupling. The circle r will be called the contact curve. In practice the teeth are constructed in such a way that the tops are parts of epicycloids and the feet parts of hypocycloids; the contact curve consists in this case of two arcs of two circles (fig. 273).

2. *The general problem*

The question arises whether other profiles of gear wheel teeth apart from cycloidical ones are possible and we shall now proceed to solve the general problem.

What is required is the transformation of a rotation ω round the axis O_1 into a proportional rotation $-(r_1/r_2)\,\omega$ round the axis O_2, r_1 and r_2 being the radii of the two pitch circles, which may eventually be immaterial and have only a geometrical meaning. Their tangent point is A (fig. 267). The material teeth

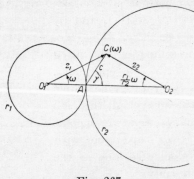

Fig. 267

rotating together with the pitch circles will make contact at the point C. The locus of the contact points C will be called the contact curve c:

$$c = c \exp (j\gamma), \quad . \ . \ . \ . \ . \ . \ . \quad (1)$$

where $|c|$ and γ are functions of the parameter ω, the angle over which the left circle is rotated.

Denote the profile of the left wheel in the position $\omega = 0$ by z_1, taking O_1 as origin; likewise denote the profile of the right wheel in the position $\omega = 0$ by z_2, taking O_2 as origin. Along the contour of the profiles we adopt ω-scales so that $z_1(\omega)$ and $z_2(\omega)$ are the points making contact in the point $C(\omega)$ after a rotation ω, respectively $-(r_1/r_2)\,\omega$ of the wheels. Then:

$$c(\omega) = z_1(\omega) \exp (j\omega) - r_1 = z_2(\omega) \exp (-j\,(r_1/r_2)\,\omega) + r_2. \quad (2)$$

This equation enables us to calculate two of the three curves $c(\omega)$, $z_1(\omega)$ and $z_2(\omega)$ if one of them is known. However, we cannot choose this third one arbitrarily as by (2) alone it is not certain that the teeth are tangent to each other in the position ω. A second condition is provided by the so-called gear-tooth law which requires that the velocity components of the two profiles at the point C normal to the common tangent be the same. If b_1 and b_2 (fig. 268) are the perpendiculars let down from O_1 and O_2

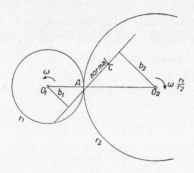

Fig. 268

on the common normal at the point C, these velocity components are proportional to ωb_1 and $(r_1/r_2)\omega b_2$. Equality of these means that $b_1/b_2 = r_1/r_2$, which in its turn means, geometrically, that the normal has to go through the tangent point A of the two pitch circles. The condition, that the instantaneous tangents of the two profiles shall be perpendicular to the vector c takes the following analytical form:

$$\frac{\dot{z}_1 \exp (j\omega)}{\dot{z}_1^* \exp (-j\omega)} = \frac{\dot{z}_2 \exp (-j\,(r_1/r_2)\,\omega)}{\dot{z}_2^* \exp (j\,(r_1/r_2)\,\omega)} = -\frac{\exp (j\gamma)}{\exp (-j\gamma)} \quad . \quad (3)$$

From (2) and (3) we can eliminate two of the three functions c, z_1 and z_2 and find the condition to which either of these three functions is subjected. On carrying out this elimination, we find

$$z_1 \dot{z}_1^* + z_1^* \dot{z}_1 = r_1 \dot{z}_1 \exp{(j\omega)} + r_1 \dot{z}_1^* \exp{(-j\omega)}, \qquad . \quad . \quad (4)$$

$$d|c|/d\omega = r_1 \sin \gamma, \quad . \quad . \quad . \quad . \quad . \quad . \quad (5)$$

$$z_2 \dot{z}_2^* + z_2^* \dot{z}_2 = - r_2 \dot{z}_2 \exp{(-j\,(r_1/r_2)\,\omega)} - r_2 \dot{z}_2^* \exp{(j\,(r_1/r_2)\,\omega)}. \quad (6)$$

Admissible tooth shapes have to be in accordance with (4) and (6) respectively. (6) is similar to (4) and actually takes the form (4) on passing to the new variables z' and ω', defined by $z' = - z_2$, $\omega' = - (r_1/r_2)\omega$.

From (5) we see that the contact curve may have any shape; (5) only fixes the ω-scale on this contact curve.

In designing a tooth-wheel coupling we may start by trying to find a solution of (4), i.e. an admissible tooth profile of the left wheel. With the aid of (2) we then find the corresponding shape of the right wheel teeth. If desired, (2) also teaches us the shape of the corresponding contact curve. We shall now give a number of examples.

3. Evolvente wheel teeth

Try to solve (4) by the equation of a circle evolvente:

$$z_1 = kr_1 (1 + j\omega) \exp{(-j\omega)} \exp(-j\psi). \quad . \quad . \quad . \quad (7)$$

This curve emanates from a circle of radius kr_1 at the point D (fig. 269) and is bent downwards. Substituting (7) in (4) we find that this solution is admissible, provided $k = \cos \psi$, which means geometrically that the tangent at the point D goes through A. From (2) we calculate for the contact curve

$$c = r_1 (- \sin \psi + \omega \cos \psi)\, j \exp(-j\psi). \quad . \quad . \quad (8)$$

This is a straight line going through A and making an angle ψ with the imaginary axis; in other words it is the tangent DA. It is described at a velocity $\dot{c} = r_1 \cos \psi = kr_1$.

The contact point falls on A ($c = 0$) if $\omega = \tan \psi$. If we wish to use this position of the profile as a starting profile, we have to multiply (7) by $\exp(j \tan \psi)$. And if, moreover, we wish $\omega = 0$ to fall on the point A, we have to shift the ω-scale over the amount $\tan \psi$. These two operations applied to (7) give us for the profile equation

$$z_1 = kr_1 \{1 + j(\omega + \tan \psi)\} \exp(-j\omega) \exp(-j\psi),$$

from which, with (2), we find for the contact curve

$$c = kr_1 . j\omega . \exp(-j\psi),$$

and for the engaging profile

$$-z_2 = kr_2 \{1 - j(\omega r_1/r_2) - \tan \psi\} \exp(j\omega r_1/r_2) \exp(j\psi),$$

which is again a circle evolvente emanating from a circle of radius kr_2 (see fig. 269).

As the argument of the contact point C is constant, the normal pressure exerted by one wheel on the other is invariable in direction, which is of importance for smooth running. This, combined with the ready way of machining evolvente teeth, has made this profile very popular; ψ is standardized at 15° or 20°.

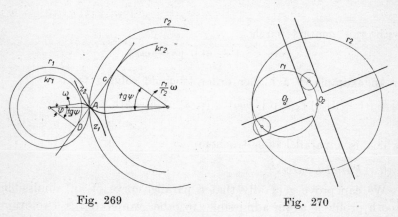

Fig. 269 Fig. 270

4. Pin wheels

A circular pin, $z_1 = a_0 + a_1 \exp\{jf(\omega)\}$, solves (4).

Equ. 4 is to be considered as a differential equation for $f(\omega)$. This $f(\omega)$ determines the way in which the contact point moves on the pin during the rotation.

If in particular $a_0 = -r_1$, $f(\omega) = \omega/2$ (fig. 270). The engaging profile consists of straight lines (Compare section 6).

5. *Trochoids*

Trochoids of the form

$$z_1 = a_1 \exp (jn_1\omega) + a_2 \exp (jn_2\omega)$$

conform with (4), if $n_1 = -a_2/(a_2 - r_1)$, $n_2 = -1$.

A special class is the one for which $a_2 = r_1 (n + 1)/n$:

$$z_1 = a_1 \exp \{ -j(n + 1)\omega \} + \frac{n + 1}{n}\, r_1 \exp (-j\omega),$$

the contact curve of which is the circle $c = r_1/n + a_1 \exp(-jn\omega)$.

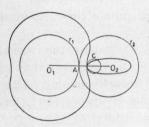

As an example fig. 271 shows the coupling of an ellipse (considered as a trochoid, $n = -2$) and a shortened nephroid ($n = 2$). Both pitch circles have radius r_1; radius contact curve $= a_1$.

Further specifying $a_1 = r = r_1/n$, z_1 is the cycloid:

Fig. 271

$$z_1 = r \exp \{ -j\, (n + 1)\, \omega \} + \\ + (n + 1)\, r \exp (-j\omega)$$

with the contact circle

$$c = r \left\{ 1 + \exp (-jn\omega) \right\}.$$

An example of a higher order trochoid solving (4) is:

$$z_1 = ((n + 1)/n)\, r_1 \exp (-j\omega) + (r_1/n) \exp \{ -j\, (n + 1)\, \omega \} + \\ + p \exp (-j\omega\, (n + 2)/2).$$

which is a parallel of a trochoid.

6. *Parallel curves*

We can prove generally that a parallel curve of an admissible tooth profile is again admissible; in other words, if z is a solution of (4), its parallel curve $z(p)$, defined by $z(p) = z + jp\, \sqrt{\dot{z}/\dot{z}^*}$, is likewise a solution.

Indeed $\dot{z}(p)$ differs from $\dot{z}$ only by a real factor which is the same for the conjugate functions and cancels out when introduced into (4). What remains to be proved is that

$$jp\, \dot{z}^* \sqrt{\dot{z}/\dot{z}^*} - jp\, \dot{z} \sqrt{\dot{z}^*/\dot{z}} = 0,$$

which is obviously true.

The contact curve changes generally also when passing to parallel curves of the tooth profiles. The contact curve $c(p)$ may be derived from the original one, c, by

$$c(p) = c + jp \sqrt{\dot{z}/\dot{z}^*} \exp(j\omega).$$

By (3) the second term on the right of the last equation is $- p \exp(j\gamma)$, so that

$$c(p) = c - p \exp(j\gamma) = (|c| - p) \exp(j\gamma).$$

The interpretation is that all moduli of c are increased by a constant stretch $- p$; in other words, $c(p)$ is the conchoidal transform of c. In the case of cycloidal teeth c is a circle passing through A, its conchoidal transform is a limaçon so that we find the limaçon as contact curve for teeth in the shape of parallel curves to cycloids. In the special case where $p = - 2 r_1/n$, the limaçon becomes a cardioid:

$$c = (r_1/n) + (r_1/n) \exp(- jn\omega) + 2 (r_1/n) \exp(-j(n/2)\omega).$$

In the case of trochoidal teeth the contact curve is a circle, not passing through the origin A; on introducing the parallel

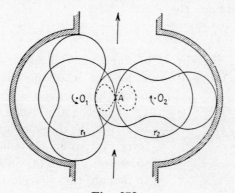

Fig. 272

tooth shapes we are led to a contact curve in the form of the general circle conchoid.

Lecocq's tooth wheel pump (1866) (fig. 272) is of this kind. The teeth are circles which are considered to be the parallel curves

of points lying inside the pitch circle, these points being considered as hypotrochoids with $n = -1$. The feet are parallel curves
of limaçons, which can be considered as epitrochoids with $n = +1$.
The contact curve consists of parts of two conchoids.

7. Slip

The point of contact moves over the two profiles at velocities
equal to the absolute values of $\dot{z}_1$ and $\dot{z}_2$. The slip is the difference
between these two quantities:

$$\text{Slip} = |s| = \sqrt{\dot{z}_1 \dot{z}_1^*} - \sqrt{\dot{z}_2 \dot{z}_2^*}$$

Now, from (3) we have:

$$\sqrt{\dot{z}_1 \dot{z}_1^*} = \pm j \exp{(j\gamma)} \, \dot{z}_1^* \exp{(-j\omega)},$$

and from (2):

$$\dot{z}_1^* \exp{(-j\omega)} = \dot{c}^* - j c^* - j r_1 ;$$

so that

$$\sqrt{\dot{z}_1 \dot{z}_1^*} = \pm j \, (\dot{c}^* - j c^* - j r_1) \exp{(j\gamma)} .$$

In the same way we find

$$\sqrt{\dot{z}_2 \dot{z}_2^*} = \pm j \, (\dot{c}^* + j \, (r_1/r_2) \, c^* - j r_1) \exp{(j\gamma)},$$

so that we find for the slip

$$|s| = ((r_1 + r_2)/r_2) \, |c| \; ; \; s = \pm j \, ((r_1 + r_2)/r_2) \, c .$$

The sign of the slip is of importance if we are interested in
the frictional forces exerted by one wheel on the other. These

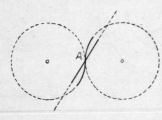

forces have opposite directions for the
two wheels and we shall reckon s so as
to give it the direction of the frictional
force exerted on the wheel under consideration. Applying this rule we have
to assign the $-$ sign to s_1 and the
$+$ sign to s_2.

Fig. 273   In order to keep the slip small, we
have to keep the dimensions of the
contact curve small and to make it pass through A. In the
case of evolvente and cycloidal teeth the contact curve passes
indeed through A; in order to keep it small we have to take a

small pitch, choosing many teeth which are parts of evolventes and cycloids. Fig. 273 shows the comparison of the contact curves of evolvente and cycloidal teeth consisting of epicycloidal tops and hypocycloidal feet.

As the contact curve of trochoidal teeth is a circle not passing through A, the slip must be more serious in this case than in the corresponding case of cycloidal teeth. By a conchoidal transformation this contact curve may be attracted towards A, so that we find profiles of low slip amongst the teeth in the shape of parallels to the trochoids. Profiles of this kind are applied in tooth wheel pumps like Lecocq's.

APPENDIX I

ANALYTICAL FORMULAS

Euler's rule:

$$\exp(\pm ju) = \cos u \pm j \sin u.$$

Goniometric functions:

$$\cos u = \frac{\exp(ju) + \exp(-ju)}{2}$$

$$j \sin u = \frac{\exp(ju) - \exp(-ju)}{2}.$$

Hyperbolic functions:

$$\cosh u = \frac{\exp u + \exp(-u)}{2}$$

$$\sinh u = \frac{\exp u - \exp(-u)}{2}$$

$$\cosh^2 u - \sinh^2 u = 1$$

$$\frac{d \cosh u}{du} = \sinh u \ \ ; \ \ \frac{d \sinh u}{du} = \cosh u$$

$$\cos ju = \cosh u \ \ ; \ \ \sin ju = j \sinh u.$$

De Moivre:

$$\exp(jnu) = \cos(nu) + j \sin(nu) = (\cos u + j \sin u)^n$$

Logarithms:

$$\exp(\pm j\pi/2) = \pm j \ \ \therefore \ \ \lg \pm j = \pm j\pi/2$$

$$\exp(jn \cdot 2\pi) = 1 \ \ \therefore \ \ \lg 1 = 0 + j \cdot n2\pi$$

$$\lg a = \lg a + j \cdot n2\pi$$

$$\exp(j \cdot \pi) = -1 \ \ \therefore \ \ \lg(-1) = j\pi$$

$$\lg(-a) = \lg a + j\pi$$

$$\lg(-a) = \lg a + j(2n+1)\pi.$$

Roots:

$$\sqrt{j} = \pm \tfrac{1}{2} \sqrt{2}\,(1+j)$$
$$\sqrt{-j} = \pm \tfrac{1}{2} \sqrt{2}\,(1-j)$$
$$\sqrt[n]{1} = \exp\,(j\,2\pi k/n)\ ,\ k = 1, 2, \ldots, n.$$

Decomposition:

$$z = |z|\,\exp\,(j\zeta) = x + jy$$
$$z^* = |z|\,\exp\,(-j\zeta) = x - jy$$
$$x = \operatorname{Re} z = \tfrac{1}{2}\,(z + z^*)\ ;\ y = \operatorname{Im} z = \tfrac{1}{2}\,(z - z^*)$$
$$|z| = \sqrt{zz^*}\ ;\ \exp j\zeta = \sqrt{z/z^*}\ ;\ \zeta = (1/2j)\,\lg\,(z/z^*).$$

TABLE OF PLANE CURVES

Straight line:

general equation: $z = \dfrac{z_1 + z_2 u}{m + nu}$

in line coordinates: $p^* z + p z^* - 2 = 0$.

natural equation: $\varrho = \infty$.

Circle:

general equation: $z = \dfrac{z_1 + z_2 u}{z_3 + z_4 u}$

special case: $z = \exp (ju)$

special case: $z = \dfrac{1}{1 - ju}$

through three points: $u = \dfrac{z_1 - z_3}{z_1 - z} \div \dfrac{z_2 - z_3}{z_2 - z}$

spanning angle $\varDelta$: $\dfrac{z - z_1}{z - z_2} = u \exp (j \varDelta)$

Apollonius' circle: $\dfrac{z - z_1}{z - z_2} = a \exp (ju)$

natural equation: $\varrho = \text{constant}$.

Conics:

general equation: $z = \dfrac{z_0 + z_1 u + z_2 u^2}{m + n u + r u^2}$

Kepler orbits: $z = p \dfrac{\exp (ju)}{e \cos u + 1}$; $e = 1$ $\begin{array}{l} < \text{ellipse} \\ \phantom{<}\text{parabola} \\ > \text{hyperbola.} \end{array}$

Ellipse:

origin in centre: $z = a \cos u + jb \sin u$

$$z = \frac{a + b}{2} \exp (ju) + \frac{a - b}{2} \exp (-ju)$$

origin in focus: $z = \tfrac{1}{2} \{ \sqrt{a+b} \exp (\tfrac{1}{2} j u) \pm \sqrt{a-b} \exp (-\tfrac{1}{2} j u) \}^2$.

Parabola:

origin in focus: $z = \frac{1}{2} p (u + j)^2$.

Hyperbola:

origin in centre: $z = a \cosh u + jb \sinh u$

$$z = \frac{a + jb}{2} \exp(u) + \frac{a - jb}{2} \exp(-u)$$

origin in focus: $z = \frac{1}{2}\{\sqrt{a+jb} \exp(u/2) \pm \sqrt{a-jb} \exp(-u/2)\}^2$

orthogonal hyperbola: $z = \sqrt{1 + ju}$.

Cubics:

general equation: $z = \dfrac{z_0 + z_1 u + z_2 u^2 + z_3 u^3}{m_0 + m_1 u + m_2 u^2 + m_3 u^3}$

special formula: $z = \mathsf{p} + j\dot{\mathsf{p}}$; $\mathsf{p} = $ Weierstrass' function.

Circle evolvente:

$z = (1 - ju) \exp(ju)$

natural equation: $s = \frac{1}{2} \varrho^2$.

Norwich spiral:

$z = \frac{1}{2} (1 - ju)^2 \exp(ju)$.

Semicubic parabola:

$z = pu^2 (1 - ju)$.

Catenary:

$z = u + j \cosh u$

natural equation: $\varrho = 1 + s^2$.

Tractrix:

$z = u + \dfrac{j - \exp u}{j + \exp u}$

natural equation: $s = \lg \sqrt{1 - \varrho^2}$.

Cissoid:

$z = \frac{1}{2} p \dfrac{u^2}{1 + ju}$

Strophoid:

$$z = \tfrac{1}{2} p \frac{1 - u^2}{1 + ju}.$$

Archimedes' spiral:

$$z = u \exp (ju).$$

Hyperbolic spiral:

$$z = (1/u) \exp (ju).$$

Logarithmic spiral:

$$z = \exp \{(1 + ja)\, u\}.$$

Hyperbolic (co) tangent:

$$z = (\text{co}) \tanh \{(1 + ja)\, u\}.$$

Cornu's spiral (= klothoid):

$$z = \int_0^u \exp (js^2)\, ds.$$

natural equation: $\varrho s = \text{constant}.$

Common cycloid:

$$z = \tfrac{1}{4} p \{u + j \exp (ju)\}$$

natural equation: $\varrho^2 + s^2 = p^2.$

Sinus spirals:

$$z = \frac{2\,p}{\sqrt[n]{2}} \frac{1}{(1 + ju)^{1/n}}$$

$n = \tfrac{1}{2}$: cardioid   ; $n = -\tfrac{1}{2}$ parabola

$n = 1$: circle   ; $n = -1$ straight line

$n = 2$: lemniscate ; $n = -2$ orthog. hyperb.

Roses:

$$z = 2r \cos (nu) \exp (ju)$$
$$z = r \{\exp (j (1 + n) u) + \exp (j (1 - n) u)\}$$

$n = 1$: circle

$n = 2$: four leaved clover

$n = 3$: three leaved clover.

Cycloids:

$$z = (n+1)\,r \exp{(ju)} + r \exp{\{j\,(n+1)\,u\}}$$

natural equation: $\dfrac{s^2}{a^2} + \dfrac{\varrho^2}{b^2} = 1$; $\dfrac{b}{a} = \dfrac{n}{n+2}$

$n \gtrless 0$ epicycloids
hypocycloids

$n = -4$ astroid

$n = -3$ deltoid

$n = -2$ diameter of circle

$n = -1$ point

$n = +1$ cardioid

$n = +2$ nephroid.

Astroid:

$$z = 3 \exp{(ju)} + \exp{(-3\,ju)}$$
$$z = \cos^3 u + j \sin^3 u.$$

Cardioid:

$$z = p \exp{(ju)} + \tfrac{1}{2}\,p \exp{(2\,ju)}$$
$$z = \frac{2p}{(u+j)^2}.$$

Limaçon:

$$z = (e \cos u + 1) \exp{(ju)}.$$

Trochoids:

$$z = a_1 \exp{(j\,n_1\,u)} + a_2 \exp{(j\,n_2\,u)}.$$

APPENDIX III

TABLE OF OPERATIONS

Elementary operations:

$z_1(u) = z_2(v)$: points of intersection

$z_1 \pm z_2$: vectoral addition and subtraction

$z_1 z_2$: multiply moduli, add arguments

z_1/z_2: divide moduli, subtract arguments

$z_2 = jz_1$: rotation over angle $\pi/2$, anti clockwise

$p = 2\,\dfrac{z_2 - z_1}{z_1^{\cdot} z_2 - z_1 z_2^{\cdot}}$: line vector of line through z_1 and z_2

$z = 2\,\dfrac{p_2 - p_1}{p_1^{\cdot} p_2 - p_1 p_2^{\cdot}}$: point of intersection of lines p_1 and p_2.

Criteria:

$z_1 z_2^{\cdot} - z_1^{\cdot} z_2 = 0$: vectors z_1 and z_2 are parallel

$z_1 z_2^{\cdot} + z_1^{\cdot} z_2 = 0$: vectors z_1 and z_2 are orthogonal

$z_1/z_2 = z_3/z_4$: similar triangles O $z_1 z_2$ and O $z_3 z_4$

$z_1 z_3 = \text{Real} \,.\, z_2^2$: z_2 bisects angle z_1 O z_3.

$\begin{vmatrix} 1 & 1 & 1 \\ z_1 & z_2 & z_3 \\ z_1^{\cdot} & z_2^{\cdot} & z_3^{\cdot} \end{vmatrix} = 0$: The three points z_1, z_2 and z_3 are collinear

$\begin{vmatrix} 1 & 1 & 1 \\ p_1 & p_2 & p_3 \\ p_1^{\cdot} & p_2^{\cdot} & p_3^{\cdot} \end{vmatrix} = 0$: The three lines p_1, p_2 and p_3 are concurrent.

Derivatives:

$t = \dot{z} = |t| \exp(j\tau)$: tangent

$n = j\dot{z} = |n| \exp(j\nu)$: normal

$\text{Im}\{(z - z(P)) \,.\, \dot{z}^{\cdot}\} = 0$: tangents from point P to curve z

$\text{Re}\{(z - z(P)) \,.\, \dot{z}^{\cdot}\} = 0$: normals from point P onto curve z

$s = \int |\dot{z}|\, du$: arc length

$$\frac{1}{\varrho} = \frac{\partial \tau}{\partial s} = \frac{\mathrm{Im}\,(\dot{z}^{*}\,\ddot{z})}{|\dot{z}|^{3}} = \frac{1}{2j}\,\frac{\dot{z}^{*}\ddot{z} - \dot{z}\,\ddot{z}^{*}}{(\dot{z}\dot{z}^{*})^{3/2}} : \text{ curvature}$$

$$\left.\begin{array}{l} \dfrac{1}{\varrho} = \dfrac{1}{j}\,\dfrac{d z^{*}}{d s}\cdot\dfrac{d^{2}z}{d s^{2}} \\[2mm] \varrho = f\,(s) \end{array}\right\} \text{ natural equation.}$$

Transformations:

$v = f\,(u)$: transformation of parameter scale only

$u' = -\,u$: hyperbolic involution

$u' = -\,1/u$: elliptic involution.

$w = f\,(z)$: conformal transformation

$w = z_0 + z$; $z_0 = \text{constant}:$ $\begin{cases} \text{shifting the origin over } -z_0 \\ \text{shifting the curve over } z_0 \end{cases}$

$w = z\,.\,\exp\,(j\psi)$; $\psi = \text{constant}:$ $\begin{cases} \text{rotation over angle } \psi \\ \text{anticlockwise} \end{cases}$

$w = 1/z^{*}$: inversion

$w = \dfrac{z_a z + z_b z^{*} + z_c}{z_0^{*} z + z_0 z^{*} - 2}$: collineation, projective transformation

$$\left.\begin{array}{l} p = 2\,\dfrac{dz}{z^{*}\,dz - z\,dz^{*}} \\[3mm] z = 2\,\dfrac{dp}{p^{*}dp - p\,dp^{*}} \end{array}\right\} \text{ dual transformation}$$

$w = \dfrac{az + b}{cz + d}$; a, b, c and d complex: circle transformation.

Derived curves:

$z - s\,\exp\,(j\tau)$: involute

$z + j\varrho\,\exp\,(j\tau)$: evolute

$\dfrac{\varrho}{j}\,\exp\,(j\tau)$: radial

$z \pm a\dot{z}$: tractor

$z \pm j\,a\,\dot{z}/|\dot{z}|$: parallel curve

$z \pm a\,\sqrt{\dfrac{z}{z^{*}}}$: conchoidal transform

$$\frac{1}{2}\frac{z\dot{z}^* - z^*\dot{z}}{\dot{z}^*} : \text{pedal}$$

$$\frac{1}{2}\frac{z\dot{z}^* + z^*\dot{z}}{\dot{z}^*} : \text{contrapedal}$$

$$2\frac{\dot{z}^*}{z\dot{z}^* - z^*\dot{z}}\, z^2 : \text{negative pedal}$$

$$z - t\frac{dz}{ds} \quad ; \quad t = \frac{s^2 - |z|^2}{\dfrac{d}{ds}(s^2 - |z|^2)} : \text{anticaustic}$$

$$t = \frac{s + x}{\dfrac{d}{ds}(s + x)} : \text{anticaustic for parallel rays}$$

$$z = f(u, v) \quad ; \quad \frac{\partial z}{\partial u}\cdot\frac{\partial z^*}{\partial v} - \frac{\partial z^*}{\partial u}\cdot\frac{\partial z}{\partial v} = 0 : \text{envelope}.$$

Integrals involving $|\dot{z}|$

$$s = \int |\dot{z}|\, du : \text{arc length}$$

$$\left.\begin{array}{l} S_i = 2\pi \int x\,|\dot{z}|\, du \\ S_r = 2\pi \int y\,|\dot{z}|\, du \end{array}\right\} \text{surface of revolution}$$

$$z(g) = \frac{1}{s}\int z\,|\dot{z}|\, du : \text{centre of gravity of contour}.$$

Integrals involving $I = \mathrm{Im}\,(z^*\dot{z})$

$$A = \tfrac{1}{2}\int I\, du : \text{area}$$

$$\left.\begin{array}{l} V_i = \tfrac{2}{3}\pi \int x\,I\, du \\ V_r = \tfrac{2}{3}\pi \int y\,I\, du \end{array}\right\} \text{volume of revolution}$$

$$z(\mathrm{G}) = \frac{1}{3A}\int z\,I\, du : \text{centre of gravity of area}$$

$$\left.\begin{array}{l} J_v = \tfrac{1}{4}\int x^2\,I\, du \\ J_x = \tfrac{1}{4}\int y^2\,I\, du \end{array}\right\} \text{axial inertia moment}$$

$$J_0 = \tfrac{1}{4}\int z z^*\,I\, du : \text{polar inertia moment}$$

$$J_{xy} = \tfrac{1}{4}\int x y\,I\, du : \text{centrifugal inertia moment}.$$

APPENDIX IV

TABLE OF DERIVED CURVES

	inversion	involute	evolute	pedal	orthoptic curve
circle	circle straight	evolvente	point	cardioid limaçon	circle
parabola	cardioid	—	semicubic parabola	cissoid strophoid	directrix
orthogonal hyperbola	lemniscate	—	—	lemniscate	circle
log spiral $z = \exp\{(1+ja)u\}$	log spiral $z\exp(-2u)$	log spiral $(a/j)\,z$	log spiral $(j/a)\,.\,z$	log spiral $(ja/(ja-1)).z$	log spiral $\tfrac{1}{2}(1-j)\{1-j\exp(-\pi/2)\}.z$

APPENDIX V

HISTORICAL NOTES

The fact that complex quantities can be represented by the points of a plane has been discovered by several authors, presumably independently of each other. Among the names of the oldest ones we encounter those of WESSEL, ARGAND and GAUSS. The two first mentioned were not professional mathematicians, WESSEL being a surveyer and ARGAND a book-keeper.

Without any doubt CASPAR WESSEL has the priority. He was born (1745) at Josrud, in Norway and died in 1818. His paper: „Om directionens analytiske betegning" (On the analytical denotation of vectors) was presented to the Royal Danish Academy of Sciences in 1797 and published in its Transactions, vol. V, p. 469 (1799). He used the geometrical representation of complex numbers for the elucidation of the formulae of goniometry and trigonometry. He even introduced hypercomplex numbers in order to extend his considerations to spherical trigonometry. Besides, he also offers the first example of what is the purpose of the present book; he uses namely the complex calculus for the deduction of geometrical results. The example in question is the proof of a theorem due to ROGER COTES (1682—1716), stating that the product of the distances of point P to all vertices of a regular polygon described in a circle of radius r amounts to $a^n - r^n$, if P lies on one of the radii from the centre of the circle to one of the vertices at a distance a from the centre.

Transposed into our notation, WESSEL's proof runs as follows: Choose point P on the real axis: $z_P = a$ and let also one of the vertices of the polygon be situated on the real axis: $z_n = r$. As all the vertices $z_1, z_2 \ldots z_n$ are roots of the equation $z^n - r^n = 0$, the product $(z - z_1)\ (z - z_2)\ (z - z_3) \ldots (z - z_n)$ equals $z^n - r^n$. If, now, z is situated on the real axis, as is the case with z_P, this product is real and equal to $a^n - r^n$ q.e.d.

JEAN ROBERT ARGAND (Geneva 1768 — Paris 1822) reports on the representation of a complex number by a point in the plane, in a paper entitled: „Essai sur une manière de représenter les quantités imaginaires dans les constructions géométriques" (Annales de Mathématiques de Gergonne, vol. IV, p. 133 (1814)). His paper is not nearly so clear and to the point as WESSEL's. Moreover, he does not give a single geometrical application of his new discovery.

FRIEDRICH GAUSS's contribution is inserted in his mémoir: „Theoria residuorum biquadraticorum commentatio secunda" of 1831 (Gesammelte Werke Göttingen 1878, vol. II, p. 174 seq.). GAUSS observes however that traces of the same idea are to be found in his thesis of the year 1799 and it cannot be denied that there is good reason for this observation. It seems, however, that GAUSS has never used the complex notation for real points of the plane as a means of dealing with plane geometry for its own sake.

This was left to SIEBECK, in a paper „Ueber die graphische Darstellung imaginärer Funktionen" published in Crelle's Journal Vol. 55, p. 221 (1857). In this paper he represents in principle a curve in the same way as is done in the present book, viz. by $z = f(u)$, although his notation differs from ours. He deals with a number of curves which he represents (transposed in our notation) by:

straight line . . . . $z = z_0 + z_1 u$

parabola . . . . $z = z_0 + z_1 u + z_2 u^2$

circle . . . . $z = \dfrac{z_1 + z_2 u}{z_3 + z_4 u}$

ellipse . . . . $z = \cos (u + ja)$

hyperbola . . . . $z = \cos (a + ju)$

SIEBECK's paper is in many respects a forerunner of the present book and the present author is highly surprised that the work started by SIEBECK was not followed up and completed in the years after his publication.

Many years later we find the same method used again by GASTON DARBOUX. His book: „Sur une classe remarquable de

Courbes et de Surfaces Algébriques" (1873) contains a chapter
headed: „Etude de certaines propriétés des imaginaires en
géometrie" in which he derives a number of properties of the
curves that since then are known as Darboux curves. A Darboux
curve is the locus of points for which the products of the distances
to two sets of fixed points are in a constant ratio. These curves
are represented in our notation by the equation:

$$(z - z_1)(z - z_2)(z - z_3) \ldots = C \exp(ju)(z - z_a)(z - z_b)(z - z_c) \ldots$$

and Darboux takes full advantage of the simplicity of this
representation. CASSINI's ovals (product of distances to two fixed
points is constant):

$$(z - z_1)(z - z_2) = C \exp(ju)$$

and APOLLONIUS' circle (ratio of distances to two fixed points
is constant):

$$(z - z_1) = C \exp(ju)(z - z_a)$$

are special cases of Darboux curves.

The next paper that should be mentioned is that by J. BRILL:
„On the application of the theory of complex quantities to plane
geometry" (Messenger of Mathematics Vol. 16, p. 8, 1887). BRILL
tries to interpret algebraic identities as geometrical properties.
His first example is:

$$x(y - z) + y(z - x) + z(x - y) \equiv 0.$$

Now, take for x, y and z complex numbers, denoting the vectors
from an arbitrarily chosen origin O to the three vertices of a triangle,
then the equation represents a (not so interesting) property of
the triangle, $y - z$ etc being the sides. In this way BRILL derives
a number of properties of the triangle and of the parabola.

The subject was taken up again fairly recently by a number
of American authors. L. L. SMAIL (American mathematical Monthly
vol. 36, p. 504, 1929) and S. A. SCHELKUNOFF (Idem, vol. 37,
p. 301, 1930) gave the proof of a number of well-known properties
of rectilinear figures; in a later paper (School Science and Mathematics, vol. 32, p. 284, 1932) SCHELKUNOFF also treats the circle

by means of the complex calculus. All these papers, however, are elementary compared with SIEBECK's memoir mentioned above.

By this summary the author hopes to have done full justice to this predecessors in the art. Further historical information may be obtained from: RAMORINO, Giornale di matematica, vol. 35 (1897) and vol. 36 (1898); A. McFARLANE, Bibliography of Quaternions and allied Systems of Mathematics, Dublin, 1904; J. L. COOLIDGE, Geometry of the complex Domain, Oxford, 1924. The last book deals with the real representation of imaginary and complex points, and although akin to it, its subject differs from that of the present treatise. Two other domains, are still more closely related to ours, the application of the WESSEL-GAUSS plane to the theory of complex functions (GAUSS, RIEMANN, WEIERSTRASS) and the treatment by complex numbers of the alternating current theory (HELMHOLTZ, 1878). We should be carrying it too far, however, if we entered into a historical analysis of these branches of science or investigated their interaction with our own subject: the geometry of the plane, considered as the assemblage of complex numbers.

Date Due